W9-BHM-284

LIFE NATURE LIBRARY

EARLY MAN

LIFE WORLD LIBRARY
LIFE NATURE LIBRARY
LIFE SCIENCE LIBRARY
THE LIFE HISTORY OF THE UNITED STATES
GREAT AGES OF MAN
LIFE PICTORIAL ATLAS OF THE WORLD
THE EPIC OF MAN
THE WONDERS OF LIFE ON EARTH
THE WORLD WE LIVE IN
THE WORLD'S GREAT RELIGIONS
THE LIFE BOOK OF CHRISTMAS
LIFE'S PICTURE HISTORY OF WESTERN MAN
THE LIFE TREASURY OF AMERICAN FOLKLORE
AMERICA'S ARTS AND SKILLS
300 YEARS OF AMERICAN PAINTING
THE SECOND WORLD WAR
LIFE'S PICTURE HISTORY OF WORLD WAR II
PICTURE COOK BOOK
LIFE GUIDE TO PARIS
TIME READING PROGRAM

LIFE NATURE LIBRARY

EARLY MAN

by F. Clark Howell
and The Editors of LIFE

TIME INCORPORATED
NEW YORK

About the Author

F. Clark Howell has been interested in "stones and bones"—as he calls the study of paleoanthropology—since high school days, when he won a tuition fellowship to the University of Chicago. Enrolling there after service in the navy, Howell studied under two important teachers. From Sherwood L. Washburn (now at the University of California and a consultant for *The Primates* in this series) he developed a solid background in physical anthropology and the evolution of human behavior. From Robert J. Braidwood he derived an interest in prehistory. In combining the influences of his two mentors, Howell has become the outstanding representative of that new breed of anthropologists who are able to synthesize data from many fields—the earth sciences, human paleontology and prehistoric archeology. He has excavated early man sites in Spain and Africa, studied museum collections and prehistoric sites throughout Europe and the Middle East and participated in many international seminars on human evolution. Today Professor of Anthropology at Chicago, he has written numerous scientific papers, edited two books, and is the author of a forthcoming volume on *The Emergence of Man*.

ON THE COVER: This is the skull of a Neanderthaler, one of 10 skeletons found on Mount Carmel in Palestine in the 1930s. Nearly 40,000 years old, it is discussed on page 127. Men like this are believed to be ancestors of modern Europeans.

Library of Congress catalogue card number 65-20165.
School and library distribution by Silver Burdett Company.

Contents

All phases of this book, from planning and organization to final editing, were under the professional direction of F. Clark Howell. The text chapters were written by Maitland A. Edey, the picture essays by Dale Brown, Timothy Carr, Robert Morton and Peter Wood. The following individuals and departments of Time Inc. were helpful in producing the book: Yale Joel and Dmitri Kessel, LIFE staff photographers; Doris O'Neil, Chief, LIFE Picture Library; Richard M. Clurman, Chief of the TIME-LIFE News Service; and Content Peckham, Chief of the Time Inc. Bureau of Editorial Reference.

Introduction

So eager have men been to know about their beginnings that they have everywhere created legends because they could not know the facts. If you yourself enjoy this kind of curiosity you are living at a good time, because the true knowledge of man's past is at last taking shape, in these very years.

As Professor Howell shows you, discoveries of ancient man began a century ago. But for many years it was possible to describe only samples, such as Java man, and Neanderthal man. Fossils were too skimpy and dates too poorly known to establish connections, and new finds sometimes brought more confusion than clarity. The evidence has slowly grown, however, until a new understanding has lately become possible, and, in fact, necessary.

I think that only an anthropologist can see with what skill Professor Howell has combined the new knowledge with his own experience to draw a fair and honest picture of what we know and what we can say. He has left out certain fossil men, not to suppress evidence but because they are so poorly known that they are merely distracting; he has done this entirely without distorting the meaning of the whole. He avoids sensationalism, the bane of popular writing on early man. In fact, he seems to note the existence of cannibalism in prehistory with the detached distaste it deserves. He does not write from any argumentative position; having no axe to grind in what he says, he will have no hatchet to bury later on.

Writing simply is not the same as simplifying. This book does not avoid some ideas because they happen to be complex. The discussion of what constitutes a species is such an idea—a major one in biology—which will become more important in future considerations of man's evolution. Another difficult idea is the real meaning of tools in our development. Dr. Howell has managed to weave together the two threads of man's physical remains and man's advancing ability to make implements, in a way which has my admiration. It may seem easy to get this down on paper; it is not. Many have tried; few have succeeded.

Careful as he is, Dr. Howell at the same time has not been afraid to apply imagination where it counts. He offers his educated suggestions on day-to-day problems and general conditions of life in the ancient past, and on the actual uses man made of his tools. Without such a view, the fossils of man are nothing more than bones.

WILLIAM HOWELLS
Professor of Anthropology
Harvard University

A NEANDERTHAL FOOTPRINT, cast from the wet clay of an Italian cave, is the type of discovery that gives scientists a rare opportunity to reconstruct the actual form and flesh of the man who left it, which otherwise can only be imagined.

1

The Case for Man's Antiquity

WHERE did man come from? This question has preoccupied human thought for thousands, conceivably for tens of thousands, of years. It is responsible for a large number of myths and for many of the world's religions, each of these grounded in efforts to explain the creation of the earth and of men. Many of these explanations are exceedingly interesting and beautiful, but much of their detail is no longer regarded as strictly factual. Instead, they are more properly interpreted as reflections of man's past yearning to fathom mysteries he could not possibly understand, his fear of the unknown and his often poetic attempts to construct a kind of theological prehistory to satisfy his desire for a good and moral world. Man cannot get along without faith, and the highest ornament of any great civilization is the ethical system by which it lives. The strength of any such system lies in its ability to continue to serve as a moral force while adjusting itself to changes in man's knowledge about the universe and his place in it.

The story of creation, as told in the Bible, is a fine case in point. It is seldom taken literally now. Its simple, sweeping concepts are interpreted by most modern Christians and Jews as being symbolic of the spirit and majesty of God. The world, in effect, was not created in six days even though the Bible

PIONEERS IN PREHISTORY

JOHN FRERE
1740-1807

An English archeologist, Frere found hand-axes in undisturbed strata in a brickyard in Suffolk and he recognized them as being of human origin. In 1797 he wrote to the Society of Antiquaries ascribing them to "a very remote period indeed, even beyond that of the present world." A landmark in prehistoric research, his letter was promptly forgotten.

JACQUES BOUCHER
DE PERTHES
1788-1868

A French customs official with a flair for archeology, Boucher de Perthes also found flint tools and speculated that they were old because they occurred with the bones of extinct elephants. He reached the conclusion that the tools had come from a race of men before the Great Flood. Experts were impressed by his writings; eventually some were converted.

says it was, and this discrepancy no longer troubles most devout people. Still, old ideas die hard; there are men and women in the United States today who believe that the earth is flat. How else, they argue, can angels preside over its four corners—as the Bible says?

Three hundred years ago most self-respecting citizens took their Bible as literally as that. Hell was a fiery place beneath their feet. Heaven was "up there" somewhere. Even the age of the earth was known to a nicety. It had been carefully calculated from Biblical references by Archbishop James Ussher of Armagh, Ireland, in 1650. His date for the morning of creation was 4004 B.C. Subsequently this was inserted in the margins of authorized versions of the Bible and before long came to acquire the infallibility of Scripture itself. At about the same time, another cleric working independently of Ussher came up with the exact date and time—9 a.m. on October 23.

WHO was there to dispute these men? Nobody, really. There was not yet any such thing as modern science and, outside of a rare genius or two like Galileo or Isaac Newton, there were no proper scientists. Such men as were interested in poking into the ground and in collecting and measuring things were amateurs. They were motivated only by their own curiosity and they took their own risks. In the 17th Century a Frenchman named Isaac de la Peyrère made a study of a large collection of oddly chipped stones gathered in the French countryside. He then had the temerity to publish a book suggesting that these stones had been shaped by primitive men who lived before the time of Adam. His book was publicly burned in 1655.

But odd-shaped stones continued to turn up. So did even odder-shaped bones. Gradually a few skeptical men began to realize that the earth had been inhabited at one time by a great number of creatures that no longer existed—huge mammoths, woolly rhinoceroses, saber-toothed tigers. More digging produced more puzzles. In 1771 human bones were found, associated with the remains of extinct cave bears in a site in Germany—which not only suggested ancient animals but ancient men too. Their finder, Johann Friedrich Esper, was flabbergasted. "Did they belong to a Druid or to an Antediluvian or to a Mortal Man of more recent times?" he wrote. He would not face the logical answer and concluded that the fragments must have come together by chance.

Others guessed right but could not get a hearing. In 1790 John Frere found unfamiliar stone tools in the same beds with the remains of extinct animals at Hoxne in England. Working in Belgian caves in 1830, P. C. Schmerling found many stone artifacts associated with the bones of long-since vanished rhinoceroses and mammoths, and in addition uncovered two human skulls. These astonishing finds went generally unnoticed.

It was even difficult to get anyone to pay serious attention to the idea that stone "tools" were tools at all. The first man to attempt to prove this in a systematic way was a French customs official named Jacques Boucher de Perthes. Interested in archeology, he began poking about in gravel banks near Abbeville in northern France and was perplexed by the number of flint objects which not only did not "belong" in the pits because they were made of a different kind of stone, but which also bore unmistakable signs of human workmanship. Many of them were carefully chipped around the edges and looked enough like axes to set even a less observant person than Boucher de Perthes to thinking. He began collecting and organizing his finds, and some years later had what he considered an overwhelmingly strong case for the existence of men far older than any hitherto known. In 1838 and 1839, his findings were laid before two French learned societies and rejected by both. He published them anyway in a five-volume edition; it was ignored for many years.

These early investigators were laboring under two separate handicaps. The first was a general lack of scientific method, which often made it easier for critics to argue that tools and human bones and extinct animals had gotten together by accident (or even by the sinister design of the scientist) than to prove that they had come there naturally. A Catholic priest, Father J. McEnery, was to suffer from this. In 1829 he dug his way through an absolutely unbroken layer of stalagmite to find flint tools and ancient bones below a cave floor on the south coast of England. When he reported this, other geologists, led by the erudite Dean of Westminster, William Buckland, insisted that the tools belonged to ancient Britons who had dug ovens in the stalagmite floor of the cave and accidentally dropped some of their stone implements into the holes. Father McEnery's earnest rebuttal that there were no such holes fell on deaf ears; his findings, to which he had devoted some 15 years, were not published until after his death.

A second and much more serious handicap was that scientists and laymen alike were instinctively suspicious of stone tools and fossils because of a severe limitation in their thinking: they still had not the faintest notion of how old the earth actually was. But by the end of the 18th Century a few of them were beginning to get some alarming ideas about its long history. This they read in the "testimony of the rocks"—in the various layers of different kinds of sediments—river gravels, sands and marine limestones that they encountered, one beneath another, some of them dozens of feet thick, indicating that they had been laid down over long periods of time. Intense interest was generated by these discoveries and speculations, and it duly led to the establishment of the science of stratigraphic geology. By the early 19th Century, a British geologist, William Smith, had identified 32 different strata in England alone.

IT remained for another Briton, Charles Lyell, to synthesize a theory—uniformitarianism—from the growing avalanche of evidence. This is a long word but it embraces a very simple and logical idea: If the earth's mantle is now affected by wind and flowing water, by frost action, by volcanic activity, by faulting along lines of crustal weakness, by mountain building—then it stands to reason that such forces have been operating in a similar, or "uniform," fashion in the past also. Thus, if one assumes the passage of immense amounts of time, this will explain the presence of such diverse strata as exist in the earth's crust. The world is constantly remaking itself, and the only reason we are not continually aware of it is that it happens so slowly. A man who watches a few pebbles fall from a crag may not realize it but he is watching the disintegration of a mountain. Muddy water flowing down a river can eventually move billions of tons of material from the center of a continent to the bottom of the sea. This immense layer of mud may harden and be covered in turn by other layers—on and on in a process extending over great amounts of time. To a society accustomed to believing that the earth was only about 6,000 years old, this was a staggering revelation.

Lyell's great work on geology was published between 1830 and 1833. Among its readers was a young man named Charles Darwin, who, in another 26 years, was to publish an even more shattering book, *On the Origin of Species*. Like Lyell, Darwin organized a great amount of evidence into a theory. Impressed

CHARLES LYELL
1797-1875

Following Boucher de Perthes' lead, Lyell studied tool-rich layers in the Somme Valley and argued that they were at least 100,000 years old. If the tools that Boucher de Perthes found were of human manufacture—and they appeared to be —man must be as old. Lyell advanced this theory in "The Geological Evidence for the Antiquity of Man," now a classic.

GEORGES CUVIER
1769-1832

Despite the fact that he was an authority on fossil fishes, reptiles and mammals, Cuvier rejected the notion of the antiquity of man. A leading spokesman for catastrophism (see page 19), he personified the opposition that plagued human evolutionists. But his fossil work is highly respected, and he is regarded as the father of vertebrate paleontology.

by the great variation in living organisms and aware of the obvious relationships of fossils in different strata of the earth, he began to speculate about how the different species now in existence might have become differentiated. He proposed a theory of evolution with natural selection as the principal mechanism which directed change.

Darwin was an extremely cautious man and the evidence he used to support his theory was limited to plants and some animals but did not include man. He mentioned the origin of human beings only once in his entire book. And then he permitted himself a single timid sentence in his conclusion: "Light will be thrown on the origin of man and his history."

But the implication was plain and nobody missed it. Thus, at this turning point in the history of human knowledge, we have the emergence of two great and related ideas about the emergence of man: that the earth is an extremely ancient place, long populated by many kinds of animals, some of which are no longer living; and that man himself, a mutable creature like the animals, has his origins far back in time. But how far back, and who those ancestral men were, nobody as yet had even the slightest notion. Everything that we now know about our ancestry we have learned in the last century—most of it during the last couple of decades.

In 1863 Thomas H. Huxley published a book, *Man's Place in Nature,* that was the first to address itself in an orderly and scientific way to the problem of man's development. By making many telling anatomical comparisons between man and the apes, particularly the chimpanzee and gorilla, he established that these were the two living creatures that were the most closely related to man. He further established that the evolutionary development of apes and men had taken place in much the same way and according to the same laws. His book was followed in 1871 by another by Darwin, *The Descent of Man.* Both were widely misunderstood. Most people—and even some scientists, unfortunately—jumped to the conclusion that both Darwin and Huxley thought that men were descended directly from the living apes. In short, a person who accepted evolution apparently was obliged to believe that a chimpanzee or a gorilla was his ancestor.

This was terribly disconcerting, for man obviously was *not* an ape, and a widespread aversion to the idea that he might have been, doubtless held back acceptance of evolutionary theory. It also produced another bothersome misconception that was to plague anthropologists for decades—the idea of a missing link. If men were men and apes were apes, it was argued, the connection could be proved by discovering a fossil that stood halfway between the two. Unfortunately for the early proponents of the theory, no missing-link fossils were found, nor would they ever be, for we know today that while both men and apes are descended from common ancestors, they bear the relationship of cousin to cousin and not grandparent to grandchild.

WHAT the fossil hunters did not realize for a time was that they already had a bona fide extinct human in their possession. This was the skullcap and some limb bones dug out of a cave in the limestone cliffs of the Neander valley near Düsseldorf, Germany, in 1856. To experts familiar with human skeletons and skull structure, there were some very peculiar things about this "Neanderthal" man, as he came to be known. The skull had strongly developed eyebrow ridges, a retreating forehead, and was much flatter on top and bulging in the back than the skull of any modern human being. One who examined it was the renowned German anatomist-anthropologist Rudolf Virchow, who promptly declared that its peculiarities were the result of pathological deformities and did not indicate primitiveness, as some less eminent examiners had suggested.

So it lay in a kind of limbo for 30 years. Then in the course of digging in a cave at Spy, Belgium, two skeletons similar to the Neanderthal one were recovered. This time their antiquity had to be accepted without question. The human bones occurred in deposits with bones of woolly rhinoceros, mammoth and other mammals that no longer exist, as well as with a number of chipped stone implements of a distinctive type. All of this extraordinary material was carefully removed layer by layer so that there could be no mistake about what was associated with what. At last, after half a century of groping, of misunderstanding, of contradictions, disputations and ridicule, a demonstrably ancient find had been made by scientists working under what were, for that time, controlled conditions. The evidence was unmistakable. This Neanderthal type was a man, but not a man identical with the ones who now walk the earth.

SPURRED by such discoveries, other students of the rapidly expanding field of early man devoted their lives to pushing the record of man's ancestry even further back. One such was Eugène Dubois. This young Dutch doctor resolved in the 1880s to do his searching in the Dutch East Indies and, in due course, discovered on Java what proved to be a primitive fossil human. This was the famous Java man, who now bears the scientific name of *Homo erectus*, a creature so seemingly primitive that Dubois himself thought at first that he was dealing with the scattered remains—a skullcap, lower jaw fragment and several thigh bones—of a fairly large tropical ape.

There is an almost childlike freshness in the idea of this young man setting out so confidently to find human fossils and so confidently selecting the Dutch East Indies from among all the places on earth he might have picked, as the one where he would dig. Actually, his choice was by no means as whimsical as it may seem. As he put it, "Since all apes—and notably the anthropoid apes—are inhabitants of the tropics, and since man's forerunners, as they gradually lost their coat of hair, must certainly have continued to live in the warm regions, we are inescapably led towards the tropics as the area in which we may expect to find the fossilized precursors of man." Find them he did. Starting in Sumatra and having no luck there, he turned to Java in 1890, and within two years he had in his hands what many other men before and after him have hunted for unavailingly throughout their lives.

Dubois' find was a blockbuster. It rocked the anthropological world, provoking so many arguments and such widespread disbelief that he eventually locked up his specimens and refused to let other scientists see them. Over the years he became increasingly suspicious and eccentric, and anthropologists had to wait until the 1920s before they could make a proper examination of Dubois' treasures, even though the original dispute over their authenticity had long since died down and they were universally regarded as the oldest human remains discovered up to that time.

One thing that worked against Dubois—and about which he could do absolutely nothing—was that he was a little ahead of his time. Sometimes a discovery is made and the world is not ready for it; sometimes even science is not ready. This was one of those times. Another 30 years and the story of Dubois' life might have been an entirely different one. Dubois had the further misfortune to do his work in the East Indies, a part of the world about which next to nothing of a geological nature was known. Thus it was only natural for other scientists to be skeptical about his claims.

Since then other finds have been made of men similar to Java man: a substantial number in a huge cave in a China hillside near Peking, a couple of others in Java, still others in Algeria and most recently in Eastern Africa. To these might be added an enigmatic jaw found in 1907 at Mauer near Heidelberg, Germany. However, their close relationship was not recognized at first and is, in fact, still being argued about. There is a natural tendency among the discoverers of dramatically ancient fossils—and these appear to be about half a million years old—for each man to think he has hit on something entirely new. For a long time there was a "Heidelberg man," a "Peking man," a "Java man," each given its own Latin name. For one thing, the skeletal parts of these ancient people were often incomplete and very fragmentary. For another, the science of evaluating them was still fumbling its way along. It is only in the last decade or so that the growing number of finds and increasing familiarity with the fossils themselves have begun to convince scientists that, for all of their geographical dispersion, they all represent a single species of man. Clearly *Homo erectus* was both widespread and highly successful.

His discovery led, naturally enough, to a very troublesome question: who preceded him? For a long time no one knew. There was an immense gap running back all the way to some possible ape ancestors known from fossils believed to be ten to twenty million years old. Then in the 1920s an anatomist, Raymond A. Dart, announced another epochal discovery, this time in South Africa—a child's skull of a totally new type. After intensive study and further finds, this turned out to be a small creature about four feet tall, manlike in that it apparently ran about on the ground on its (or his) hind legs, apelike (but still not an ape) in some characteristics of skull and jaw. Dart christened this curiosity *Australopithecus*. Since then other extremely interesting South African discoveries have been made including examples of a slightly less primitive type who may have been the first manlike creature to make stone tools. New methods of dating applied there have established that the earliest of these premen are nearly two million years old.

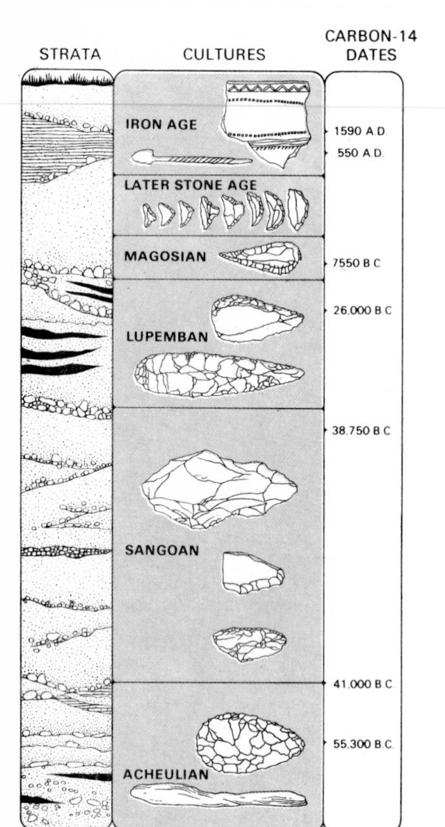

DIGGING FOR DATES

A sort of master index of tool finds in strata dating back over 50,000 years, this so-called "stratigraphic column" at Kalambo Falls in Northern Rhodesia illustrates how scientists use such a site for relative and absolute dating of finds.

Relative dating is based on the fact that strata get older as one goes down. Thus a find made in an upper layer is younger than one from a lower layer. Absolute dating—i.e., age in actual years—is made by chemical or radioactive methods, such as carbon-14. Since Kalambo Falls shows a consistent and largely undisturbed record of cultures dating from the primitive stone tools of the Acheulian to the sophisticated pottery and iron implements of the Kalambo culture of about 1590 A.D., its stratigraphic column provides a detailed and handy cross-reference for other finds from similar strata elsewhere in Africa.

ONE aspect of paleoanthropology, the branch of science dealing with the study of early man, that puzzles the layman is the way sweeping conclusions about dates and fossils can apparently be drawn from the study of bits and pieces. An entire head may be reconstructed from a patch of skull, a way of life from a few charred animal bones and some stone tools. How is this possible? The answer is extremely complicated and most of the rest of this book will be taken up with an attempt to explain it. Within it lies the real triumph of paleoanthropology during the past 50 years. Almost all the sciences have contributed: botany, with its studies of fossil pollen as a way of judging past vegetation and from this, inferring past climates; physics, and more lately atomic physics, with its precise methods of dating by measuring decay products of certain isotopes of radioactive elements; chemistry, with its varied techniques for analyzing substances; biology, and particularly comparative anatomy, with their contributions to knowledge about the similarities and differences between closely related organisms; and at the very foundation, of course, geology.

Today the wheel has come full circle. The public accepts the enormous age of the earth as readily as it does the succession of the seasons. The problem now is to get accurate dates for human fossils, to figure out their relationships more precisely, to learn how such people lived and to discover more of them. For man is a maddeningly poor source of fossils. As recently as 1956, the paleontologist G.H.R. von Koenigswald, who spent much of his earlier life looking for them, calculated that if all the then-known fragments of human beings older than Neanderthal man were gathered together they could be comfortably displayed on a medium-sized table.

WHY so scarce? Why can one go to good fossil sites here and there almost anywhere in the world and find literally millions of mollusc remains or thousands of extinct reptiles and mammals, when peoples earlier than Neanderthal men are known from only a handful of sites at which investigators have worked through tons of deposits, piling up other finds by the bushel basket before recovering a single human tooth? There are many reasons. First, the great commonness of marine fossils is a direct reflection of their enormous abundance when they were alive. It also reflects the tremendous span of time during which they were abundant. Many of them swarmed through the waters of the earth for millions of years, sinking steadily to the bottom when they died and being covered there by sediments. Their way of life helped preserve them, as did their shells, which are extremely durable and the only parts of them that now remain. Men, by contrast, have never been as numerous as oysters and clams. They existed in small numbers, reproduced slowly and lived a long time. They were more intelligent than dinosaurs, for example, and were less apt to get mired in bogs, quicksands and tar pits. Most important, their way of life was different. They were not river browsers but lively, wide-ranging gatherers and hunters. They often lived and died out in the open where their bones could be worried by scavengers, nibbled by ants, bleached and decomposed by the sun and rain. In hot climates, particularly in the tropical grasslands and savannas, the soil is apt to be markedly acid. This is an exceptionally poor preserver of bones, and any early men that may have lived and died in such an environment would have had a very poor chance of lasting until today. Finally, men have only been with us one or two million years. There simply has not been as much time for them to scatter their bones about as there has been for some of the longer-lasting types of animals.

What is needed to catch a glimpse of a clever, elusive uncommon animal like early man is a nice quiet cave where a corpse can be gently covered by blown-in dust, leaves or even sand and mud from the rising water level of a river. Or the cave can be a large one with a deep rock fissure serving as a garbage dump at the back into which dying old men or dead babies can be thrown along with the bones of game animals, just to get them out of the way. Finally, the cave may simply be one that is occupied steadily for a long period of time. The dirt and mess of mere living will gradually build up the floor so that it becomes deeper and deeper, and if people live in it long enough their story will be revealed—from recent to increasingly primitive—just by carefully digging down from one layer to another.

Layers in a cave, like strata of gravel in a riverbed, tell a rich story if they are investigated and analyzed carefully and their evidence is read right. This is something that earlier investigators usually failed to realize. Too often they dug with reckless abandon, throwing great shovelfuls of material every which way to recover only the largest bones and major pieces of worked stone. What they did not appreciate was that the position of things relative to each other was important, as was the surrounding earth itself for what it might give up

DATING PROCESS	MATERIAL TESTED	POTENTIAL RANGE: YEARS	HALF-LIFE: YEARS
CARBON-14	WOOD, CHARCOAL, SHELL	70,000	5,730
PROTACTINIUM-231	DEEP SEA SEDIMENT	120,000	32,000
THORIUM-230	DEEP SEA SEDIMENT, CORAL, SHELL	400,000	75,000
URANIUM-234	CORAL	1,000,000	250,000
CHLORINE-36	IGNEOUS AND VOLCANIC ROCKS	500,000	300,000
BERYLLIUM-10	DEEP SEA SEDIMENT	8,000,000	2,500,000
HELIUM-4	CORAL, SHELL	------	4.5 BILLION
POTASSIUM-40 ARGON-40	VOLCANIC ASH, LAVA	------	1.3 BILLION

NATURE'S TIMEPIECE

Most of the elements found in nature are mixtures of several isotopes—atoms that are chemically identical but have different atomic weights. Some of these isotopes, such as the ones listed above, are radioactive; that is, they emit nuclear particles and gradually disintegrate into other elements. Carbon, for instance, has a radioactive isotope, carbon-14, that disintegrates into nitrogen.

Each radioactive isotope has its own fixed rate of decay, expressed by the term "half-life"—the time required for half of the atoms in a sample to disintegrate. Therefore, if one knows an isotope's half-life, it is not hard to calculate the age of a specimen—simply by measuring how much of the isotope is left.

This is the basis of many of the dating methods science is using to find the absolute age of fossils and fossil-bearing deposits. Above is a chart of eight such methods, along with the materials to which they are applied, their characteristic half-lives and potential time ranges.

to analysis in the way of chemical secrets. Many questions shout themselves at the curious and well-trained observer. Was there evidence for fire? Was it natural or controlled by man? Did certain kinds of animal bones predominate at one level and decrease at another, indicating a change of diet or climate? Do the deposits preserve pollen grains, which are often more sensitive clues to vegetation, and hence climate, than the deposits themselves?

When this kind of a study is made—in three dimensions—of an occupation place of early man, then the information contained in it can be compared with that gained from another site. There may well be an overlap between the two, permitting the matching-up of several layers and an even better understanding and dating of both than was possible with one alone. Work of this sort is made still more precise when stone tools are brought into the picture, for each culture had different kinds of tools and different techniques for making them.

Modern work at sites occupied by early man is infinitely time-consuming and demanding. The tools of today's field worker are not so much picks and shovels as surveyor's transits, dental instruments and small camel's-hair brushes. Using such tools, it may take weeks to excavate properly a very small area. Every scrap that is gently and patiently worked free must then be mapped both horizontally and vertically, everything recorded, everything labeled. Thus, the full development of an important site may take many years, many specialists to analyze the findings in different ways, and substantial amounts of money. But the scientist will not select his site haphazardly. Something—bones or tools—must first be exposed by the erosional forces in nature to suggest that here is a site worth investigating. Then a series of test trenches are opened in order to expose the stratigraphy and to pinpoint concentrations of interesting material. In these ways the paleoanthropologist vastly improves his chances; otherwise he may dig out an entire hillside, using up large sums of research money in the process, and find nothing.

DOES this "nit-picking" phase mean that the great, exciting days of paleoanthropology are over? Not at all. It is true that the basic concepts are nailed down and there can no longer be the kind of eye-bugging sense of absolute astonishment that greeted the geological time-concepts of Lyell or the evolutionary concepts of Darwin or even the amazed disbelief that greeted the unveiling of Java man. Nevertheless, these are vastly exciting times for paleoanthropologists. Not only is the body of evidence growing almost faster than it can be analyzed but each fact, each new bit of proof that is hammered home speeds up the over-all process of understanding. We now know as much about Cro-Magnon man as the Pilgrim settlers of this country knew about the ancient Greeks. That is what is so thrilling about paleoanthropology today, and it is all unfolding itself before the eyes of living workers in the field. It is the highlights of that story that will be dealt with in the following chapters of this book. First we will deal with what is known about fossil apes and their possible connections with fossil pre-men. Then will come the pre-men themselves: the australopithecines of one to two million years ago; followed by *Homo erectus*, the first of the true men; next, the remarkably well-documented life of Neanderthal man and his contemporaries, those ice-age hunters of large animals; then Cro-Magnon man, who lives just over the hill from us in time and is really no different from us physically; and finally some Stone-Age people who are still walking the earth today and who still practice a way of life that would be entirely familiar to their ancestors of twenty or thirty thousand years ago.

THE NEANDERTHAL SKULLCAP, DISPUTED UNTIL MORE COMPLETE FINDS WERE MADE, WAS THE FIRST AND MOST FAMOUS CLUE TO EARLY MAN.

The Era of Discovery

The theory of man's evolution aroused a storm of controversy in the Victorian world. Many people denied even the fossil evidence of their primitive ancestry; others exploited the confusion with elaborate hoaxes. But as methods of investigation were increasingly refined, the doubters were silenced; today, modern dating methods show man to be older than Darwin could have imagined.

The Quagmire of Tradition

Until the 18th Century, few men were curious about the age of the earth, nor did many question the tradition that all life had been created in 4004 B.C., a date calculated by Archbishop Ussher *(above)*. But as fossils of extinct animals were found in deeper geologic strata, it became clear to some that the earth must be far older. How to reconcile evidence with tradition? One answer was catastrophism. This doctrine stated that the formation of strata was accelerated by a series of creations whose products were eliminated by subsequent catastrophes—like Noah's flood. But evidence was mounting to the contrary. By 1833, Charles Lyell had dealt catastrophism the death blow. The only correct way of interpreting geologic strata, he said, is to assume that the forces of nature have always acted in a uniform manner. The implication was enormous: at last the door was opened to the realization of the immense age of the earth. The next step was the acceptance of the age of man himself.

LITERAL GENESIS, this 16th Century scene shows all life created almost simultaneously. The story of Adam and Eve is shown in sequence, proceeding from left to right.

THE ANCESTRY OF MAN, traced by naturalist Ernst Haeckel in 1867, was one of the first attempts to deal with the specifics of evolution. Although his genealogical chart, starting with a blob of protoplasm and continuing to a modern Papuan, is filled with misconceptions and fictitious creatures, it is fairly accurate, considering the dearth of knowledge in his day.

The Pangs of Evolution

The first evolutionists had their work made doubly difficult for them. Despite their growing faith in the evolution of man, they had so little fossil evidence to go on that their theories were of necessity largely speculative *(opposite)*. Darwin, in fact, wrote his epochal *The Descent of Man* without a single subhuman fossil as evidence to support his theory. Another bane to evolutionary pioneers was the press, which exploited the widespread anti-evolutionary sentiment to titillate its readers with ridiculing cartoons *(right and below)*. But the tide was turning. In valleys and caves through Europe, human remains were being found along with ancient tools and artifacts. Slowly the Victorian qualms about early man died down; evolution became a reputable word.

MR. BERGH TO THE RESCUE
THE DEFRAUDED GORILLA: "That Man wants to claim my pedigree. He says he is one of my Descendants."
MR. BERGH: "Now, MR. DARWIN, how could you insult him so."

Man Found only in a Fossil State—Reappearance of Ichthyosauri

A LECTURE: "You will at once perceive," continued Professor Ichthyosaurus, "that the skull before us belonged to some of the lower order of animals; the teeth are very insignificant, the power of the jaws trifling, and altogether it seems wonderful how the creature could have procured food."

LAUGERIE
BASSE
ici
RESTAURANT
BAR
CHAMBRES
SANDWICHS

The Role of the Amateur

Archeology as a science did not come into being suddenly; rather it was to a great extent the product of a cadre of dedicated amateurs who, however crudely, had long been digging back into prehistory on their own. Educated people from all walks of life, some had made discoveries that were of great significance. But as the new science became more sophisticated, new skills and new techniques were needed to excavate, evaluate and date the mounting evidence of tools and fossils: where amateurs once led the way, professionals eventually took over.

ON THE TRAIL OF PREHISTORY, scientists pose at Laugerie Basse in France in 1908. The deposits here were discovered in 1863 by Edouard Lartet, a magistrate turned archeologist.

THE CLIFFS OF LAUGERIE BASSE have sheltered humans for some 15,000 years. This area of southwestern France was densely inhabited by Neanderthal and Cro-Magnon peoples.

EXCAVATING, amateurs display their trophies and, incidentally, the kind of careless digging which in some cases rendered valuable sites worthless for careful scientific investigations.

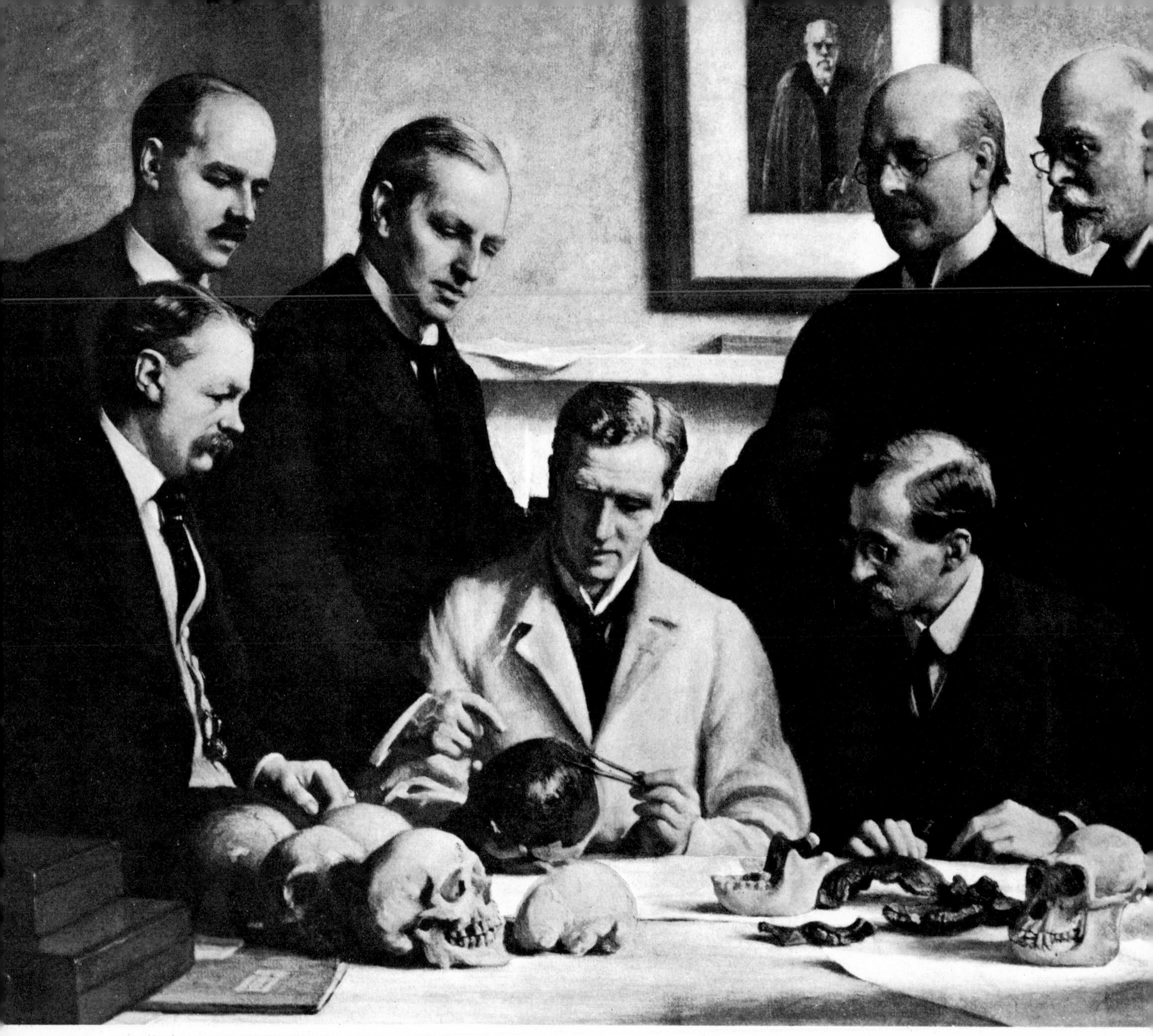

CHARLES DAWSON (STANDING RIGHT CENTER) WATCHES AS PILTDOWN SKULL IS MEASURED BY ANATOMIST SIR ARTHUR KEITH, WHO PIECED ▶

WASHING GRAVEL from the Piltdown pit, Dawson *(left)* hunts for pieces of skull. The remains were found in dubious geological circumstances, which helped to render them suspect.

An Ape Man That Never Was

The most intensive search conducted by early investigators arose from an attempt to reconcile Darwin's theory of the descent of man with the doctrine of a "chain of being" leading back to Creation. If man had indeed evolved, this reasoning ran, then somewhere in his past there must exist an original creature, a "missing link" between him and the apes. Here was a situation ripe for wild surmises. By 1912 Charles Dawson, an amateur archeologist, had turned up portions of a skull which, when reconstructed, proved to be a modern human cranium with a lower jaw that was fully apelike. This startling find launched an argument that lasted 40

TOGETHER AND ACCEPTED IT AS GENUINE.

KENNETH OAKLEY (STANDING) EXAMINES PILTDOWN JAW BEFORE BORING A SAMPLE FOR TESTS.

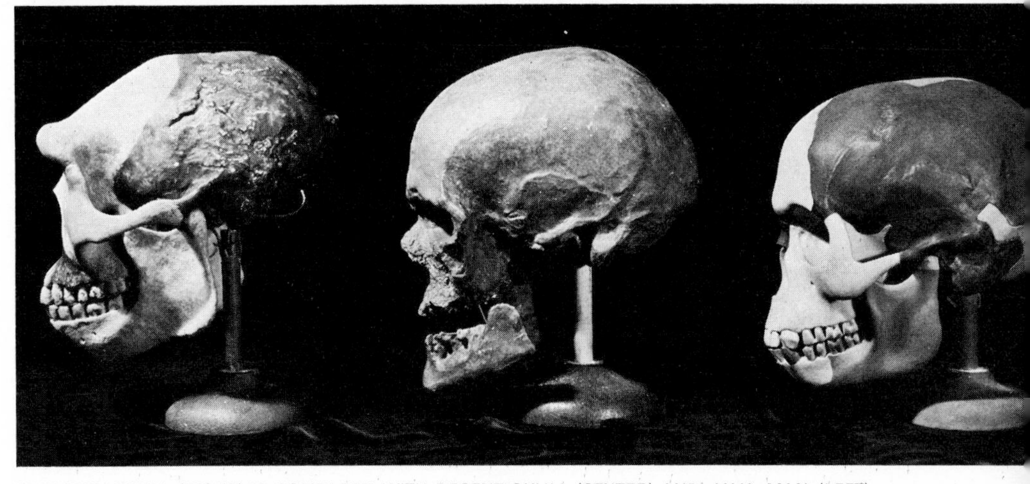

PILTDOWN SKULL (RIGHT) IS COMPARED WITH RECENT SKULL (CENTER) AND JAVA MAN (LEFT).

years. Popularly known as "Piltdown man" from the English hamlet where it was found, the fossil was accepted as genuine by some and named *Eoanthropus dawsoni*, or Dawson's "dawn man."

Dawson was widely acclaimed, and the case for Piltdown man was further strengthened in 1915 when he came up with another find, some pieces of skull and a molar. As the years passed, however, the Dawson fossils were increasingly difficult to reconcile with other, unquestionably authentic finds. Java man and the African pre-men, with skulls more apelike and jaws more manlike, made Piltdown man seem like an evolutionary paradox.

By the early 1950s, three British scientists determined to settle the Piltdown question once and for all. Modern testing methods could now determine a fossil's age with accuracy, and while Kenneth P. Oakley applied chemical tests, J. S. Weiner and W. E. Le Gros Clark subjected the fossils to exhaustive anatomical analysis. In 1953, their conclusions were published: the skull of Piltdown man was that of a modern man, his jaw that of an ape with teeth filed to disguise them. Dawson was long since dead and so could not explain the hoax. The moral of the story is that, with modern dating methods, no "fossil" like the Piltdown man could ever get by today.

ARGON IS ABSORBED in activated charcoal. Geophysicist J. F. Evernden chills a tube of charcoal with liquid air so that it will take up the gas.

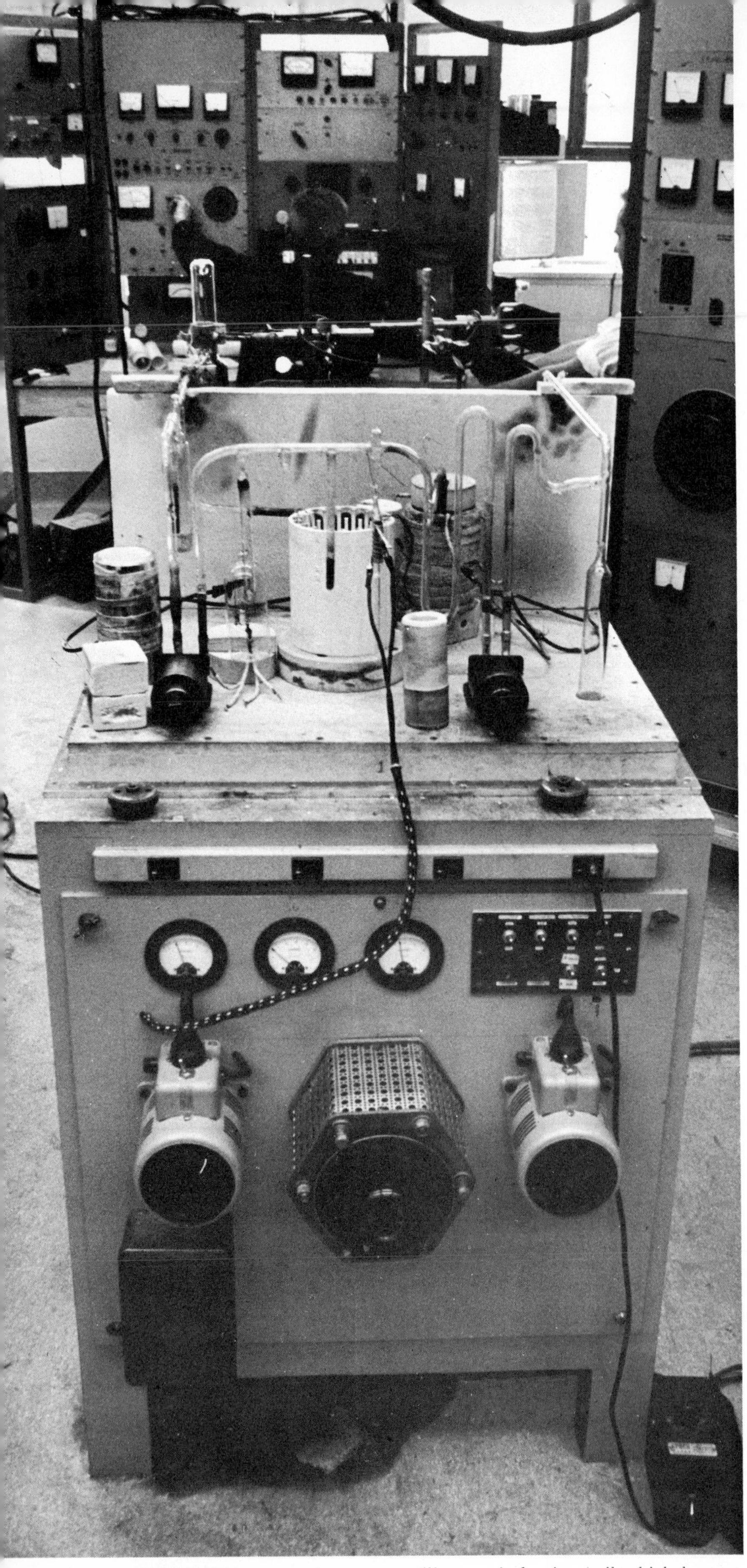

FIRST STEP in extracting argon utilizes an induction coil which heats a volcanic rock sample to 2,200° F. As the sample melts, argon gas trapped inside for perhaps millions of years is released in measurable amounts.

A Matter of Time

The exposure of Piltdown man gave dramatic emphasis to a basic fact of paleoanthropology: the full significance of any fossil can only be determined after its age is known. The relative age of fossils is usually determined by reference to the deposits in which they are found. With the growth of atomic knowledge, however, dating techniques were devised which could provide absolute age—a revolution in paleoanthropology.

Such methods of absolute dating, described in more detail on page 15, measure the amount of radioactive decay in a sample; with this data scientists can determine the age of the sample. For purposes of dating early man the two most widely used methods are carbon-14 dating, for organic materials, and potassium-argon dating, shown on this page, which can reveal the age of volcanic strata and, by extension, any fossils associated with them. With the latter method, scientists are now able to state confidently that erect-walking, tool-using prehumans existed nearly two million years ago.

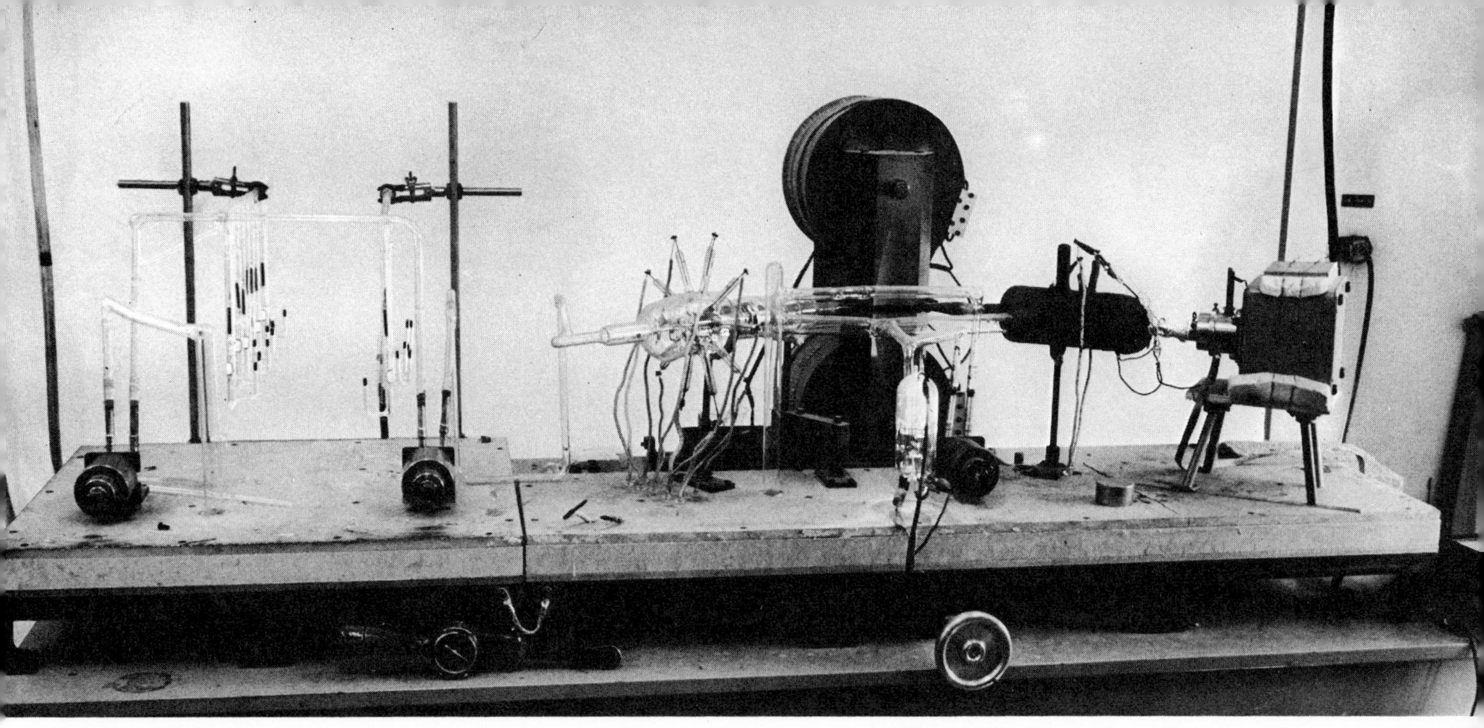

ARGON IS MEASURED by using a mass spectrometer to fire charged argon atoms past a powerful electromagnet that deflects them toward an electronic cup where they are counted. Since argon is a product of the decay of a radioactive potassium isotope with a half-life of 1.3 billion years—half of it decays in that time—it is now easy to determine the sample's age.

MONITORING THE EXPERIMENT, Evernden and G. H. Curtis read the results of the mass spectrometer test from a control console. Their experiments at the University of California in Berkeley have so refined the potassium-argon method that today it can date samples ranging in age from 100,000 years to the age of the earth—with a very small margin of error.

Special Skills to Study Early Man

The pioneer days of paleoanthropology, when just one man working alone might locate, excavate and evaluate an entire fossil bed, are largely gone. A growing body of specialists is today participating in the search for early man—sometimes a dozen or more different experts may be involved with a single

IN THE FIELD

THE PALEOANTHROPOLOGIST is in charge of investigations from start to finish. He must pick the site, obtain financial support, hire the labor and organize, plan and supervise the work in progress. Finally, he must integrate the data collected by each of the specialists and then publish his conclusions.

THE GEOLOGIST often assists in picking the site. His knowledge of the geologic history of the region is indispensable in determining the relative ages of fossil finds. His study of the strata at the site will also determine the natural processes—erosion, volcanic action, mountain-building—which laid them down.

THE SURVEYOR maps the general region of the site. If a local map does not exist, he makes it himself, often using aerial photographs. Next he draws a map of the site itself, plotting it in relationship to natural landmarks and making a detailed record of its contours before they are obliterated by digging.

IN THE LABORATORY

THE PETROLOGIST identifies and classifies the rocks and minerals found around the site. He can determine the nature of rocks from which tools were made, identify stones which do not naturally occur in the area—indicating importation by early man—and answer specific questions of the field geologist.

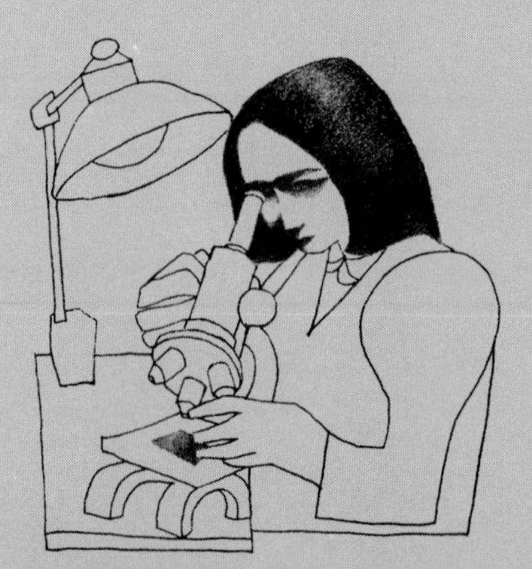

THE PALYNOLOGIST specializes in fossil plant pollen. Separated from deposits with acid solutions and classified and counted to determine the relative frequency of species, these pollen grains may tell the expert which trees, shrubs and grasses grew in the area—shedding light on early man's habitat and diet.

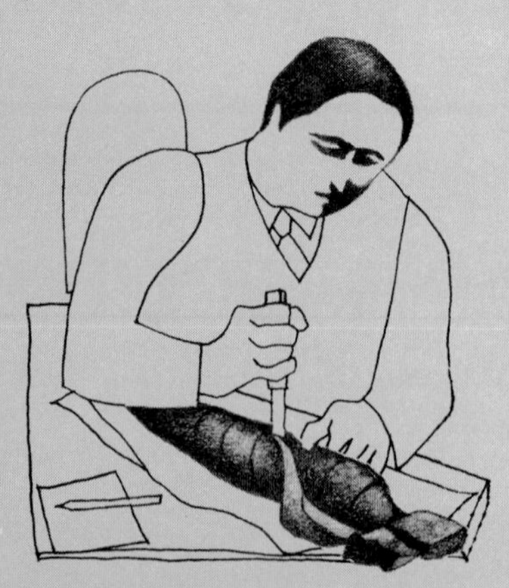

THE PEDOLOGIST, an expert on soils and their chemical composition, is shown here studying a core bored from the bed of a lake. His findings round out the picture of the habitat as it once was, supplementing the palynologist's ideas about the vegetational conditions which prevailed when the site was inhabited.

fossil site. Every phase of the operation—from the selection of the site to the analysis of the specimens—requires skills so specialized that no one man could handle it by himself.

An even greater revolution, however, has taken place in the laboratory. New sciences like geochemistry and palynology have contributed to it. They, and the new techniques and equipment that have been introduced into established sciences like geology and human anatomy, are increasing the knowledge about early man so fast that the data from a single site may take years to process and evaluate.

THE DRAFTSMAN records the exact position of all fossils, tools and other artifacts as they are excavated, marking their relationships to each other in both the horizontal and vertical planes. His work must be meticulous, for it is from his records that the position of all finds will be reconstructed for later analysis.

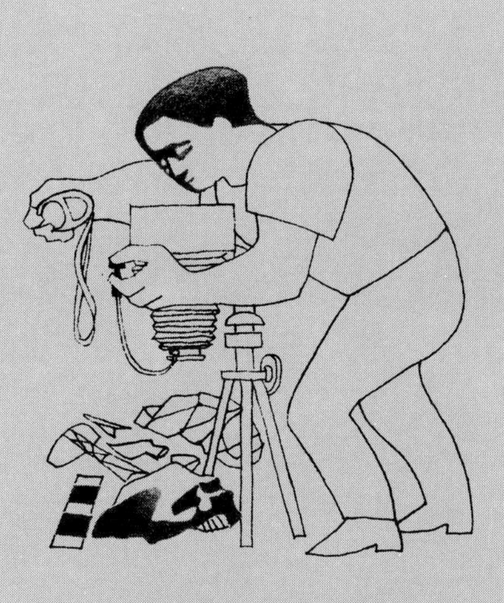

THE PHOTOGRAPHER documents fossil remains and artifacts and their associations as they are uncovered, photographing them alongside a metric rule for scale. He also records work in progress, the use of special equipment and provides over-all views of the site as well as of personnel at work, for publication.

THE PREPARATOR preserves and protects fossils and artifacts with various hardening agents like epoxy and makes plaster casts for particularly fragile bones and other organic remains. Later in the laboratory, the preparator will clean and restore the specimens, making them ready for study by various specialists.

THE GEOCHEMIST, with the geophysicist, conducts chemical and physical tests in the laboratory—the potassium-argon method is one—to determine the absolute age of material found at the site. He may also study the chemical composition of bones and artifacts, and help other specialists evaluate them.

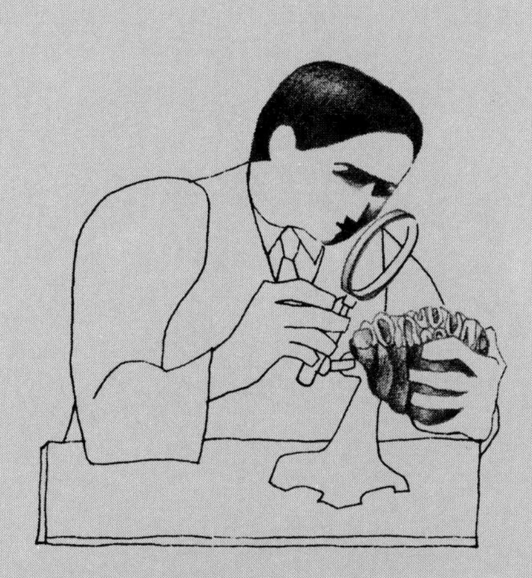

THE PALEONTOLOGIST studies the fossil animal remains found throughout the stratigraphy. From the kinds of finds, he can learn much about the ecology of the habitat and the eating habits of early man. By comparing the fossil sequence with that of other sites, he can deduce relative dates and faunal succession.

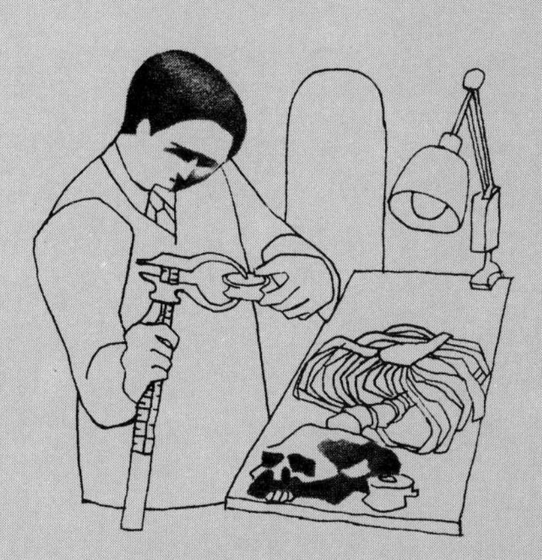

THE PHYSICAL ANTHROPOLOGIST is a specialist in the comparative anatomy of apes and man. This, plus his familiarity with the skeletal remains of early man, permits him to evaluate the human remains found at the site and form judgments about the evolutionary status of the fossil man who inhabited the site.

RAREST OF FINDS, the almost complete skeleton of *Oreopithecus* lies in a coal deposit in Italy where it turned up in 1958. Predating *Australopithecus* by 12 million years and possibly bipedal, it led some scientists to think it was an even earlier link between apes and man. It is now believed to lead to a dead end.

2

Back beyond the Apes

ONCE the idea of man's evolutionary development is accepted, his origins can theoretically be traced back to the origin of life itself—a matter of some two billion years. For practical purposes, however, the point at which to study the beginnings of man is when he began to have the first faint traces of "mannishness." How far into the past to dig for such traces—what, even, to keep an eye out for—is something of a problem. It was first stated by T. H. Huxley 101 years ago in a series of questions: "Where, then, must we look for primaeval Man? Was the oldest *Homo sapiens* pliocene or miocene, or yet more ancient? In still older strata do the fossilized bones of an Ape more anthropoid, or a Man more pithecoid than any yet known await the researches of some unborn paleontologist?"

An ape more anthropoid (manlike); a man more pithecoid (apelike)—that would seem to sum it up with surgical neatness but it does not go back quite far enough. To tell the story properly, we must look behind apes to monkeys and, behind them, to the earlier animals from which monkeys sprang, because traits that would later begin to emerge as distinctly human are believed to have had their origins in the shapes and behavior of these shadowy creatures.

At the start of our search we know only one thing: we know what we are like. It is as if, in putting together a jigsaw puzzle, we have only the top edge (ourselves) fastened together. Below that is an interesting row of hooks and loops to which we can hopefully begin fitting other pieces. Unfortunately the other pieces do not come to our hand in any orderly way. They are all mixed up in a box from which we are permitted to take them out one at a time. The first piece that we take out and examine does not fit anywhere so we set it aside and take out another. These may belong in the middle, near the bottom, or they may even be from another puzzle entirely. It is only when we have a considerable number of pieces before us that we begin to realize what the pattern of the puzzle as a whole may turn out to be. The extraordinary thing about recent researches into man's ancestors is that we have learned a great deal about them with an incredibly small number of pieces. For the first pieces that belong in the puzzle of man—those at the very bottom edge—we should begin with the first hints of primates: the group to which monkeys, apes and men all belong. This takes us back about 70 million years to the Paleocene epoch, a time when human ancestors still looked more like squirrels than people.

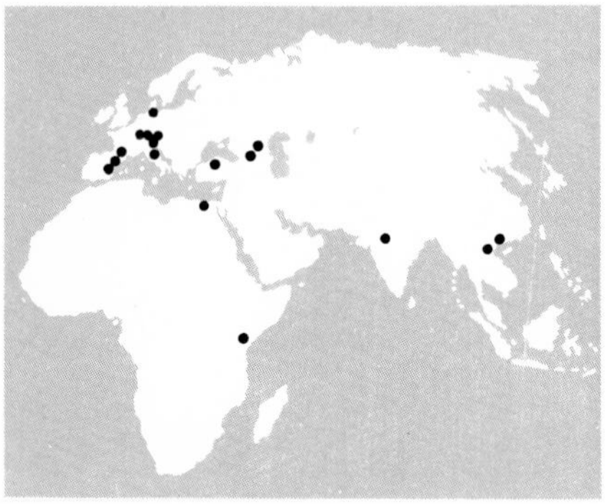

WIDE-RANGING EARLY APES

The surprisingly wide distribution of the dryopithecines, the group of primitive apes to which Pliopithecus and Proconsul (opposite page) both belonged, is shown in this map of their fossil finds, each designated by a black dot. Chief reason for this multicontinental spread was a forest habitat which extended in an almost continuous blanket across much of Africa and Eurasia, with fewer physical barriers—seas or mountain ranges—than exist today to limit the dispersal of various animals.

THE Paleocene opened on a warm and placid world, with enormous tropical forests spreading much farther north and south from the equator than they do today. France and Germany had a moist, jungly, humid climate; so did South Africa—and nearly everything in between. Among the inhabitants of these immense expanses of forests was a large population of what are believed to have been the forerunners of today's tree shrews and tarsiers. Long-tailed, rodent-shaped and -sized, they were probably adept at leaping about in the trees, seeking out fruit and seeds, slow-moving grubs and insects, buds, birds' eggs and an occasional nestling. What on earth had they in common with us? At that point very little—notably a tendency to hunt with their eyes rather than with their noses and a tendency to hold objects in their claws, much as a squirrel or a raccoon does today. Holding and looking as ways of eating and survival, it turned out, were extremely important to these small animals. For as these traits developed, their eyesight became better and better, their eyes working farther and farther around to the fronts of their heads until their depth perception was very keen indeed. This encouraged a more and more precise manipulation of objects, which, in turn, led to a slow evolution away from claws and toward separate fingers with flat nails. Along with these two developments went a marked increase in the size of certain parts of the brain, and—at some point—the ability to distinguish colors.

These were the ancestral primates. Enough of their fossils have been recovered to indicate that many of them were not radically different from several kinds of prosimians that still survive in Africa and Asia. For 30 or 40 million years the prosimian stock was tremendously successful in the tropical forests of the world, and during that time it began to produce a variety of types that were increasingly like what we would now recognize as monkeys or apes. In the process, most of the earlier types faded away; surviving prosimians are much reduced in number and variety from what they were in the past, and the prevailing opinion among anthropologists is that the newer-model monkeys—bigger, stronger, better coordinated, and above all much more intelligent—have largely taken over from them.

What were those ancestors, those prosimians-on-the-way-to-becoming-monkeys, like? Unfortunately we do not know very much about them. Like human fossils, those of the other primates and proto-primates are scarce. The reasons are generally the same—they were animals following a mode of life that did not lend itself to fossilization and living in areas that hastened the disintegration of their bones. Actually, conditions were even a little worse for them. For one thing, we must search farther back in time for them, with every step into the past decreasing the likelihood that any of their remains will have survived to the present. For another, many of them were small creatures; small bones and teeth are harder to find than large ones. Thus it is that the 40 million years of gradual edging toward "monkeyishness" that the early prosimians underwent has produced only a few drawersful of fossils—enough, however, to indicate that their evolutionary development was very slow. It was not until the late Eocene, about 40 million years ago, that anything like a monkey showed up. What appeared then was a creature named *Amphipithecus*, a small piece of whose jaw has been found in Burma; but this animal is so dimly seen on this distant boundary line between prosimians and monkeys that it is hard to tell if it actually foreshadowed monkey development or not.

For a better clue, we must move ahead 10 million years to the Oligocene, and to a spot in the Egyptian desert about 60 miles southwest of Cairo. This is a shallow dip in the landscape known as the Fayum Depression. It is one of the driest places on earth today but in Oligocene times the Mediterranean reached this far inland and the Fayum lay on the borderline between sea and forest, with tropical rivers emptying into the Mediterranean along this early shore. In the Fayum is a uniquely rich deposit of early primate fossils, and among these one in particular stands out. This is named *Oligopithecus*, after the epoch in which it lived; it is the oldest known candidate for inclusion in the line of Old World monkeys. (It should be noted here that the Old World monkeys are a distinct group from those of Central and South America, the so-called New World monkeys, which split off from the prosimian line considerably farther back in time and are not closely related to Old World monkeys at all, though they much resemble them in form and habits. Thus, these New World monkeys play no part in human evolution.)

WHAT makes *Oligopithecus* seem like a monkey or an ape, instead of a prosimian? This brings up the question of teeth, and also gives us the first opportunity to illustrate how the paleontologist can deduce as much as he does from one piece of fossil evidence. Teeth, being the hardest substances in the body, endure the longest. As a consequence, there are more of them than there are of other bones knocking about in the fossil collections of the world, and they have been more intensively studied. It did not take long for anatomists to realize that most prosimians (fossil and modern types alike) have some 34 or more teeth, whereas nearly all Old World monkeys—also apes and men—have only 32. This is a radical difference and represents a huge evolutionary jump. It also makes a rather special exhibit out of *Oligopithecus*, for it is the oldest known primate to have 32 teeth—a sure sign of monkeyishness.

In addition, its teeth have a very revealing shape. Looked at from the top, its molars each have four bumps, or cusps, for chewing. All grinding teeth are cusped, and such animals as horses and elephants have some extremely elegant corrugations on the tops of their molars. But a bilophodont pattern—four cusps connected in pairs by small ridges—is found only among Old World monkeys. A four-cusped fossil tooth, therefore, can only belong to a fossil monkey or to some sort of creature on the way to becoming a monkey.

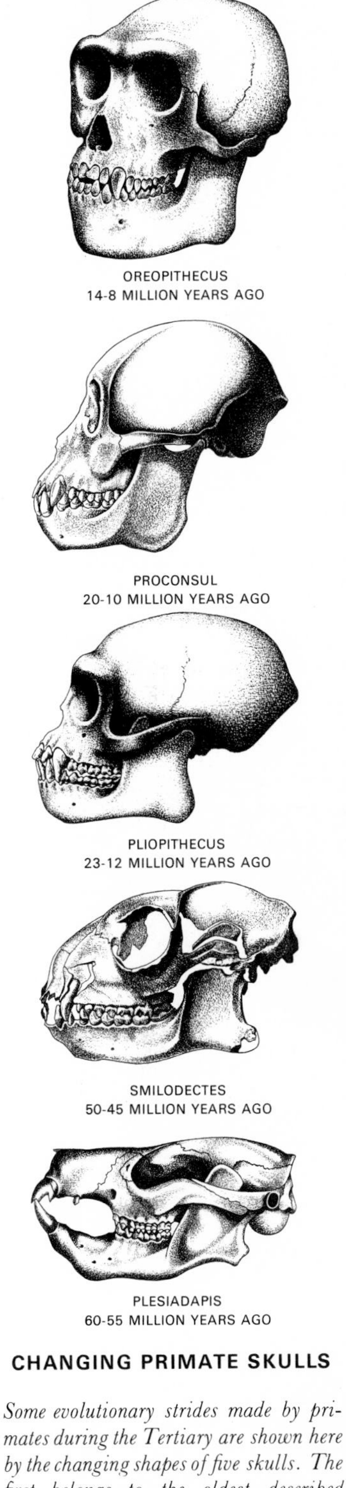

CHANGING PRIMATE SKULLS

Some evolutionary strides made by primates during the Tertiary are shown here by the changing shapes of five skulls. The first belongs to the oldest described prosimian, the rodentlike Plesiadapis. In the next, the skull of the prosimian Smilodectes, an enlarged cranium and forward-directed eyes are already seen. Pliopithecus, in addition to a development of these features, shows a radical flattening and foreshortening of the face. Proconsul's apelike skull is still further refined, while Oreopithecus looks like the aberrant ape it was.

Thirty-two teeth, then, with the bilophodont cusp pattern, is diagnostic of monkeys. But one swallow does not make a summer, nor do a few cusps necessarily make a monkey out of a fossil. Hopefully, the comparative anatomist will be able to find other things that all monkeys have in common and that separate them from all other animals. Such a list of characteristics is known as a "grade of organization." Each genus of living animals has its grade of organization, and how closely one overlaps with others will determine how closely two or more genera are related. For example, dogs and wolves have so many structural and behavioral characteristics in common that even a non-scientist would have no difficulty in recognizing that they are very closely related. In the same way, though both dogs and wolves share with cats the traits of four-leggedness, warm-bloodedness, infant-care, sharp-toothedness and a great many others, they are still less like cats than they are like each other.

It is by systematically and laboriously building up grades of organization for fossils that the paleontologist begins to get a pattern of relationships among long-extinct types. His evidence may be frustratingly meager, but each fragment that is added to it will either increase the similarity of one animal's grade of organization to another animal's or decrease it. And as the bits of evidence are sorted out, enough characteristics like bilophodontism may finally be nailed down for an expert to state with a considerable degree of conviction, "Yes, this one is a monkey or a direct monkey ancestor, while that one has too many un-monkeyish characteristics and is something else."

FROM this kind of detective work it has been concluded that *Oligopithecus* lies probably on the main monkey-ancestral line. Aside from its teeth we do not know much about it. It was apparently about a foot high—no bigger than a chicken, really—and, like all monkeys, it was a true quadruped. It probably lies a little off to one side as a direct ancestor of man, for even then it was not the only pithecoid scampering about in the forests of the Fayum. There were, in fact, a great many of them. One in particular, named *Propliopithecus*, had characteristics that are not so much monkeylike as apelike—which is another way of saying that it was more manlike, for apes and men are actually closer together in their grades of organization than apes and monkeys.

When the principal differences between apes and monkeys are spelled out, the "mannishness" of the former is unmistakable. The most obvious of these are in the trunk skeleton, reflecting the fact that monkeys are quadrupedal animals

WHAT TEETH CAN TELL

Enduring teeth, often the only fossils an anthropologist has to work with, are an enormous help in classification. Canines, incisors, premolars and molars differ widely in numbers, shape and size among primates. Thus, the lemur with 36, combines canines and incisors in a "dental comb." In the baboon the canines are long and heavy; in the chimpanzee and man they are much reduced; and like all Old World monkeys, baboons have 32 teeth, as do apes and man.

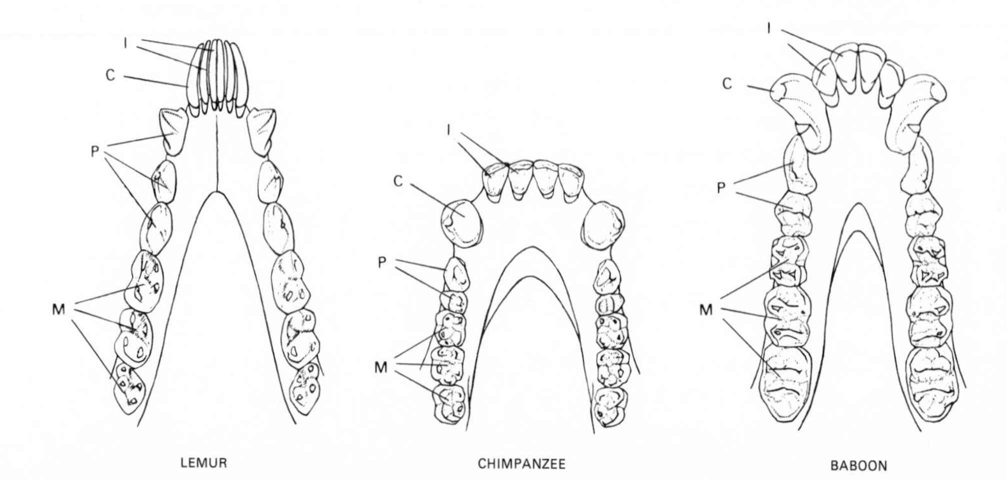

that are built to go on all fours and do so most of the time, and that apes, by contrast, tend to be upright. This does not mean that they spend their time walking around on their hind legs as men do. However, they *can* do this, and some of them quite often do so. Reflecting this tendency toward an erect posture, an ape has much more flexible arms and shoulders for hand-over-hand swinging or climbing. Its elbows and wrists are both more limber than a monkey's, and the arrangement and proportions of its limb muscles are also different. Its spinal column is shorter and stiffer than the more springlike spinal column of a typical monkey. Its pelvis is broadened and enlarged to support the weight of its body over its legs. The ape head is balanced more or less atop the spinal column, rather than being thrust forward, and its brain is larger and more complex. Its viscera—those internal organs like the stomach, intestines and liver—are also arranged and attached differently to the inner body wall. They would have to be, or else they would tend to sag and crush one another when their owner was in a semi-erect posture.

These are some of the major differences that we find today between monkeys and apes. Unfortunately we do not have conclusive vertebral or pelvic evidence from either *Oligopithecus* or *Propliopithecus* to confirm their apelike condition, but we do have teeth.

We have seen that Old World monkeys have four-cusped molars. By contrast, apes have five-cusped lower molars, as do ape prototypes and men. *Propliopithecus* has left us a legacy of teeth from the Fayum, and they have five cusps. It, therefore, must be considered on or near the main line of ape and human descent. This small but exceedingly important bit of tooth evidence proves that already the lines that would lead to monkeys and the lines that would lead to apes had begun to differentiate. When and how the fifth cusp that underscores this branching apart first made its appearance is not yet known. In fact, little or nothing was known about either *Oligopithecus* or *Propliopithecus* until expeditions from Yale University to the Fayum in 1961 and 1963 recovered enough fragments to reach the dramatic conclusions about them that are printed here. Now that more *Propliopithecus* fossils are known to exist, the hope of finding others is quickened. Like a man struggling to solve a problem in mathematics, his chance of success is much greater if he knows there is a solution than if he is simply staring at a mass of figures that may have no significance at all. Similarly, discovery of a fossil stimulates further search. If more pieces are found, there is always the chance that they may be from other parts of the body, making it possible to deduce whether or not *Propliopithecus* was veering toward apishness in other ways than in its teeth.

The whole Fayum picture is one of exceptional interest. The fossils in it are numerous and varied, and they throw considerable light on the problem of when monkeys and apes began to differentiate from one another. They make it clear, for example, that if a joint ancestor to the two groups is to be found, the search will have to be conducted somewhat farther back in time than students have been accustomed to thinking. Already in the Fayum there is good evidence that some of the primates were on the monkey line and a whole array of others on the ape line. More than that, it is beginning to be apparent that the apelike ones even then had begun to show some of the characteristics that now account for the differences among today's apes. There were little tree-swinging pre-gibbons, indicating that there was already a division between the types that would lead to modern gibbons and modern great apes, for these

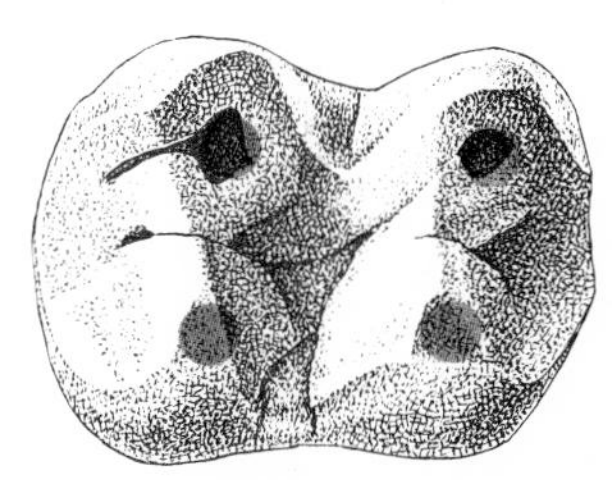

BABOON

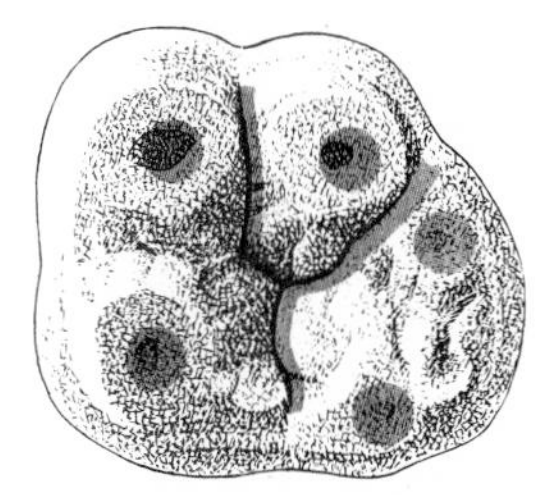

CHIMPANZEE

THE "Y-5" PATTERN

Often a single tooth can indicate whether its owner was a monkey, an ape or possibly a man. Old World monkeys, like the baboon at top, have four ridges or cusps on their molars. Only apes and man have five, and these are arranged in such a way that a figure "Y" can be drawn in the valleys between the cusps. This "Y-5" pattern, shown here on a chimpanzee, may vary according to the size of the cusps. Basically, however, it has persisted for more than 24 million years since it appeared among the ancestors of the dryopithecines, the stock from which came the apes and eventually man.

BONES OF CONTENTION

Ramapithecus punjabicus, whose jaws are shown here in reconstruction, was not only the most advanced of the dryopithecines but perhaps even a hominid. It might have been so classified much earlier had not confusion surrounded its pitifully few remains. For almost three decades, fragments of upper and lower jaws found by George E. Lewis in 1934 (black) were thought to belong to two entirely different genera, while other similar fragments, unearthed in India in 1910, had long been assigned to a third, more primitive genus. In 1963 Elwyn Simons, examining a canine (solid color) dug up in Africa, decided to reevaluate the whole Ramapithecus question. He discovered that the African canine fitted the upper jaw from India—and that both sets of jaws belonged to the same creature, Ramapithecus, a primate that had ranged throughout Africa and Asia 14 million years ago.

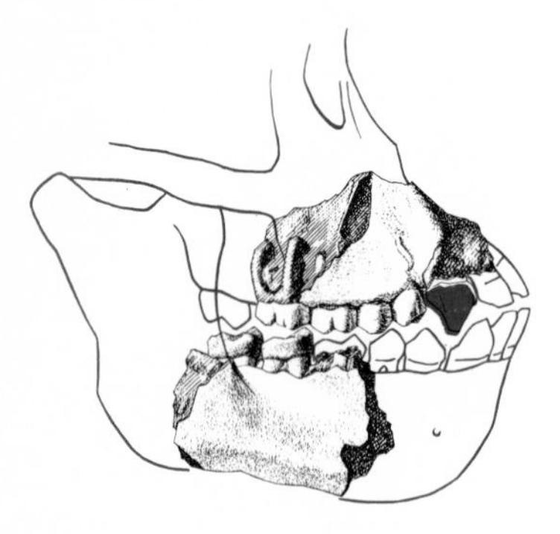

early swingers were already so specialized that they could not be ancestral to chimpanzees or gorillas. In addition there were examples of an aberrant apelike type that no longer exists. There were also both large and small types whose relationship to the other modern apes is suspected but which has not yet been worked out because of the scarcity of their fossil remains. Further work in the Fayum, and more study of the bones that come out of it, cannot fail to throw more light on this fascinating subject.

One Fayum fossil about which we know somewhat more is some 10 million years younger than *Propliopithecus*. It bears the shorter name of *Pliopithecus* and it lived during the Miocene epoch about 20 million years ago. Its remains have been known to scientists for well over a hundred years, but good evaluation of them has not been possible until the recent recovery of additional fossil fragments from a number of places both in Europe and Africa, the newest of these being from Czechoslovakia in 1957.

These latest finds of *Pliopithecus* have produced a skull and most of a skeleton, and we can reconstruct it in some detail. It had an unmistakably flat apish face, five-cusped teeth, free-swinging arms, a semi-upright posture and most definitely occupies a position somewhere along the ape ancestral line. With it we have at last emerged from the murk of trying to decide whether a given creature is more like a monkey or more like an ape; now we are confronted with the narrower problem of which kind of ape *Pliopithecus* might most resemble. The general consensus is that it is probably ancestral to the gibbon. It has a face, jaws and teeth that are all strongly suggestive of modern gibbons, but it lacks the extremely elongated forearm and hooking fingers which were presumably developed later by gibbons as special adaptations for efficient brachiation.

Of the four kinds of apes—the gibbon, orangutan, gorilla and chimpanzee—the gibbon is considered to be the least like a human being and the chimpanzee or gorilla the most. Therefore, if we could hit on a chimpanzeelike or gorillalike fossil from the Miocene, we presumably would have something even closer to ancestral man. Such an animal exists. Its name is *Proconsul*, and it was discovered on a small island in Lake Victoria, Kenya, in the 1930s. The man who discovered it was L.S.B. Leakey, who, with his wife Mary, has devoted an entire life to primate fossil hunting in East Africa. The first *Proconsul* finds were a sensation. They were shipped to England where their close affinity to chimpanzees was immediately recognized. Indeed, the very name *Proconsul* is a kind of professional anthropological joke, "pro" meaning before, and "consul" being the name of an actual chimpanzee very well known to zoo-goers in London. It is an apt name; *Proconsul* is either a pre-chimp or the next thing to it. As the Yale geologist and paleontologist Elwyn Simons puts it, it shows "some monkey-like traits of hand, skull and brain, but hominoid and even partially hominid characteristics of face, jaw and dentition." Hominoid, in its literal translation, means manlike. Actually, however, it is used to describe both apes and men in order to distinguish them from monkeys. Hominid also means manlike but it excludes apes; a hominid is an actual man or a manlike creature directly ancestral to man. Simons' statement, therefore, describes a type that has some of the attributes of a monkey, some of an ape and some that might even be construed to lead directly to man.

Confusing? Indefinite? Tentative? Yes—all these things. But we must not forget that *Proconsul* lived 20 million years ago, at a time when monkeys and apes—to say nothing of men—had yet to appear. It is not surprising that at this early date it had some of the characteristics of all three. Another puzzle about *Proconsul* is that it comes in a number of sizes. Some are as small as pygmy chimpanzees, others are as large as gorillas. But they all have structural characteristics in common that place them in the same genus. Large or small, we may guess, but we cannot yet state with any conviction, that *Proconsul* may have fathered both chimpanzees and gorillas.

This brings us very close to the ancestral human line; can we place *Proconsul* on it? Unfortunately, not quite. To understand why, we must go back to teeth and jaws once more. If the reader of this book will open his mouth wide and stand in front of a mirror, he will notice two things about his upper jaw. The first is that his hard palate—the roof of his mouth—is arched. The second is that his teeth go back on each side in a broad curve, with the widest part of the curve at the very back. By contrast, the hard palate of an ape is flat and its jaws are U-shaped. The sides of the U are parallel, with the result that the backmost molars are no farther apart than those nearer the front of the mouth, clearly different from the human condition.

Proconsul has those apelike parallel rows of molars. From this it must be inferred that his descendants were apes and not men—unless, of course, we assume that the broadly curving jaw was a later evolutionary development. It was quickly proved not to be. Digging in the Siwalik Hills of India in the 1930s, G. E. Lewis of Yale University found one of those wide-curving jaws with an arched palate. He named his find *Ramapithecus*, and on the strength of these two manlike features, announced that of all the tangle of Miocene ape-forebears, this one not only belonged to a different genus from the others but also was the most manlike of the lot. This was a sanguine step—too sanguine, many specialists felt, for Lewis' specimen consisted of only part of an upper jaw with a few teeth attached. To anchor the entire human line to such a small fragment of fossil seemed to be rushing things. Furthermore, there was another wide-jawed type rattling about in the museums. He bore the confusing name of *Bramapithecus* and was known only by a lower jaw. With commendable caution the scientific fraternity sat back to see whether the upper-jawed *Ramapithecus* or the lower-jawed *Bramapithecus*—or perhaps another pithecus entirely—would end up with the honors.

NOTHING much happened for a quarter of a century. Then Leakey—the finder of *Proconsul*—hit pay dirt again in Africa with an upper jaw that so closely matched that of *Ramapithecus* that it, too, is now called *Ramapithecus*. Furthermore, potassium-argon dating of this new jaw was possible. It confirmed an age of 14 million years—contemporaneous with *Ramapithecus*. From these two finds, a pretty good upper jaw with all its teeth could be reconstructed. Now there was no blinking the unmistakably manlike sweep of those upper teeth. Furthermore, with a whole set of them now in place, another strongly human characteristic revealed itself; they were all about the same size. Among apes, the front teeth—the incisors and canines—tend to be conspicuously longer.

The matching up of the Lewis find and the Leakey find into one good *Ramapithecus* jaw was suggested by Elwyn Simons of Yale, and the identification of the two as a single species (although one came from India and one from Africa) was pushed by him. Hoping to further strengthen *Ramapithecus*' credentials, he decided to search all the fossil collections at Yale and other places to see if he could not find some clues that had been overlooked by previous examiners. For one thing, he was puzzled by the fact that of the only two curve-jawed types

OF TEETH AND PALATES

How can scientists claim, on the basis of some teeth and part of a palate (top), that Ramapithecus was manlike? One sure sign is that the canines are relatively small as compared to those of the apes; another is that the pre-molars are evenly proportioned. Most important of all, the palate is arched and curves outward toward the back, like man's; all apes and monkeys have flat palates in a U-shape, with teeth in parallel rows. By superimposing Ramapithecus' teeth and palate first on an orangutan's (middle) and then on a human's, their manishness becomes immediately apparent.

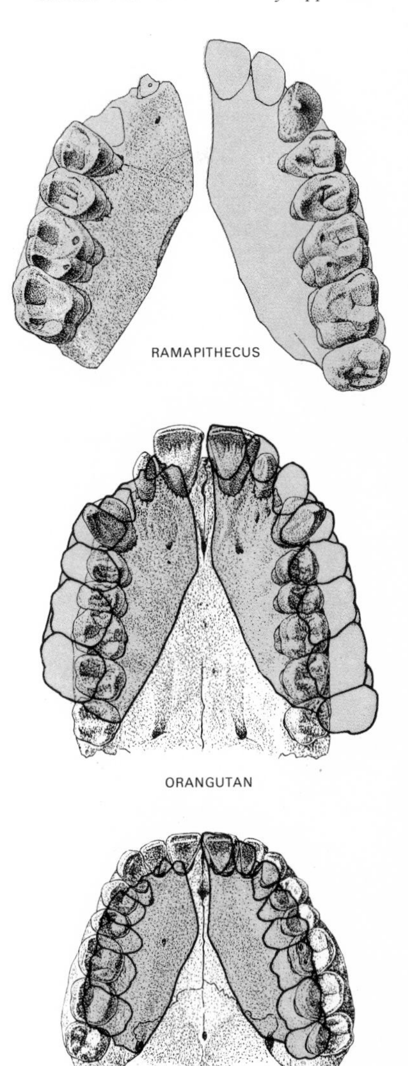

known, one *(Ramapithecus)* was represented only by upper jaws, and the other *(Bramapithecus)* only by lowers. Puzzling over this, it occurred to him to put them together. They fitted—*Bramapithecus* and *Ramapithecus* are the same. Thanks to Simons, the name *Bramapithecus* is now dropped from the list and *Ramapithecus* has both an upper and a lower jaw. Its credentials as man's oldest known direct ancestor are thus advanced one step further.

The impressive thing about *Ramapithecus* is that each bit of additional evidence about it has tended to strengthen rather than weaken the claim being made for it. If this continues a bit longer, its position in the human ancestral line should be secure. For—going back to grades of organization again—the more evidence that can be assembled leading toward one kind of creature, the more likely it becomes that further evidence will fit. Very quickly this likelihood becomes overwhelming; one simply does not find a jaw like *Ramapithecus'* on the body of a quadrupedal animal, any more than one would find grasping toes associated with the fossil remains of a horse.

So anthropologists are eagerly awaiting the next *Ramapithecus* find—if it should come. They are also following Elwyn Simons' example and taking some sophisticated second looks at the bones now in their possession. As more and more of this rechecking goes on, the clouds that have obscured the Miocene primate picture can only begin to thin out. The situation is far more complicated than has been indicated in this necessarily brief chapter. There are many pithecuses that have not been mentioned at all—*Parapithecus*, *Oreopithecus*, *Dryopithecus*, *Aeolopithecus*, *Aegyptopithecus*, *Limnopithecus*—to mention just a few. All exist in lamentably small fragments; and which definitely belongs with which is still being unraveled. What they do make clear, from the abundant and varied fossil beds of the Fayum in particular, is that the primate tree had nothing like a central trunk but was a luxuriant vine with many shoots and tendrils growing side by side, sometimes withering and dying, sometimes branching. And in those branches we see extremely ancient prosimianlike types, more advanced monkeylike and apelike types, and finally a group that belongs definitely in the ape line alone and from which it is possible to begin to pick out the directions which the apes themselves would go. Some of these were more like gibbons; and *Pliopithecus*, for example, might almost be called a gibbon that had not yet become specialized. Others certainly—but which ones we do not yet know for sure—were ancestral to the larger apes.

ALL this falls into the category of anthropological "hot news" since much of the organizing of the Miocene's primate fossil record is only a couple of years old, some of its most significant interpretations even newer. It is a far clearer picture than was possible as recently as five years ago. That it may be turned inside out by other discoveries is always a possibility, but like grades of organization among individual animals, there are what might be called grades of organization for larger scientific assumptions too. The more evidence that is collected to support them, the more unlikely it becomes that they will be upset.

The Miocene, then, during about 10 million years, saw the development of a number of proto-apes. They were widely distributed through Europe, Asia and Africa; they were evolving rather rapidly; and they may well have been exceedingly numerous. Toward the end of the Miocene, about 14 million years ago, one of them, *Ramapithecus*, began to show unmistakable hominid traits, and until a better candidate comes along, may be considered ancestral to man. The longer its claim is allowed to stand, the stronger it will become.

DATING BACK SOME TWO MILLION YEARS, THE JAWS OF AUSTRALOPITHECUS HAVE ADDED DETAILS TO THE STORY OF HUMAN EVOLUTION.

Becoming Man

It is now a proven scientific fact that man was millions of years in the making. The path of his evolution is marked by dead ends and new beginnings, the wayside strewn with relics of his various forms. Though many of these remains are at best minimal, they are enough to sketch out the key stages of his march through time; the chief problem facing anthropologists today is to fill in the gaps.

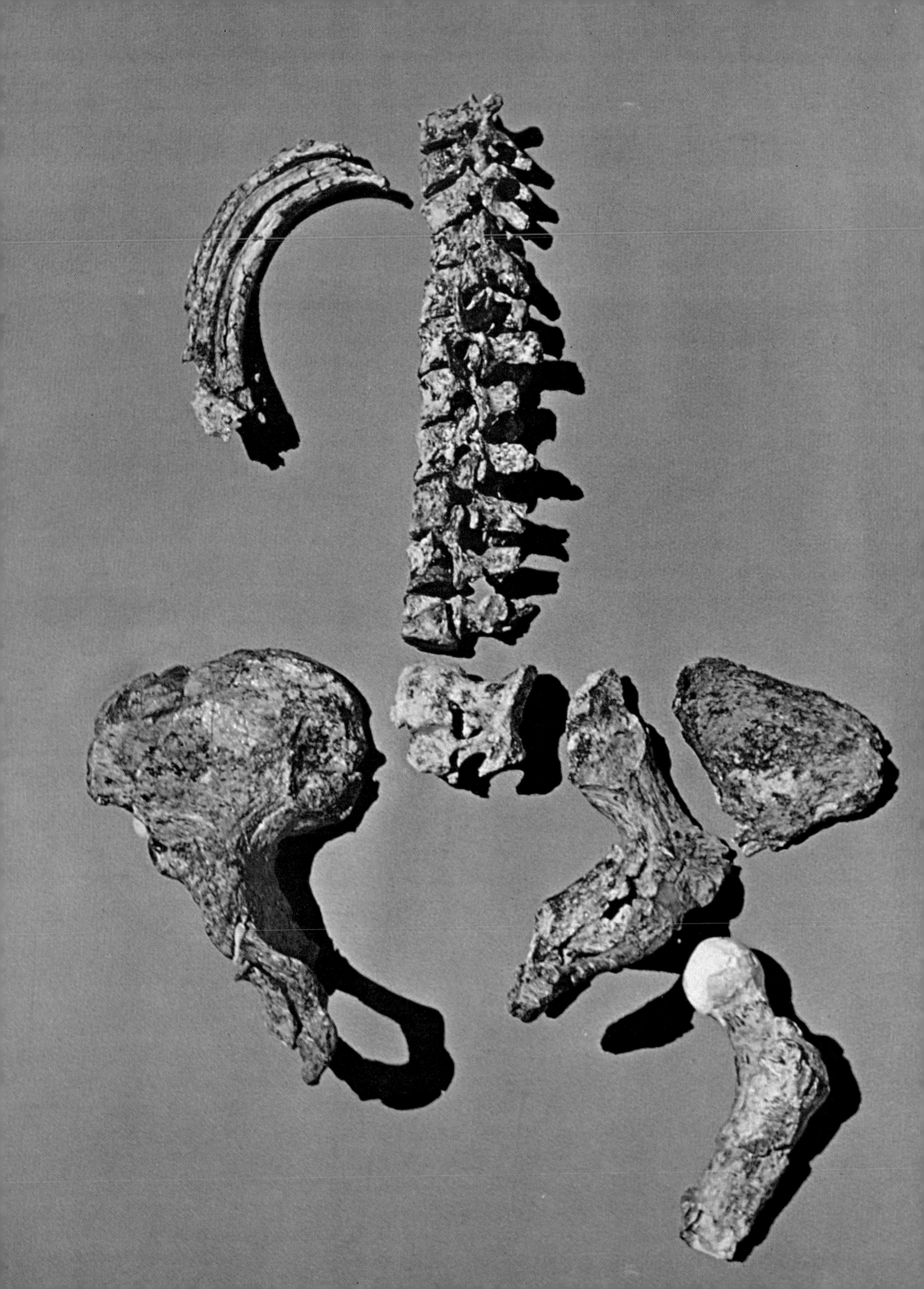

The Road to Homo Sapiens

What were the stages of man's long march from apelike ancestors to *sapiens?* Beginning at right and progressing across four more pages are milestones of primate and human evolution as scientists know them today, pieced together from the fragmentary fossil evidence. It is a revealing story, not only for the creatures it shows, but also because it graphically illustrates how much can be learned from how little: the seemingly chaotic collection of bones at left, for example, can give a quite complete picture of how *Australopithecus* might have walked—a bipedal creature at the very dawn of man.

Many of the figures shown here have been built up from far fewer fragments—a jaw, some teeth perhaps, as indicated by the white highlights—and thus are products of educated guessing. But even if later finds should dictate changes, these reconstructions serve a purpose in showing how these creatures might have looked. When they lived can be seen from the geological time scale across the top—blue for the proto-apes, red and purple for the hominids and the first men, green for *Homo sapiens*. Breaks in the ribbons signify extinction of a line or gaps in the fossil record. Although proto-apes and apes were quadrupedal, all are shown here standing for purposes of comparison.

A SPINE, ribs and hip bones of *Australopithecus* reveal not only his approximate height and weight but, most important of all, his upright posture and bipedal gait.

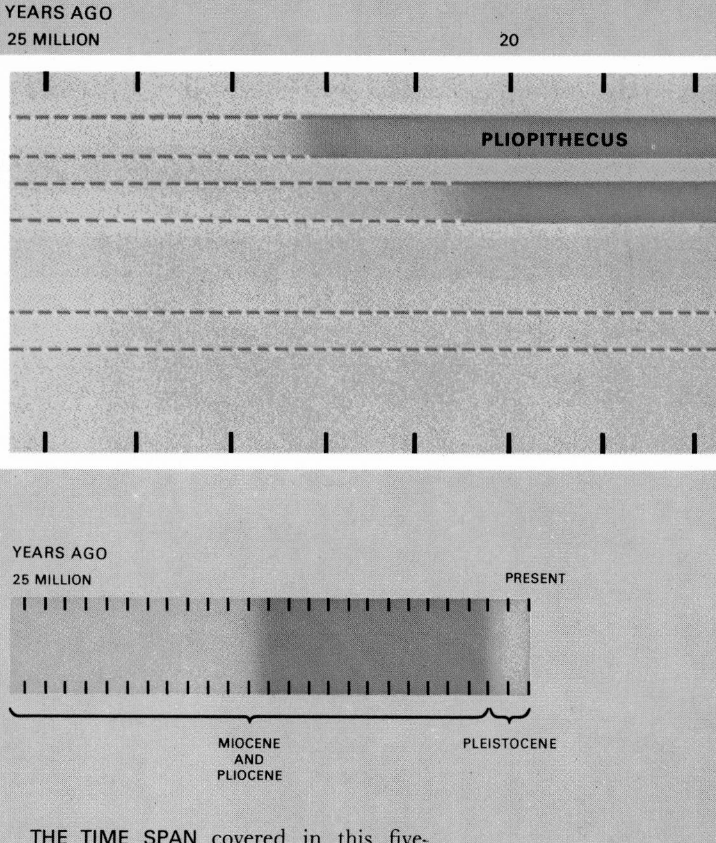

THE TIME SPAN covered in this five-page foldout is 25 million years, beginning with the Miocene and ending with the present. Years are marked off first in millions, then, in hundreds of thousands.

PLIOPITHECUS

One of the earliest proto-apes, *Pliopithecus* had the look of a modern gibbon although its arms were not as disproportionately long and specialized for swinging through the trees. On the basis of its teeth and skull it is now classed as an ancestor of the gibbon line.

PROCONSUL

Known from numerous fragments adding up to almost complete skeletons, *Proconsul* is considered to be a very early ape, the ancestor of the chimpanzee and perhaps of the gorilla. A contemporary of *Pliopithecus*, it is often found with it in the same fossil site.

LIFT AND UNFOLD, DO NOT TEAR

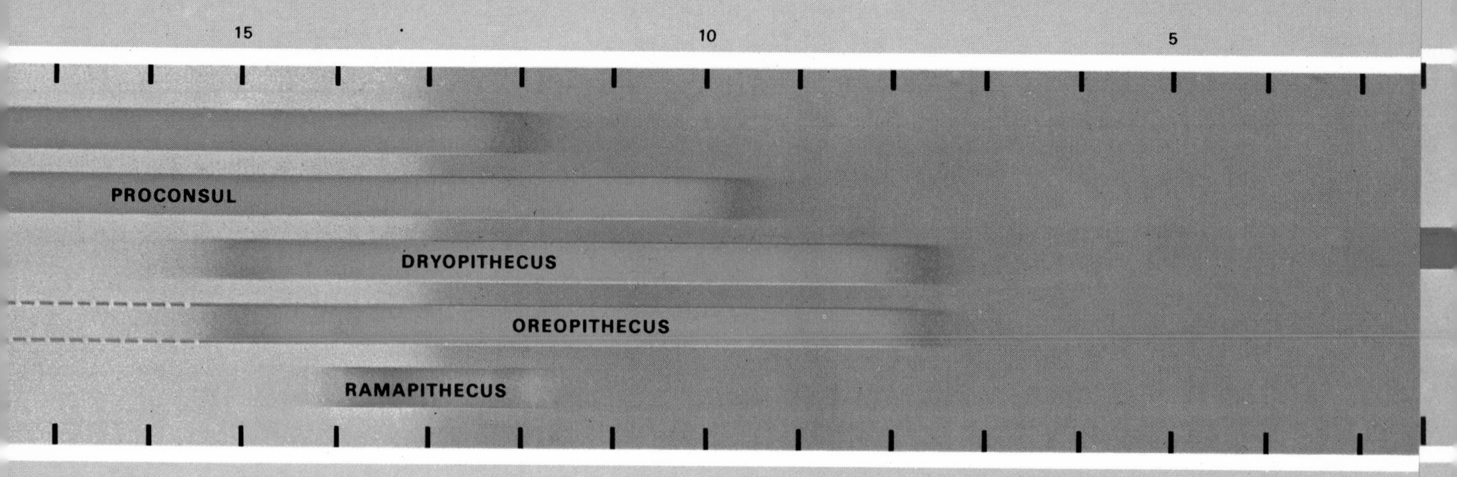

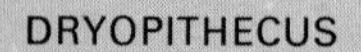

DRYOPITHECUS

Though its skeleton is tantalizingly incomplete, *Dryopithecus* can be fairly described from a few jaws and teeth. First of the fossil great apes to be discovered, it was widely distributed; remains have been unearthed throughout Europe, in North India and China.

OREOPITHECUS

A likely side branch on man's family tree, *Oreopithecus* is believed to have stood around four feet tall and weighed about 80 pounds. Its teeth and pelvis led scientists to wonder if it could be ancestral to man, but apparently it became extinct some 8 million years ago.

RAMAPITHECUS

The earliest manlike primate found so far, *Ramapithecus* is now thought by some experts to be the oldest of man's ancestors in a direct line. This hominid status is predicated upon a few teeth, some fragments of jaw and a palate unmistakably human in shape.

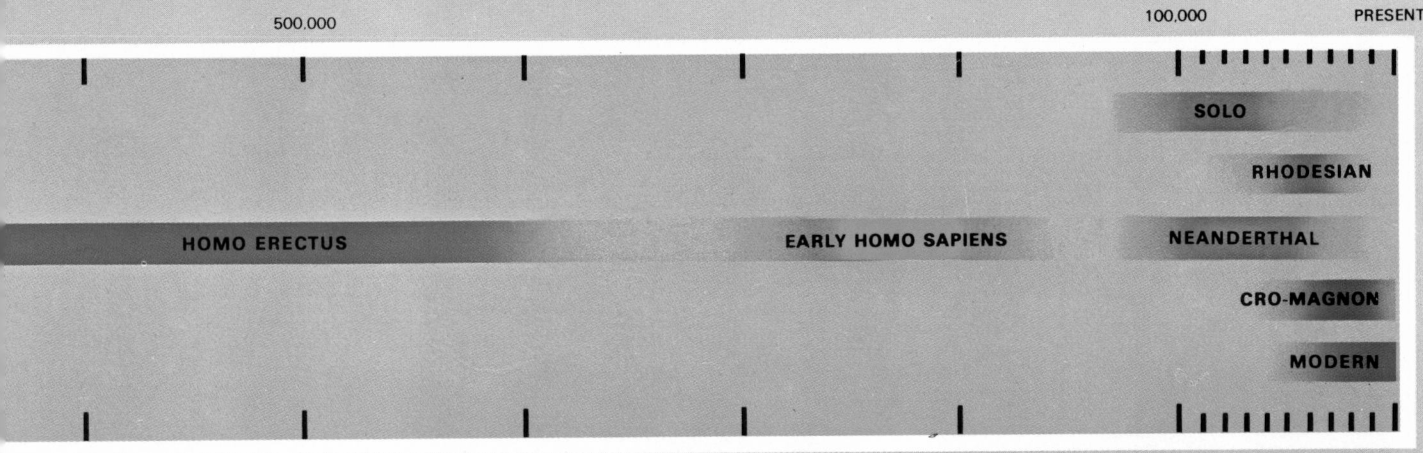

500,000 100,000 PRESENT

SOLO
RHODESIAN
HOMO ERECTUS
EARLY HOMO SAPIENS
NEANDERTHAL
CRO-MAGNON
MODERN

NEANDERTHAL MAN

Not nearly as brutish a fellow as his name has come to connote, Neanderthal man, whose peoples rimmed the Mediterranean and dotted Europe, had a cranial capacity in some cases larger than that of modern man. He made a variety of tools advanced in design.

CRO-MAGNON MAN

Only a cultural step away from modern man, Cro-Magnon man has left the world his art—cave paintings, stone engravings and carved figures. He replaced the Neanderthals in Europe and, diversifying in many populations, seems to have colonized the world.

MODERN MAN

Physically, modern man differs little from Cro-Magnon man. What sets the two apart is culture; by learning how to grow his own food and domesticate animals, man could afford to give up his nomadic life and found permanent settlements—and civilizations.

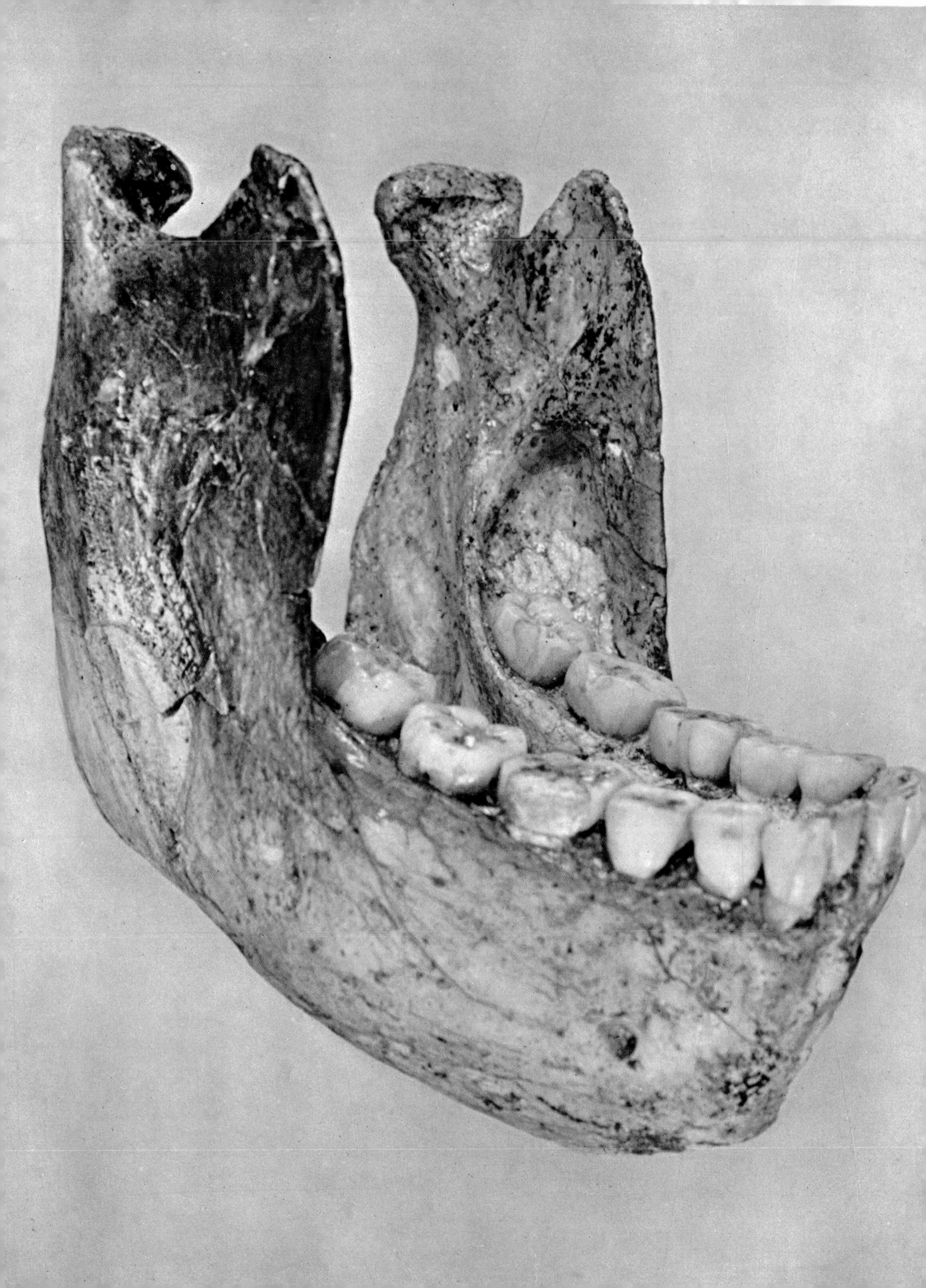

HUGE MOLARS and premolars and diminutive front teeth set in a massive jaw characterize the man-ape *Paranthropus*. Many remains of this creature have come from intensively dug sites in sub-Saharan Africa.

3

Forward from the Apes

In the last chapter we left *Ramapithecus* teetering between apishness and mannishness. But how far it teetered in our direction is still impossible to say since all we have of it is jaws and teeth. We have no leg or hip or spinal bone to tell us whether it stood erect like a man or only aspired to, like an ape. However, considering the number and variety of primate fossils recovered in recent years from the late Miocene and early Pliocene, we should be able to look confidently ahead to finding even more illuminating ones to fill the gap between this time and the beginning of the Pleistocene.

Astonishingly, and maddeningly, we find nothing. Almost the entire Pliocene, for reasons that science is still trying to explain, is a total blank as far as human ancestors are concerned. For some 10 million years that exasperating and cryptic epoch lasted, and during it profound evolutionary changes occurred among certain of the higher primates. New creatures emerged, primates unlike any that lived before. No longer forest apes, they made their living increasingly on the open plains, moving erect on two legs.

The importance of bipedalism—two-leggedness—cannot be overestimated. It is much more than a mere rearing up and running about. Readers of the previous book in this series, *The Primates*, will remember that apes and monkeys have all sorts of structural handicaps that hamper them in this respect; they stand in a perpetual crouch, unable to extend their legs fully; they walk on the sides of their feet. They *can* move on two legs, and sometimes do for short distances, but they are not made for it. For man, however, this is the way of life; he cannot function properly in any other way. With bipedalism are associated other equally important matters: the freeing of the hands for using tools and the development of larger, more complex brains. Somehow, somewhere, in the long blank space of the Pliocene, these adaptations made their appearance in at least one kind of Miocene primate.

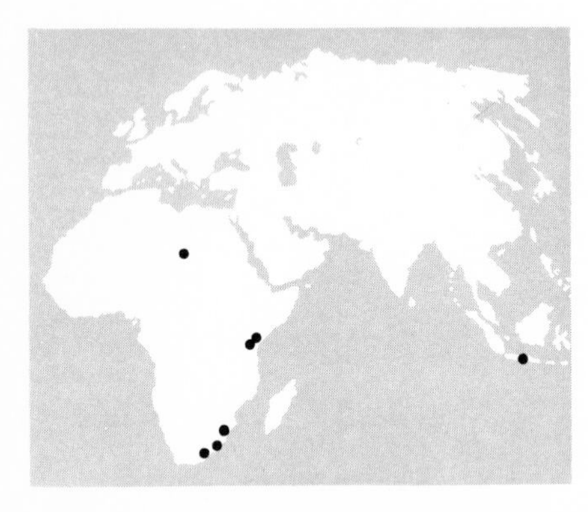

WHERE AUSTRALOPITHECINES HAVE BEEN FOUND

With only one exception, australopithecine finds (black dots) have been limited to Africa and that exception is still in dispute. This map indicates all the sites known to date: South Africa, East Africa, Chad and a suspected find in Java.

The first tangible evidence that something so endowed actually existed came in 1924. Raymond Dart, a professor of anatomy at the University of Witwatersrand in Johannesburg, South Africa, had the habit of encouraging his pupils to collect fossils and bring them back to the anatomy museum. One student brought in an unusual fossil baboon skull that had come from a limestone quarry 200 miles away. The quarry owner was persuaded to save other bone-bearing material for Dart, and in due course he was sent two boxes of broken rock containing fossils. Opening these up, Dart found nothing of interest in the first box, but his eye hit on something very strange in the second. This was the cast, or mold, of the interior of a skull, but it was not like any baboon skull that Dart had ever seen. Its proportions were different, and it was larger, impossibly larger. Scarcely allowing himself to think what this might mean, he went through the remainder of the box and found another piece of rock with a curved depression into which the stone skull-cast fitted perfectly. In this second rock Dart could dimly perceive the outline of a broken piece of skull and the back of a lower jaw. He was looking from the rear at the inside of something's —or somebody's—head, which had been broken away by the quarry workers.

Working intensively at his discoveries during every spare moment for months, painstakingly picking away tiny bits of rock, Dart gradually revealed the face and most of the skull of a child five or six years old. He named it *Australopithecus africanus*, the South African Ape, declaring that it stood "intermediate between living anthropoids and man."

CONFIDENT from the beginning in the nature of his find, Dart published a description of it less than four months after he had discovered it—record time for the deliberate treatment usually given such momentous events. His report was intensely interesting to a number of scientists in Europe—not so much for the manlike attributes he claimed for it as for the inexplicable presence of an ape so far south. The general conclusion was that this was some kind of chimpanzeelike or gorillalike species, but how it had wandered way down there, where no ape had ever before been known to go, was extremely puzzling. For this suggested the existence of large tracts of forest in South Africa—an awkward suggestion indeed, because the Pliocene was a dry period, with forests shrinking away toward the equator. As a result of these puzzles, the Taung baby—as Dart's skull came to be known, from the local name of the place where it was found—had to endure a long apprenticeship of skepticism.

But Dart stuck to his guns. One thing that made him feel sure that he was dealing with a true bipedal creature was that the foramen magnum, the hole through which the nerves of the spinal cord pass into the skull on their way to the brain, faced almost directly downward. This indicated that in life the Taung baby had carried its head over its spine like a rock balanced on the top of a pole; in apes and monkeys the foramen magnum is near the back of the skull, reflecting the more nearly horizontal position of the spinal column. Whatever verdict the scientific establishment would eventually pass on the Taung baby, Dart was certain that it stood erect.

Soon he had an ally. A paleontologist working in South Africa, Robert Broom, examined the Taung baby, became convinced that Dart was right, and said so in print. But the two men had no adult skull to confirm their belief, nor did they have any leg or pelvic bones to support the evidence of erectness that the foramen magnum suggested. Broom was determined to find them, but it was not until the 1930s that he was free to begin a serious search. Then, from two new South African fossil sites, he was able to recover enough fragments to piece together several almost complete adult skulls. He found other body bones as well, and finally parts of several pelvises that confirmed that their owners had been two-legged. All this evidence fitted and strengthened Dart's original concept of *Australopithecus*, although the individuals from the two sites were not quite alike. Apparently more than one kind of erect pre-man had once wandered about South Africa.

For his part, Dart continued to pick away at his baby skull, working almost daily for more than four years, and eventually succeeded in separating the upper and lower jaws, which had been cemented together in the rock-hard mass of breccia that enclosed them. Now he could examine the teeth from all sides and in particular get a look at their grinding surfaces. What he found further strengthened his case. Although these were the milk teeth of a child, they were not fundamentally different from those of a human child—less different, in fact, than they were from those of a young ape. One striking thing about them was that the front teeth, the incisors and canines, were relatively small. In apes they are large; they have to be—for tearing up the large amounts of vegetable matter that forms so much of their diet, and also as an aid in defense. Large canines have another characteristic; they extend so far that space must be provided between the teeth of the other jaw to accommodate them. In a previous chapter the reader was invited to look at the inside of his mouth in a mirror. Let him go back and do this again. All his teeth, both uppers and lowers, should be touching those next to them. Let him now look into the mouth of the family dog. Dogs have large canines, and their mouths clearly show the wider spacing of teeth and longer jaws that are necessary to accommodate canines that must interlock instead of merely coming together as human teeth do. Similarly with apes; their jaws are longer than human jaws. They are also heavier, and the muscles needed to move them are more massive, which leads to the development of bony ridges on the skull as anchors for the whole chewing, grinding muscle system. The Taung baby is hominid rather than apelike in all these characteristics. Its jaws are shorter and more lightly made than those of an ape, and its skull lacks the characteristic bony ridges that denote large muscles.

All this is extremely neat and logical, but it leaves some awkward questions unanswered. Why did these australopithecine ancestors come down from the trees? Why did they begin moving out of the relative lushness of the forests into more open country? Why did they get up on their hind legs? What became of their long sharp canine teeth?

The first question—why did they come down from the trees—can be answered fairly confidently. They almost certainly came down for food. But the way of asking it suggests that there was some kind of rational willful decision in the matter, something that the apes themselves elected to do. A decision also suggests a single spot in time and space. A pioneering ape makes it, his descendants follow, and—lo and behold—they are ground dwellers.

A more sophisticated modern view, held by a number of scientists, has recently been summarized by the University of California's Sherwood Washburn. He visualizes the situation as it may have existed at the very end of the Miocene or early in the Pliocene. At that time, in his view, there was a great expanse of tropical forest extending through most of Europe, Asia and a good part of Africa. This, of course, means that there also existed a comparably large amount of forest edge, with opportunities for tree dwellers to descend to the ground and eat the berries, roots, insects and other edibles that abounded in the open. Advanced proto-apes, including *Ramapithecus*, thronged in the forests, probably existing in a number of species, some of which must have been forest-edge animals. Like a good many monkeys and apes today, some of these undoubtedly came to the ground when opportunities for feeding there presented themselves. If it is understood that these "decisions" to come to the ground were repeated billions of times by millions of apes in thousands of different places, then one begins to get a better idea of the process; it was a gradual one, so gradual as to be imperceptible, except over great spans of time. Opportunity and aptitude went together. One was not possible without the other, one encouraged the other. No single decision by a single ape or group of apes had any meaning whatsoever. But, in places which provided a better living on the ground for apes increasingly able to exploit it, and where this situation prevailed for century after century, the ones best adapted to living and feeding on the ground were the ones that spent the most time there, and whose descendants were still better adapted—and so on.

Another point that Washburn makes is that the apes were not "forced" out of the trees. It is true that the drying out and retreat of the Pliocene forests ultimately subtracted several million square miles of arboreal living space from the theoretical ranges of tree-dwelling apes. But here again the process was so gradual that at no time could it conceivably have had any effect on the evolving habits of individual animals. Variations of climate from one year to the next were all that concerned them. If a river goes dry and the trees along it die, the animals that formerly thrived there simply move away, taking their various ways of making a living with them. They do not abandon the trees because the trees disappear; they find other trees.

WASHBURN's third and perhaps most striking observation has to do with erect stance and tool using. Most views on this matter have always been on the side that erect posture came first, that it freed the hands and that tool using followed. Washburn suggests that the reverse is true: tool using preceded walking on two legs; more than that, it led to it. This is an astonishing idea, but the evidence for it and the logic behind it are impressive.

We should not forget that apes, unlike monkeys, already had a tradition of uprightness even before they left the trees. Whereas monkeys jumped about in trees, apes climbed hand over hand. They swung from branches, sat upright in them, and sometimes even stood on them. Their arms were well articulated for reaching in all directions, and an important hand-in-hand development of stereoscopic eyesight, larger brain and improved manual dexterity, had already begun. Apes, in short, had the physical equipment and the dawning brain potential to use their hands in new and useful ways. That certain of them did is suggested by the fact that chimpanzees, man's nearest relatives, come close to being tool users today. They throw stones and sticks. They use sticks, rocks and handfuls of leaves for digging, cracking nuts, wiping themselves and sopping up water. They seek out thin twigs or vines to use as probes, poking them into termite nests and then carefully withdrawing them and eating the insects that cling to them. More significant, if they cannot find appropriate tools for this task, they will make them, stripping the leaves from vine stems. They carry tools around with them and take them to their nests. All of these activities have been observed in the wild state by Jane Goodall, a chimpanzee expert working in East Africa. Miss Goodall also reports that these techniques are learned; young chimps are apt to produce unsuitable tools and become proficient at making acceptable ones only through practice.

From here on, all is speculative. But the speculations have an uncanny way of hanging together. For a tool user, the most useful way of getting about is on two feet since that leaves the hands free to carry things. Chance success with throwing stones and sticks may have led to a dawning realization that rocks and clubs were useful as weapons, even for bringing down small game. In due course, these talents could have made rather formidable animals out of their owners, allowing them to venture farther and farther from the safety of the trees. Eventually they could have become completely ground-oriented, with natural selection operating on them physically to produce animals that were more and more adept at running on two legs.

To a creature increasingly involved with tools, brain development becomes increasingly important, and changes in skull size and shape can be considered as possible results of selection pressure to provide increased brain space. By this time there is no separating the tangled triple influence of bipedalism, brain development and tool using. They are hopelessly interlocked, each depending on and stimulating the others. As one develops, a faster development in another takes place, and this in turn encourages a further development in the first. The process is called positive feedback by scientists, and its operation could well have produced as specialized a creature as *Australopithecus* from the ground-venturing apes that preceded him.

So, it would seem, tools are vital. Indeed, in Washburn's view it appears that they have been vital not for half a million or a million years, as the boldest anthropologists thought not so long ago, but for two, four, five, possibly ten million years—long before men were men. How long may ultimately depend on what one's definition of a tool is. In any event, if two-leggedness does depend on tool use, it stands to reason that *Australopithecus*, who was unquestionably two-legged, must have been a tool user. It would be nice to be able to confirm this by producing some chipped-stone artifacts from the same strata that Dart's and Broom's fossils come from, but here again we are stymied. Experts searched for stone tools to go with *Australopithecus* for years but did not find a single one.

Dart and Broom were themselves not too preoccupied at first with stone tools. *Australopithecus* was such a stunningly ancient and controversial character that for a number of years after his discovery the argument was less over whether he was or was not a tool user than it was over whether he was or was not an ape. All Dart's and Broom's energies were directed to puzzling over the extraordinary anomaly of finding a skull with manlike characteristics in a creature so ancient that it must have been an ape. The fact that it walked erect was an added puzzler. To cap it all, and as already mentioned, was that Dart and

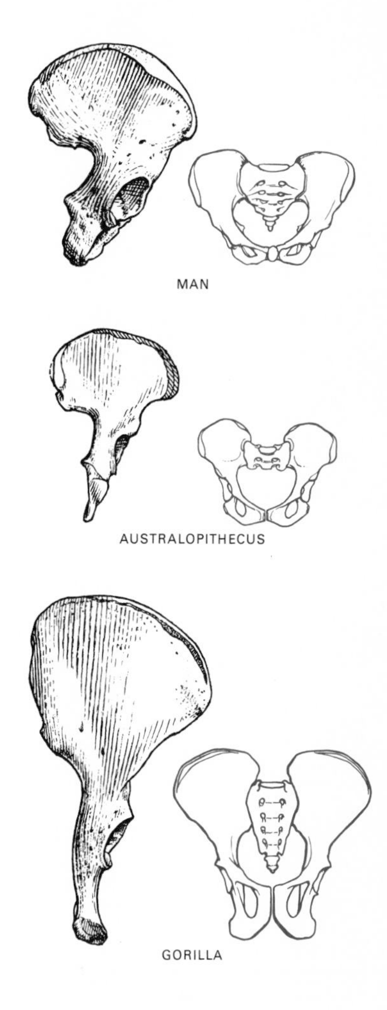

HIPS FOR ERECT WALKING

How the pelvis is shaped has a great deal to say about whether or not a creature can walk upright. In the gorilla, the pelvis is large and extremely long and prevents the animal from standing up straight. For erect posture, the pelvis must become shorter, as in Australopithecus, and its blade must become proportionately broader, with a bigger flange projecting to the rear. This flange not only anchors the large buttock muscles needed for walking erect but the whole structure of the pelvic girdle becomes a kind of basket to support the weight of the torso directly over it. These qualities that the australopithecine pelvis shares with the human pelvis prove that this form was a hominid and not an ape.

Broom apparently had two kinds of australopithecines on their hands. The first, of which the Taung baby is the prototype, represented a species of rather small creatures—lithe, slender, and weighing about 60 or 70 pounds. Their age was calculated by Broom to be between a million and two million years.

This was the roughest of rough guesses and had to be arrived at in a very roundabout way. Most of the South African finds were made in breccia, a cementlike mixture of sand, soils and pebbles, and this had to be gotten out of quarries or ancient caves by blasting—which, of course, destroyed the stratigraphic pattern. In addition, whatever stratigraphic clues could be gotten were very hard to read since so little was known about the geology of South Africa that match-ups with better known and better dated layers in other parts of the world could not be made. About the best that Broom could do was make a careful examination of the considerable numbers of animal fossils associated with the australopithecine remains. These represented 15 species of animals, ordinarily a large enough sample for making useful comparisons with datable fossils from other places. But to Broom's frustration, not only were all of these 15 animals extinct but they were unknown from any other place; there was nothing he could compare them to. However, the very fact of their extinction indicated that they must have been at least a million years old, possibly much older. His guess of two million years for the age of the Taung baby was, by its very nature, a shaky one, but as will be seen, it was an extraordinarily shrewd one.

THE second type of australopithecine fossil that Broom identified he recovered from a quarry at Kromdraai. He named this type *Paranthropus*. The choice of this name is extremely significant. Its owner lay with less archaic kinds of animals than *Australopithecus* and in what seemed to be a different layer of breccia. Therefore *Paranthropus* had to be considerably younger—perhaps half a million years was his age-estimate—and presumably that much closer to man. Thus he was honored with a scientific name that linked him with humans: *Para* (Greek for "akin to"), *anthropus* (Greek for "man").

At first *Paranthropus* seemed a good name for this second type. But as more fragments were recovered and more learned about him, an uncomfortable suspicion arose that he might actually be more primitive than the earlier *Australopithecus*. Discoveries of this sort are dreadfully unsettling to scientists because they suggest that somewhere in the long, carefully assembled chain of evidence and deduction there has been a gross error. Most distressing, it is not always possible to tell at first how far back in the chain the error has been made.

Whatever his private thoughts, Broom was quick to discover some very peculiar things about *Paranthropus*. He was a veritable fullback among australopithecines. He stood more than five feet tall and weighed between 130 and 150 pounds. His skull and jaw were much more massive, almost gorillalike in one or two respects, particularly in the presence of a bony ridge on the top of his skull. This ridge helped anchor the strong muscles required to work his heavy jaws and also suggested that he did a lot of powerful chewing. His molars and premolars were huge in proportion to the size of his front teeth, and, together with the evidence of the skull ridge, hinted strongly that *Paranthropus* may have been a vegetarian.

How could a more primitive type occur so much later than a more advanced one? This question not only nagged at Broom, but it also bothered his dedicated young assistant, J. T. Robinson. Meanwhile, fossil evidence on both types continued to accumulate. By the mid-1950s a total of five sites had yielded several dozen individuals of both *Australopithecus* and *Paranthropus*. There was no longer the slightest doubt that they were different species; ultimately they were put into different genera. Furthermore, more intense studies of the sediments in the sites by another South African, C. K. Brain, had begun to produce better evidence on their relative ages. A vague kind of order for australopithecines began to assert itself. The smallest ones were invariably the oldest and the most primitive, and from them there was an apparent, rather rapid evolution into larger and increasingly manlike forms. By contrast, *Paranthropus* was big and bulky from the start and stayed that way. It seemed that throughout his existence he evolved little or not at all.

Most interesting of all, the suspicion grew that tools might be involved with *Australopithecus*. Dart had speculated about this some years before, particularly about the use of broken animal bones as digging sticks or weapons, but his evidence is fragmentary and has not been generally accepted. It was not until 1957 that Robinson and Brain were able to state positively that they had recovered primitive stone implements and australopithecine remains from the same layer of breccia.

Once again an enormously important discovery from South Africa failed to make the impact it deserved to make. A reason for this may have been that Robinson was not the first man to find tools in Africa. For that we must turn once again to Louis Leakey and his wife Mary. The Leakeys found tools, so many of them that they were able to give their culture a name—Oldowan. Their trouble was that they could find no men to go with them.

The place where most of the Leakeys' work has been done, and where most of their discoveries have been made, is a miniature Grand Canyon in northern Tanzania known as the Olduvai Gorge. Like the Grand Canyon, its sides resemble a layer cake of different strata laid bare by the cutting action of an ancient river. Leakey did his first collecting in the gorge in 1931 and since then he has taken a great number of fossils from each of the four principal beds that overlie one another from the bottom to the surface of the plain some 300 feet above. All in all, more than 150 species of animals have been recovered from Olduvai, many of them extinct.

ONE of the most striking things Leakey noticed in the lowest deposits was a number of very primitive stone tools. To an untrained eye it might have appeared that they were natural stones since they bore only the faintest resemblance to tools. They were hopelessly crude; some of them were large pebbles, others were fist-sized chunks, but all had a few chips struck from one end to make them jagged. Leakey, however, recognized that these tools had been chipped by some directing—if dim—intellect and that the fractures were not the result of natural accident.

But who had made them was an utter mystery. All he knew was that he was the possessor of a small collection of the oldest implements ever seen. For years he had to live with this mystery unsolved. Not only was Olduvai far away from the museum in Nairobi where he worked but it was also virtually inaccessible because of the lack of roads. He had neither the time for intensive field research nor the money. He went there when he could, always hoping for hominid fossils, but collected only on the surface and did not find any. It was not until the 1950s that he and Mary Leakey were able to begin systematic excavation at Olduvai. The story of how their hopes were finally realized is a dramatic and well-known one. He was lying in camp with a fever, unable to work, when

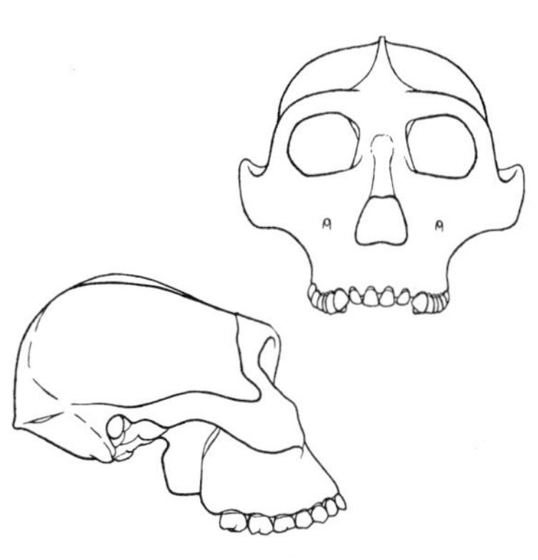

PARANTHROPUS

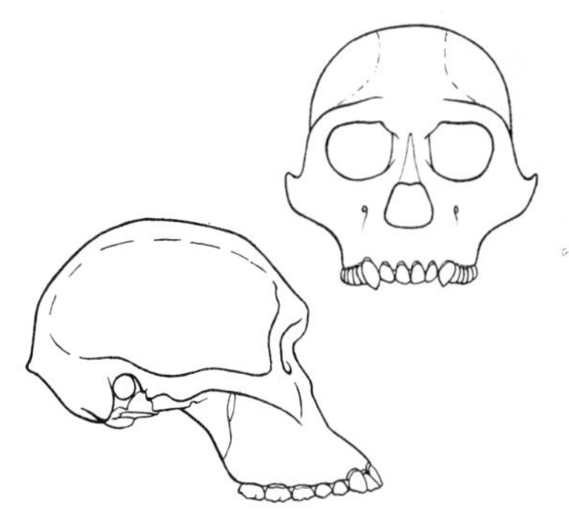

AUSTRALOPITHECUS

AFRICAN HOMINIDS: HEAD TO HEAD

The essential differences between Australopithecus and Paranthropus can be seen at a glance in these two adult female skulls. Australopithecus has the more delicate skull with a narrow face, arched forehead and rounded brain case. Paranthropus has an extremely wide, flat face, a low cranium with no forehead and an apelike crest which anchors the heavy musculature of the jaw atop the massive skull. Seen from the side, Paranthropus' molars are much larger than those of Australopithecus; Paranthropus is thought to have been a vegetarian.

Mary rushed in with the electrifying news that she had found a hominid fossil. His fever forgotten, Leakey leaped into his Land-Rover and careened back to the site with her. There it was, an unmistakable hominid jaw and teeth just beginning to emerge, together with more of those primitive tools, from the eroding slopes of Bed I, the lowest and most ancient of all the layers at Olduvai. Now, in addition to having the oldest tools in the world, he also appeared to have found their owner, the world's oldest hominid.

Just how old the Leakeys' fossil was, was determined through the unusual coincidence of its having been found sandwiched between two lava flows. Analysis of these layers by the new method of potassium-argon dating gave the Leakeys' fossil the fantastic age of nearly two million years.

THIS seemed unbelievably old for a toolmaker, but it gave a few grains of support to the equally fantastic discoveries made by Robinson and Brain a couple of years earlier. They had found tools associated with australopithecine teeth in the famous cave at Sterkfontein, but there had always been some skepticism about this association. The reason was that the lower layer of breccia in the cave contained a great number of australopithecine fossils but no tools at all. The next layer contained numerous tools—300 of them—but almost no fossils, only a few teeth. Why this peculiar distribution? There is still no good answer to this riddle. All that is certain is that the stones were definitely tools. The Sterkfontein cave was near the top of a hill at a place where stones of that kind did not naturally occur. They were common in the valley about half a mile away, and since stones do not climb hills unaided, they must have been carried there. What this all adds up to, together with the evidence from Olduvai, is fairly staggering: Africa, between a million and two million years ago, contained a goodly population of manlike creatures with brains not much bigger than those of apes but who already possessed dawning intellects, who presumably used the tools that are found with them, and who were thus well launched on the long climb to the human estate.

Now that these pre-men are identified as tool users, does this not tend to support Washburn's view that the use of tools might go back to a time before man got up on his hind legs? Not necessarily, according to Robinson. On the contrary, he thinks that bipedalism came before true tool use did. At this point we have come as close to present thinking and arguing about these matters as it is possible to come. The latest evidence, on which some of Robinson's argument rests, is dated 1963. Experts will continue to meet and debate this and other questions about the early African finds, altering and sharpening their views as fast as new information comes to hand. But this book must go to press and the best that can be done is to set forth Robinson's argument just as Washburn's was set forth earlier in the chapter—without prejudice to either. Sometimes on the very frontiers of science there are no sure answers.

What has continued to plague Robinson—and many other investigators—is the puzzle of *Paranthropus*. Although definitely younger than *Australopithecus*, according to the stratigraphic evidence in South Africa, he was just as definitely more primitive. Some explanation of this apparent contradiction had to be found before other matters could comfortably fall into place. Robinson had his ideas, but he needed proof. This was supplied dramatically when Leakey's man was compared to *Paranthropus*. The two were the same. In one stroke the problem of primitiveness was solved; *Paranthropus* was old after all—as old as *Australopithecus*, possibly older—and he had every right to look primitive.

But no sooner was this problem solved than another just as perplexing appeared. A much younger *Paranthropus* fossil, perhaps only half a million years old, turned up at Lake Natron in Tanzania. If he was as ancient as the Olduvai dating indicated and as recent as the Lake Natron find indicated, this meant that he had survived unchanged for about a million years. How had he lasted so long? Stranger still, why had he not evolved?

Robinson suggested that it was because he did *not* use tools.

This was a dangerously bold statement. How could Robinson make it when everybody knew that Olduvai was full of pebble tools in a stratum unmistakably associated with *Paranthropus* remains? Very easily, if one will accept that those tools were made by other hominids. But what other hominids? There were none. At this point, the Leakeys came up with another stupendous strike. They found a second hominid in the bottom bed at Olduvai—an *Australopithecus*. He, and not *Paranthropus*, it now seems likely, was the tool user.

This immeasurably strengthened Robinson's case. It removed the principal remaining sticky inconsistency and allowed him to demonstrate that although *Paranthropus* occurred in a number of places and at different times, at none of them could it be proved that he was a tool user. On the other hand, it began to be increasingly apparent that *Australopithecus* or one of his descendants was. Between 1961 and 1963 further finds had permitted a view of the over-all picture that shapes up something like this: *Paranthropus* did not change. *Australopithecus* did. Furthermore, he evolved quite rapidly. He started off small, but in half a million or a million years he was appreciably larger and more man-like. In still another half-million years, according to the latest evidence from a series of remains found at various levels in Olduvai, he had become a man. He apparently is our ancestor; *Paranthropus* is not. The burly vegetable eater stands off to one side. He is not a grandfather but a kind of great uncle, and has died out without leaving any descendants.

CLEARLY *Paranthropus* is something of a puzzle. He still leaves us with two questions: why did he not evolve and why did he die out? If we will again accept Robinson's suggestion that *Paranthropus* was not a tool user, tentative answers are possible for both of them. We have already seen that tool using and brain development act to stimulate one another in a feedback relationship. This is apparently the key to the startlingly swift changes that took place in *Australopithecus*. If such a stimulus is absent, and if a creature is already well adapted to its environment, there is not so much incentive to change. The most unusual thing about man is not that he has evolved—all living things have done that. What is surprising is the increasingly rapid rate at which man has done so. Compare him to the African gorilla, who sits stolidly in the forests of the eastern Congo and has not changed essentially in the last several million years. But the men who now live in the same forests, the pygmies, have changed profoundly during that same time. Pygmy and gorilla do not bother each other since they occupy different niches in the forest and can get along comfortably side by side. The gorilla is a vegetarian, the pygmy a mixed eater. He lives on fruits, berries, roots, lizards and other small game. Occasionally he nets a little forest deer. In short, he lives off the land, somewhat as the australopithecines did, and his diet is not so very different.

It is tempting to hazard a guess that *Australopithecus* and *Paranthropus* may have had some such casual noncompetitive relationship: *Paranthropus* making a place for himself in the bushy, parklike country between forest and plain, not

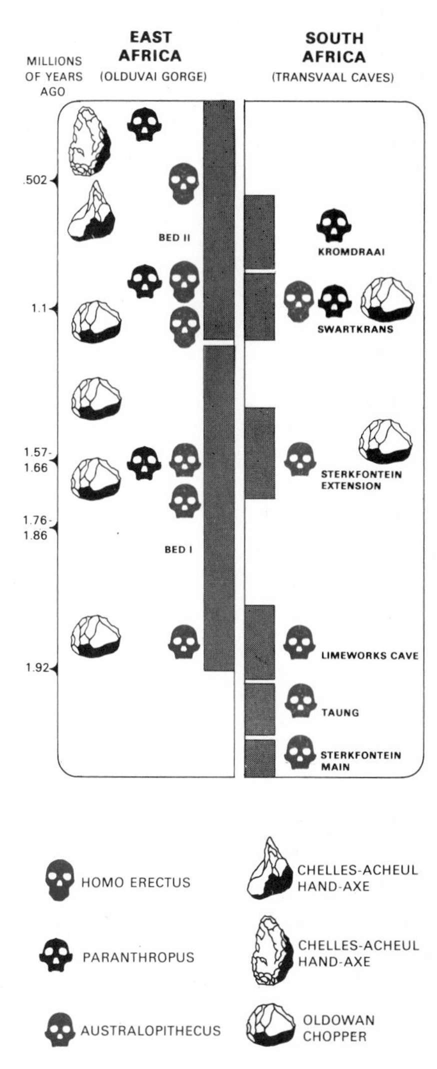

AFRICAN GENESIS

The story of early man in Africa is told in this chart. Gray bars in the center represent fossil and tool-bearing sites: those on the left are Beds I and II at Olduvai Gorge in East Africa; those on the right are the South African caves. On the left-hand edge of the diagram are absolute dates obtained from Beds I and II by the potassium-argon method. South African dates are known only by cross-checking animal fossils there with similar animals at Olduvai. The oldest find is Australopithecus at Sterkfontein Main dated at over two million years ago. He later shows up in East Africa, and is last seen in both places about a million and a half years ago, apparently later evolving into Homo erectus. Paranthropus overlaps both Homo erectus and Australopithecus but eventually he disappears.

venturing far into the latter because as a vegetarian he would have to stay close to whatever kind of green stuff he depended on for food, and *Australopithecus*, the agile wiry little fellow, ranging far, eating whatever came to hand. During the wet season he probably did pretty well on fruits and berries. But during the dry season his lot must have been hard. The need to catch and kill small animals must have been very great, the need to dig into the ground for roots, the need to defend himself, equally great. All these things are best done with sticks, stones and clubs. Bones can be smashed for their marrow, skulls cracked for their brains. On the evidence from both South and East Africa, it is increasingly clear that *Australopithecus* did all these things. In some sites there are large numbers of cracked bones and animal skulls with holes knocked in them. As he grew more proficient, he gradually grew larger, smarter and bolder. He took on bigger and bigger animals. Large antelopes, horses, even hippopotamuses show up with him in some sites.

Eventually he became a pretty formidable fellow, particularly in East Africa, where the record of his development is fairly clear. In South Africa it is much less so. His progress upward from the smallest australopithecine stage cannot be traced. There is a break in it. The small type simply disappears, suggesting that a considerably more advanced type, which appears later in South Africa, may have exterminated his little brother. Extermination is the most dramatic and easily recognizable kind of extinction. However, it is by no means the most common. What often takes place is continuous change until all members of a population are so different from their ancestors that the ancestors can properly be said to no longer exist. Whether this latter process eliminated the small australopithecines will be proved only by the discovery of intermediate stages between him and his larger descendants.

WITHOUT those intermediate stages, evolution appears to go in a series of jerky jumps. Of course it does not. It can be compared to a strip of movie film. If one examines such a strip frame by frame, the differences from one picture to another are almost imperceptible. Who can say exactly when the hero begins to smile? But if every tenth frame is examined, differences appear. In one he is not smiling; 10 frames later he definitely is. So it is with the story of *Australopithecus*, except that the examples are thousands of frames apart. The jumps are very big indeed. At the moment the African "movie" of ancestral man is limited to about four frames. In the first we see the smallest, most primitive australopithecine type, now believed to date from as much as two million or more years ago. In the next, somewhat under two million years ago, we see him somewhat larger and bigger-brained but still with strong australopithecine traits. The third and fourth frames continue this development, bringing us up to half a million years ago and to a type that begins to resemble the true men of Peking and Java. So much does the last of these early Africans resemble *Homo erectus* that he has been given the tentative label of "early Homo," and at the moment is the oldest known creature that can properly be called a human being.

The African story began about 40 years ago, and its five chief proponents —Dart, Broom, Robinson and the Leakeys—have all made conspicuous contributions, despite skepticism all along the way. However, their story, in its broad outlines, is coming to be generally accepted. Their evidence is unique; there is nothing like it known from any other spot on the globe. Africa, in the light of present knowledge, must be regarded as the place where man arose.

PARANTHROPUS, SMALL-BRAINED AND HEAVY-JAWED, MAY HAVE FAVORED THE MORE LUSH HABITATS OF SOUTHERN AND EASTERN AFRICA.

The Pre-men of Africa

Several million years ago, in the tropics of Africa or Asia, some venturesome apes gave rise to what became two distinct, erect, bipedal creatures—Australopithecus and Paranthropus. Were they man's progenitors? As yet no one is sure—but by about a million years ago in Africa the first seems to have evolved into an early human species. The second, perhaps a vegetarian, became extinct.

LECTURING TO STUDENTS, Raymond Dart holds the reconstructed skull of an adult female *Australopithecus*. Found during the late 1940s in a fossil-rich cave in the Makapan Valley, about 200 miles north of Johannesburg, this is one of many significant finds of fossil prehumans made by Dart's students and colleagues in caves uncovered by commercial mining.

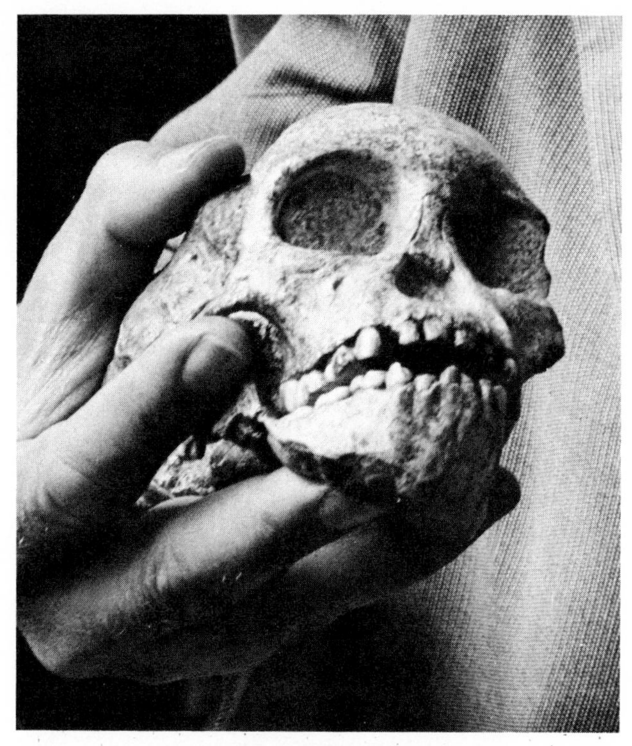

THIS IS THE SKULL OF THE TAUNG "BABY"

A Most Advanced Ape Type

The man who named *Australopithecus* was Raymond Dart, an Australian-born anatomist teaching in Johannesburg. To fully appreciate the significance of his discovery, it must be realized that ever since DuBois found his Java "ape man" in 1893, the search for more remains of very early man had been frustratingly barren. The only other fossil ancestors known to the world were some Neanderthalers and a mysterious jaw from Germany. In the scientific community there was little doubt that these were authentic early men but what was lacking was the creature—or creatures—who bridged the gap between them and the apes. And what Dart came up with was a "manlike ape" evolving along distinctly human lines.

On the basis of a single skull, that of a child taken from a limestone quarry at Taung in Bechuanaland, Dart, in 1924, defined a new genus of hominid: an erect-walking creature with a brain larger than a chimpanzee's and more human than a gorilla's, and with teeth which were distinctly nonsimian. This seemed indeed to be the intermediate animal imagined by every evolutionary theorist since Darwin—but it was a dozen years before Dart's hypothesis was fortified with dramatic new evidence.

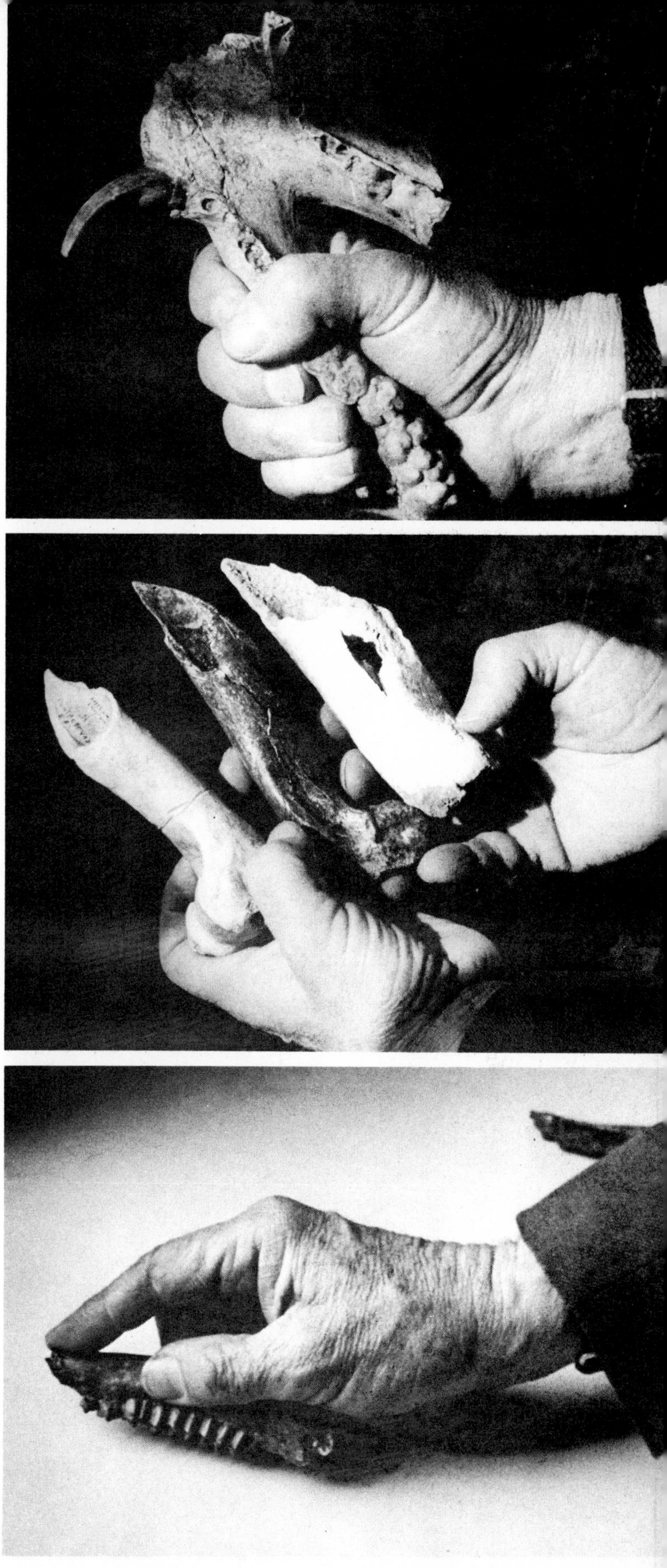

THE FIRST TOOLS of *Australopithecus* may have been fashioned from leftovers of his meals. Dart believes that tusks, femur ends and teeth *(above)* of extinct pigs, antelopes and gazelles found with *Australopithecus* remains were deliberately used in chopping, cutting and scraping activities, and as offensive weapons.

A ROCK-BOUND JAW is examined by Robert Broom in the cave at Swartkrans, which he and Robinson began exploring in 1948. Some 35 *Paranthropus* specimens were recovered there.

The Proof of a Hypothesis

Because the original *Australopithecus* fossil was that of a child, Dart's establishment of the new hominid genus was hotly debated. An adult skull was needed to prove the hypothesis and in 1936, Robert Broom, a 69-year-old physician and paleontologist, set out to find it. Within six weeks, he had it—an adult female *Australopithecus* skull dug from a limestone mine at Sterkfontein. Within a year, he had eight more, found in a quarry. By the late 1940s,

Broom and his colleague John Robinson had found many more fossils of both *Australopithecus* and *Paranthropus* and also fragments of an advanced form of *Australopithecus*, all in Transvaal caves. With many skull, teeth, limb bones and pelvic parts, they established beyond doubt that the early African prehumans stood erect, walked bipedally and that one of them, from evidence found by Robinson in 1957 and 1958, actually made and used stone tools.

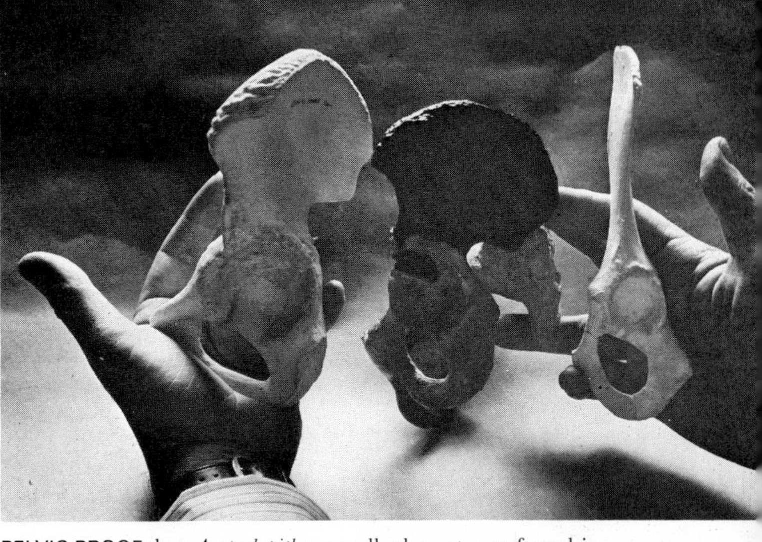

PELVIC PROOF that *Australopithecus* walked erect was found in the Makapan Valley in 1947. Its hip blade *(center)* is compared with those of a modern man *(left)* and a chimpanzee.

A LOWER CANINE is gently hammered free by Robinson as he meticulously chips away the stone surrounding an *Australopithecus* fossil. This one was found in 1958 at Sterkfontein.

GUIDING A DRILL, Robinson bores a block of breccia to break out fossils which may lie locked within. For this rock-hard material, drills and black powder are used despite the danger of damaging specimens.

Reconstructions of Paranthropus and Australopithecus

PARANTHROPUS was a barrel-chested five-footer who weighed about 140 pounds. Females were shorter and slighter, although both were big-boned and robust with slightly pushed-in faces, beetling brow ridges and massive jaws. Their brains were gorilla-sized.

The splendid discoveries and descriptions of Dart, Broom, Robinson and Leakey make it possible to reconstruct *Paranthropus* and *Australopithecus* with some exactness. To portray them for this book, artist Jay Matternes consulted scores of scientific papers, fossil casts and many experts. To enhance the realism of his charcoal drawings, he first sculpted busts of the figures, adding muscles and skin in clay, combining the latest scientific evidence with a measure of his own intelligent artistic speculation.

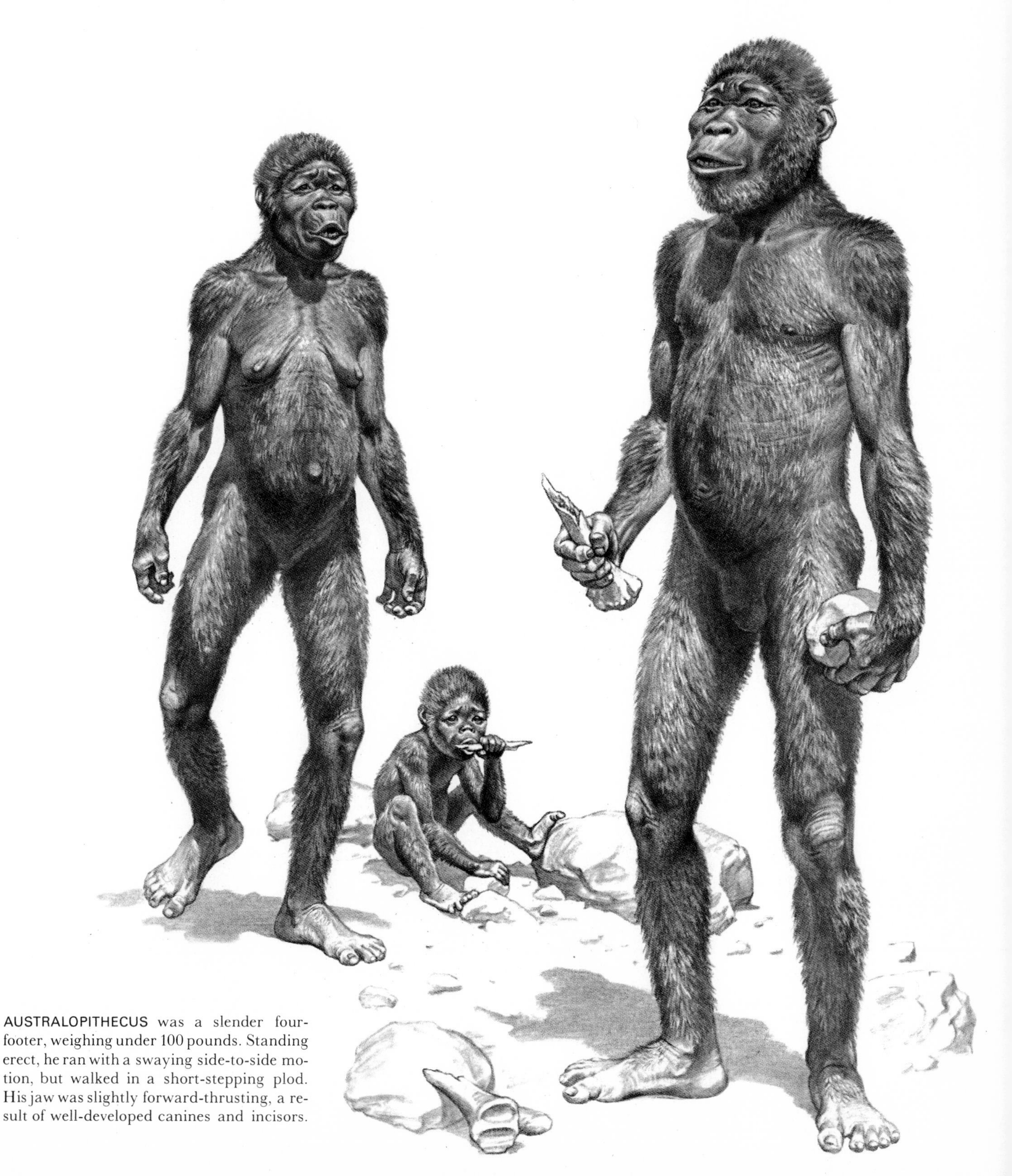

AUSTRALOPITHECUS was a slender four-footer, weighing under 100 pounds. Standing erect, he ran with a swaying side-to-side motion, but walked in a short-stepping plod. His jaw was slightly forward-thrusting, a result of well-developed canines and incisors.

THE ORIGINS OF MEAT-EATING

How and when did early man become a meat-eater? To the paleoanthropologist trying to reconstruct his behavior, this is an important question. *Australopithecus* is believed to have inhabited the formerly dry savanna lands of South and East Africa; he might therefore have supplemented his vegetable diet by eating meat. One clue in support of this idea is that broken and smashed animal bones have been found in caves with *Australopithecus* remains. Did he eat these animals him-

self, or were the bones left there by carnivores? The latter is not likely, since most big cats do not ordinarily drag bones to their lairs; they eat the soft parts and leave the rest at the kill. The high proportion of skull and leg bones suggests that somebody retrieved them from many kills and took them to certain spots. *Australopithecus* may therefore be pictured as a scavenger, competing with hyenas and jackals for the remains of animals killed by larger predators. The painting above shows a group of hunters returning with some choice pieces of Topi antelope, still beating off the tenacious spotted hyenas.

THE CASE FOR VEGETARIANISM

Although dentition is not a positive clue to diet, the massive jaw, heavy skull musculature and huge molar teeth of *Paranthropus* lead some investigators to conclude that he was essentially a vegetarian. This idea is further supported by the fact that in southern Africa the brownish breccias yielding *Paranthropus* remains indicate that a moister climate and, as a result, a richer and more densely vegetated habitat may have prevailed than exists there today. In such an ecological

situation—and with his dental equipment—it seems likely that *Paranthropus* would have subsisted largely, as some apes still do, on green shoots, edible leaves and seasonal fruits and nuts of various kinds, only rarely seeking out small game. As a vegetarian in this habitat, he might have got along perfectly well without stone tools—although such artifacts do occur in his time range. In the drawing above, a male *Paranthropus* reaches for fruit from a *Marula* tree, while a female in the foreground, attended by her young child, concentrates on foraging for edible roots with a pointed stick.

CRACKING AND TWISTING antelope long bones, these australopithecines extract the edible insides. Later they may use the sharp-ended bones as weapons. Such bones, found in great numbers with prehuman fossils, may have been the world's first deliberately manufactured tools.

Reconstructing

From scavenging the kills of predators to hunting live prey is a logical step for an animal on its way to becoming a predator itself—a step *Paranthropus* and *Australopithecus* may have taken. To the modern paleoanthropologist, speculation on such

CORNERING A BUSHBUCK, *Australopithecus* hunters use no weapons other than their cunning and knowledge of the animal's habits. Such simple methods as this are used by Bushmen living in South Africa's arid regions today.

HUNTING COOPERATIVELY, *Paranthropus* males block all but one entrance to a rodent's burrow, beat on the ground to frighten it and then brain the terrified animal when it scrabbles out and tries to escape.

STALKING A GAZELLE, the usually vegetarian *Paranthropus* takes advantage of the infant's defensive "freeze." Chimpanzees, also mainly plant-eaters, capture an occasional meat meal in just the same manner.

a Hunter's Life

questions of behavior is fully as interesting as reconstructing physical appearance. But intelligent speculation may be all he will ever achieve—sites from which the earliest prehumans are known include little in the way of tools and other cultural artifacts.

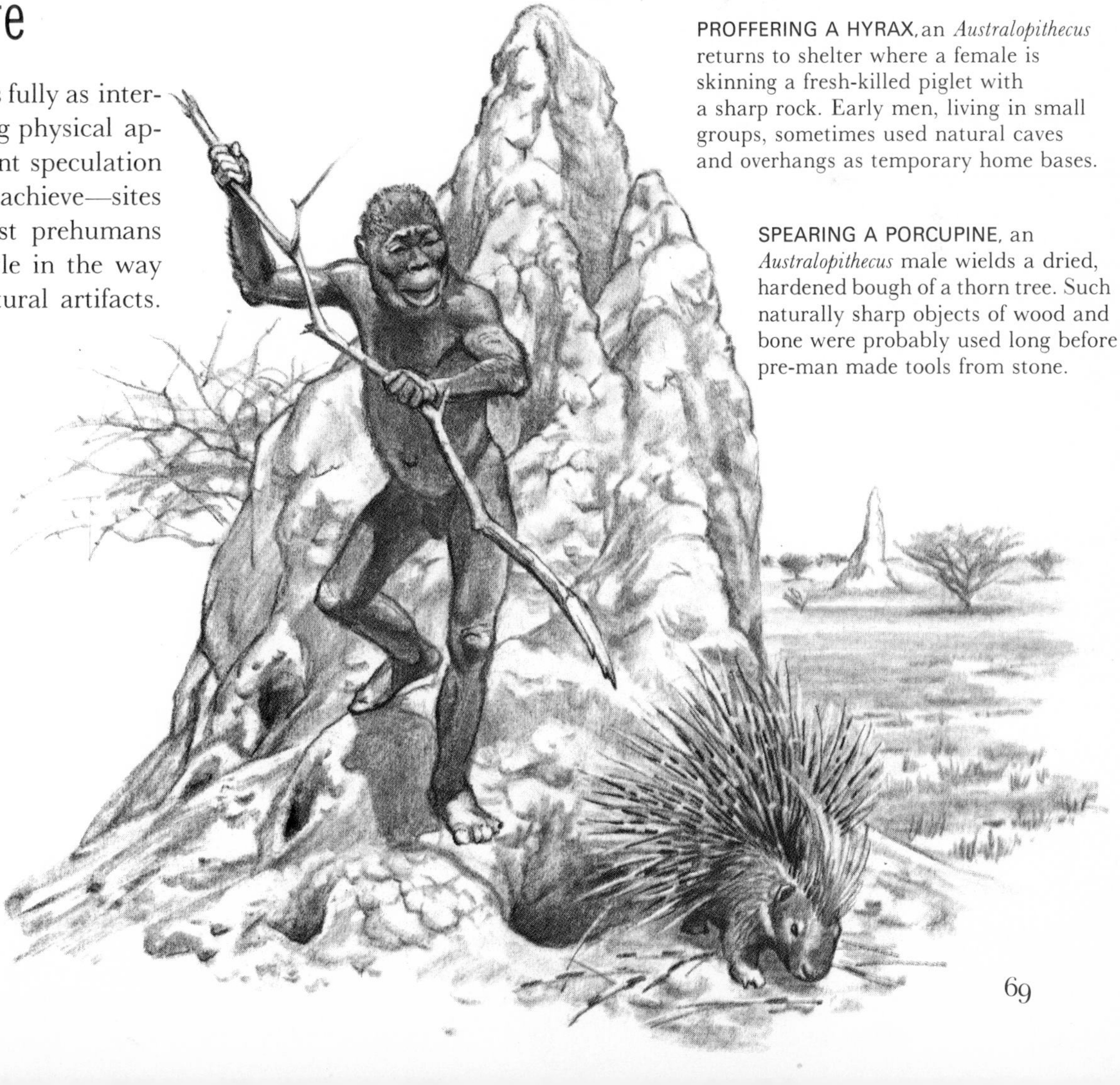

PROFFERING A HYRAX, an *Australopithecus* returns to shelter where a female is skinning a fresh-killed piglet with a sharp rock. Early men, living in small groups, sometimes used natural caves and overhangs as temporary home bases.

SPEARING A PORCUPINE, an *Australopithecus* male wields a dried, hardened bough of a thorn tree. Such naturally sharp objects of wood and bone were probably used long before pre-man made tools from stone.

VISITING SCIENTISTS get a briefing from Leakey *(right)* and his wife Mary, at work under the striped umbrella. This location yielded the first of the famous *Paranthropus* skulls in 1959.

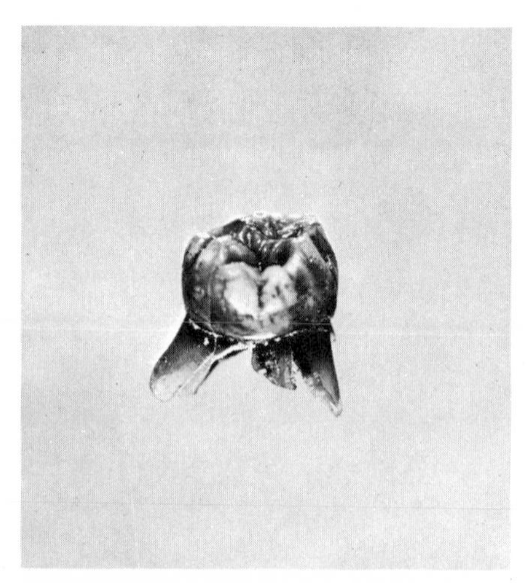

THIS CONTROVERSIAL MOLAR has stirred a long debate. Does it belong to *Homo erectus*, as Leakey asserts, or to *Paranthropus?*

SHOWING OFF TEETH, Leakey compares the controversial molar, which he ascribes to a *Homo erectus* child, with a canine found nearby and a fragment of a modern human lower jaw.

Olduvai Gorge, a Fossil Gold Mine

The place where australopithecines were first discovered in strata which could be dated absolutely is Olduvai Gorge, one of the great fossil sites of the world. Over hundreds of thousands of years, the progressive ebb and flow of lake sediments and periodic falls of volcanic ash have trapped and preserved animals, prehumans, early men and a wealth of archeological treasure.

For more than 30 years now, Louis Leakey and his wife, Mary, have been digging out and recording the geologic, animal and human history of the region with the help of geologists, paleontologists and a host of other specialists working under their direction. In recent years the pace at Olduvai has quickened, and the finds have been dazzling. Since 1959, remains of *Australopithecus*, *Paranthropus*, *Homo erectus* and even modern man have been unearthed in at least six levels in the fertile stratigraphy—an amazing, virtually unbroken record of human evolution.

Potassium-argon dating of many of the Olduvai fossils has been possible because of the volcanic minerals present in the strata. Basalt rock at the bottom of the gorge has yielded a date close to two million years ago, while volcanic ash in layers nearer the top gives an average age of half a million years. Sites at Olduvai also contain a unique succession of stone tools —from the crudely flaked chopping tools of the early Oldowan industry to the finely made hand-axes of the Chellean culture associated with *Homo erectus* in Africa.

ON THE JOB Leakey kneels before the bones of a *Dinotherium*. Tools found among the remains indicate that it may have been butchered and eaten.

THE PREHUMANS' PEACEFUL PLAIN

This is how Olduvai Gorge probably looked two million years ago, long before natural forces shaped it into a steep-sided valley. Small lakes and swamps lay at the foot of two now-extinct volcanoes, Ngorongoro *(left)* and Lemagrut. A varied population of plants and animals flourished in a climate rather wetter than it is today. Among the creatures were a giant baboon *(left)*, wild pigs, various ancestral antelopes and gazelles, birds like vultures, and flamingoes—seen feeding in the shallow lake—and many other animals, including hares and foxes similar to those which live in East Africa today. Larger

beasts included rhinos *(left)*, the elephantlike *Dinotherium* browsing in the marshes, the hefty, tree-cropping chalicothere and the oddly antlered *Sivatherium (right foreground)*, a relative of the giraffe. To feast on this wealth of flesh, there were lions, hyenas and the extinct saber-toothed tiger. Hunting and gathering food along with the animals were *Australopithecus* and *Paranthropus*. Evidence of their presence, diligently excavated and collected from many sites in the Gorge, includes a mystifying arrangement of lava rocks *(left center)*. Is this a hunting blind, a windbreak or a weapons pile? No one yet knows exactly what it is, but such provocative clues keep the dry and dusty search at Olduvai fresh and ever-exciting.

FACE TO FACE AT OLDUVAI

A fascinating conjecture offered by the fossil record in Olduvai Gorge is that two kinds of pre-men, known to have lived side by side, may have confronted one another often. This is suggested by the belief that *Paranthropus* was primarily a vegetarian browser and grubber of roots while *Australopithecus* was a hunter and scavenger of small game. With somewhat different ways of life, they could have shared their environment for many thousands of years without bothering one another. But this easy truce may not have lasted. *Australopithecus* probably became increasingly threatening to other forms of life—*Paran-*

thropus included—as his hunting ways continued to sharpen his wits. This painting shows a chance encounter between two advanced *Australopithecus* males *(left)* and a *Paranthropus* band. The australopithecines hold pebble tools that they have made. The *Paranthropus* males, grabbing whatever rocks lie handy, bluster and threaten while the females scurry off with their young ones. Meetings like this may have been accidental and were no doubt as startling to one group as to the other. But *Australopithecus* was a hunter and he might have killed a young *Paranthropus* if he could have done so safely. Constant pressure and decreasing freedom of movement, particularly during bad food years, may have led to *Paranthropus'* extinction.

FRANZ WEIDENREICH

CAST OF A CRANIUM
OF PEKING MAN

CHOUKOUTIEN CAVE, NEAR PEKING, IN 1937

PEKING MAN is known from many skulls, jaws and a few limb bones, unearthed from a great cave in China. Discovered by Davidson Black in 1927, and later extensively studied by Franz Weidenreich during the '30s, he is still the best documented example of *Homo erectus*.

4

Homo Erectus: A True Man at Last

SINCE this book is almost entirely about fossils, it may be worth noting that fossil finds, as far as their impact on knowledge goes, fall into two rough categories. There are the hitherto unknown kinds—those that provide brand-new insights into the evolutionary picture—and there are those that merely confirm or enlarge knowledge about a type already discovered. It is the first kind, the heart-stopper, the producer of wild surmises, that makes newspaper headlines. But it is not wise to underrate the second, since, to the scientist, it is perhaps the more important of the two. In order to get any good idea of the characteristics—the dimensions, one might say—of a species, one must have a series consisting of fragments or whole skeletons from a number of individuals. Without such a series, a single fossil may be simply a curiosity—a provocative and exciting one, no doubt, but still one that cannot be fitted with any sense of sureness into the over-all order of things until a number of like fossils can be found and scrutinized. So it is the patient, more obscure and always time-consuming comparative studies of later finds—often made years after the original one—that eventually turn the wild surmises into scientific conclusions.

The subject of this chapter is *Homo erectus*, and his story is a near-perfect example of the wild surmise eventually made respectable. When Eugène Dubois first turned up bits of an "ape man" fossil in Java back in the 1890s, no one knew quite what to make of it. Here, certainly, was an example of the first kind of find. It was born to make headlines. Ahead of its time, it faced a society and a scientific world both unready for it. It was by far the oldest and most primitive human fossil known. As a result, its apelike qualities were emphasized more than its manlike ones. Dubois gave it the name *Pithecanthropus erectus* (erect ape man). But so little was known of the geology of Java that there was no way of estimating its age, and its characteristics were so utterly unlike anything ever seen before, that there was no agreement on whether it was a hominid or an ape. Dubois himself changed his mind about it several times, grew increasingly resentful and suspicious of the public reception given it, and finally locked his fragments up, refusing to let other scientists study them at all.

The metamorphosis of this enigmatic fossil into *Homo erectus*, now definitely known to have been an early species of man, is the result of everything that has come since Dubois made his first Java discovery. Many anthropologists, of course, were passionately interested in what the Java man had to say about human evolution. They suspected the truth about it, and were waiting in a fever of impatience for more information to be released about it or for a breakthrough somewhere else that might throw some light on it.

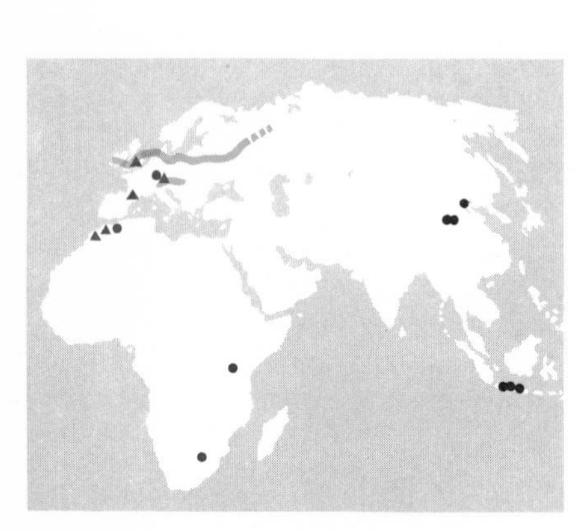

WHERE HOMO ERECTUS HAS BEEN FOUND

On this map of the Old World are marked the sites at which actual fossil remains of the first true men have been found—ranging from Dubois' Java man, in 1891, Black's Peking man, in 1927, to Leakey's recent discoveries in East Africa and to even more recent finds in central China. Dots represent Homo erectus remains and triangles his immediate successors, the first Homo sapiens, including Swanscombe man in Britain and Steinheim man in Germany.

The grayish lines show the extent of the northern ice sheet and alpine glaciation a half million years ago, about the age of most Homo erectus fossils. That these men could live at the very edge of frost shows a growing ability to cope with climate, a marked advance over the apelike Australopithecus, whose remains have been found only in warm places.

One such man was Davidson Black, a Canadian anatomy professor teaching at a medical college in Peking, whose attention was drawn to a large cave in the limestone hills about 30 miles away. This place was called Choukoutien by the Chinese, who had been digging fossils out of such spots for hundreds of years, grinding them up and selling them as medicines and magical potions. No one will ever know how many powdered fossils have passed harmlessly through the alimentary canals of dyspeptic Chinese mandarins in this fashion—certainly as bizarre a way of increasing the rarity of fossils as one could think of. But whatever the losses may have been, some of the limestone caverns in the hillside were still richly packed with material when Black was shown a fossil tooth from one of them. Struck by its size and its cusp pattern, he studied it exhaustively and became convinced that it was a human tooth of great antiquity. Although he was operating on the thinnest kind of a fossil shoestring—a single molar—he confidently announced a new genus of man who later would become known as Peking man. In due course the Rockefeller Foundation agreed to underwrite an investigation of the hill under his direction.

Work was started up at Choukoutien in 1927 and continued at a lively pace for two years. Tons of earth were excavated and sifted for signs of fossil fragments. Bits and pieces of teeth and other bones came to light, but nothing that could add to the original molar, which Black wore in a gold locket attached to his watch chain. Finally, encased in a bed of limestone, a skull was located. Black spent the next four months freeing it from the surrounding stone. When the skull was entirely clean he separated all its bones, made an exact cast of each one and then reassembled the pieces. Now he was ready to make a comparison between his find and Dubois' Java man, with which he was quite familiar through Dubois' first scientific paper about him.

The characteristics of the two skulls matched with remarkable closeness. Without question these were two specimens of the same kind of man. In each, the bones of the skull were thick, the forehead was low and sloping, with massive brow ridges jutting out over the eye sockets. Black's skull was much more complete than Dubois', and for the first time he was able to make a reliable estimate of the brain capacity of his find. It came to about 1,000 cubic centimeters, and marked its owner definitely as a man and not an ape.

Tragically, Black did not live to savor the full bounty of Choukoutien. He suffered a heart attack and died in 1934, but his work at the hill was carried on by a worthy successor, Franz Weidenreich. In a decade, 14 skulls, 14 lower jaws and nearly 150 teeth were exhumed—parts of 45 different individuals were recovered. Particularly important were the remains of more than a dozen children, for much can be learned about the nature of a species by studying the growth patterns of its juveniles. Of equal significance was that all the material came out of one cave with the stratigraphy well preserved. It tells a detailed and vivid history, and it is from this that most of our speculations about *Homo erectus* and the way he lived have come.

To begin with, the deposits are an astonishing 160 feet deep. They can best be visualized by comparing them to an apartment house 16 stories tall, each story of which is packed solid with the blown-in debris of the elements combined with the abandoned rubbish of its long-departed tenants. Similarly with the Choukoutien cave. Layer on layer, the detritus of ages filled it with strata of clay, with soil carried in by the wind, with limestone drippings, with fallen rock from the ceiling—all sandwiching other layers of human and animal debris. It is clear that large carnivores occupied the Choukoutien caves for long periods of time. Bones of big cats like the saber-toothed tiger and a huge extinct hyena, together with the remains of animals on which they preyed, occur at certain levels. At others, it is equally clear that men drove the carnivores out and took over the caves for themselves. At first the animal and human layers alternate fairly regularly, but toward the top, humans take over permanently. Their leavings include bones that vary in size from those of small rodents and bats up through bears, horses and camels to rhinoceroses and even elephants—all told, some 60 species. A favorite food was venison; there are more than three times as many deer fossils in Choukoutien as there are of any other animal.

CERTAIN horizons are rich in man's tools. These are roughly chipped of quartz or chert and are obviously man-made, for they had to be brought from natural sites several miles away, there being nothing but limestone in the caves themselves. Charcoal fragments and burned bones show up again and again in many of the upper levels from which most of the human fragments have also been recovered, positively linking man with the use of fire. Even if no charcoal had been found, it would be reasonable to suppose that *Homo erectus* used fire. He lived during times of glacial advance and bitter cold. Also, he was a vegetarian turned meat eater. Like all the apes, man has a digestive system that is built basically to accommodate greenstuff; he needs help, through cooking, in breaking down the high-energy fats and proteins contained in a meat diet. That Peking man's was not all meat is indicated by the recovery of plant remains and seeds from some layers.

But when and where he began to cook, and how he first learned to use fire will never be known. The earliest known signs that he did so come from Choukoutien, and date back some 400,000 years. They have two possible explanations. One is that they originated from natural fires, either lightning strikes or volcanoes. Early man must have seen blazes from these causes over and over again. Fire has a fascination even to quite sophisticated modern people. Perhaps this fascination also existed for earlier man, who may have approached a natural fire fearfully but curiously. A burning twig is easily managed in the hand, and one can imagine the sense of power and wonder that must have suffused the man who first gave fire to another shrub or tuft of grass by touching it with his own burning twig. The warmth of fire is quickly felt, and it would not have taken much of a leap in foresight, even for a small-brained and inexperienced ancestor, to imagine its usefulness in a cold cave and attempt to bring fire in with him.

Probably the first uses of fire were limited to occasional capture after a brush blaze caused by lightning. Certainly these early fires must have gone out many thousands of times before men became provident enough to keep supplies of fuel on hand and skillful enough to keep fires going and to transport them from one place to another. And when a fire went out, the loss must have been keen and the wait a long one before a natural blaze could be captured again.

ANOTHER possible theory for the discovery of fire, which connects man even more closely with its actual production, is that he made it himself accidentally while chipping flint tools. Sparks are often struck in this way, and these may well have landed in adjacent piles of leaves used as bedding or in the hair of animal skins, and begun to smolder. The origin of cooking was undoubtedly the result of a similar kind of accident stumbled on over and over again, in which food falling into the fire turned out to be tasty and tender when retrieved and allowed to cool. There is no way of proving any of this since behavior does not leave fossils. But the assumptions are logical, particularly when we know that at some point man did tame fire and did begin cooking his food. With increasingly well-developed brains, and with burgeoning prospects of foresight and reflection, the simple mental processes required to do these things were almost certainly within the reach of *Homo erectus*, and we may assume that most of his kind used fire for much of the three or four—or could it be six—hundred thousand years they existed on earth.

But how long was this? Thanks to the richness of its deposits, Choukoutien tells us a good deal about *Homo erectus* himself, but it leaves us with only the most enigmatic of hints as to where he came from and how he evolved, and, of course, says nothing at all about his history and distribution in other parts of the world. The obvious place to look for more evidence was Java, and there in the 1930s more fossil finds were made by the paleontologist G.H.R. von Koenigswald. These further broadened knowledge of *Homo erectus'* physical characteristics. More important, they extended his occurrence in time. Von Koenigswald was able to do more careful stratigraphic work than Dubois had done, and he discovered that the oldest individuals that he found substantially antedated Dubois' original specimen. His findings indicate that early men were in Java for more than half a million years.

Recently Javanese workers have been extending Von Koenigswald's work, doing large-scale controlled excavating for the first time on that island. Prior to this, nearly all finds had been made on the surface of the ground as they were exposed by erosion, with only a little shallow digging at those points. Now a large site is being systematically excavated. *Homo* remains have been found—also, for the first time in Java, tools. Most significant of all, there seems to be evidence of an even more primitive hominid. Could this be an australopithecine? As yet not enough of it is known to tell. As a result, Africa is still the only continent that contains a place where anything like a known sequence of types connecting australopithecines with *Homo erectus* has been discovered and studied. As might be suspected, this place is the Olduvai Gorge.

Olduvai, as a reference book of the human past, is unique on earth. Its stratigraphy is clear, its levels numerous, its succession of animal fossils amazingly rich and abundant. Equally abundant are tools of the primitive Oldowan industry. Both *Australopithecus* and *Paranthropus* appear in its lower levels dating back nearly two million years. Toward the top of Bed II, going back only half a million years, is a fine example of *Homo erectus*, falling well within the range of variations of the finds made earlier in China. What is perhaps the most important of all—a perfect example of the kind of follow-up evidence that begins to make good sense out of everything else—is what has recently been discovered between the two.

Intensive work has been conducted by Louis and Mary Leakey in this middle ground during the past five years. Their most recent efforts have been directed toward the bottom of Bed II, and there they have found parts of skulls and teeth that can only be described as being intermediate between *Australopithecus* and *Homo erectus*. These skulls are smaller than those of the more developed *Homo erectus* skulls that lie above them. Nevertheless their shape and many details of tooth and jaw make it clear that they were early members of the species *Homo erectus*. Nothing in the whole spectrum of human evolution is more dramatic than this succession of evidence that takes us from something that was not yet a man to something that was.

How *Homo erectus* spread through the continents is still unknown. All that can be inferred is that he must have been an extremely successful type since his populations were so widely scattered about the globe. It is eight thousand miles from Olduvai by land around the Indian Ocean and down to Java. It is just as far from Olduvai to Peking, in China. If, as is now thought, these men originated in Africa, then they obviously had to make it to both places on foot. They would have had to inch their way century by century from one valley to the next, settling down for a few generations, spreading again, running away from larger bands of their own kind, unable to cross any sizable body of water and thus forced to flow inexorably and unconsciously around it, adapting themselves not only to the languid damp of the East Indian tropics but to some periods of bitter cold in northern China. They also turn up in Algeria and possibly in Germany.

Physically, *Homo erectus* represents a considerable advance over *Australopithecus*, whose pelvic and leg bones indicate that while he could run well enough, he probably was not a particularly good walker, and in all likelihood proceeded

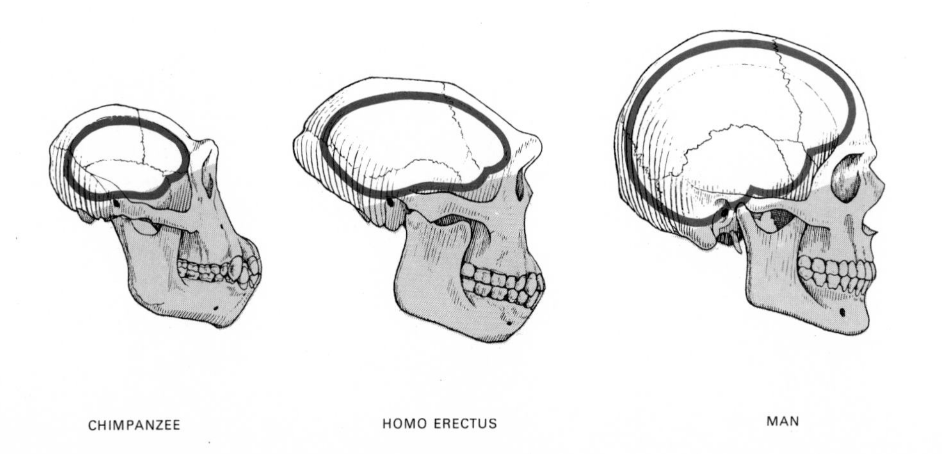

THE RATIO OF BRAIN TO FACE

From chimpanzee to Homo sapiens the evolution of the skull shows two main characteristics: the brain gets bigger and the face smaller. Homo erectus, the first true man, falls almost exactly midway between the two evolutionary extremes: his cranium takes up about half his total skull size. However, the structure of the skull still shows heavy, apelike features, notably the strong overhanging brows, with hardly a hint of the great frontal bulge and forehead of modern man.

with a rolling or waddling gait, his feet turned awkwardly out. *Homo erectus*, by comparison, was a superb walker. His legs were long and straight; in fact, except for individual or racial variations, his leg bones—those that we have specimens of—cannot be distinguished from those of a modern man. From this it is assumed that the rest of his skeleton was also much like modern man's, although it should be emphasized that, so far, this is only an assumption. As to his size, the best evidence is that females stood just under, and males just over, five feet tall.

His face is not well known. But from Choukoutien fossils we can deduce that by today's standards, he had an extremely broad flat nose, a sloping forehead, massive brow ridges and no chin to speak of. The bones of his head were uniformly thicker than are those of a modern man, his jaw was more massive and his lower canine teeth, which were still large, showed a slight tendency to interlock with the teeth of his upper jaw. His molars have an interesting cusp pattern that sets them about midway between those of *Australopithecus* and *Homo sapiens*, an important link in the evolutionary chain that is steadily being forged between the two.

His brain was large, dramatically larger than *Australopithecus'*, but still smaller than that of modern man. Its capacity varied between 775 and 1,300 cubic centimeters, as against a range of 1,200 to 1,500 in modern man. What can be said about this brain? Very little directly, although we can make a number of indirect inferences. As a general rule, all apes and men share the same basic pattern of brain configuration. Certain parts are known to be associated with certain functions. Toward the rear are areas that have to do with vision and the storage of information. In the center and sides are areas concerned with speech, memory, bodily sensations, and also movements of the body. The forebrain is where man does his thinking—and presumably where an ape does whatever thinking it is capable of. Sheer size in brains is important for two reasons. Most obviously, a small brain simply cannot hold as many brain cells as a large one. Less obvious, but more important, is that the true quality of a brain must be measured by the complexity of the linkages between cells. Inasmuch as the possible number of linkages goes up very rapidly as the brain gets larger, it is clear that a big brain can be a much more sophisticated instrument than a small one.

In an ape, certain brain areas are known to be small and undeveloped, and this is reflected in its activities. There is simply no point in trying to teach it something that these parts are not equipped to do. Talking is a perfect example of this. Apes have been brought up from infancy in human households, and intensive efforts have been made to teach them to talk; but unfortunately there are no speech centers in their brains and they are unable to repeat more than a word or two, and even this is not speech in the true sense of communication. With a wider head, and bigger speech centers in his brain, man has no such trouble.

To say whether *Homo erectus* could talk or not by examining his skull is extremely difficult, if not impossible. In the matter of size, it was large enough to do most, if not all, of the things a modern brain can do—particularly since there are men of marked intelligence walking about today whose brains are as small or smaller than his. But of the all-important internal circuitry we know nothing. The shape of his brain, which is easily determined by making a cast of the inside of his skull, is somewhat different from a modern man's. His head was narrower, pinched in at the sides, and his crown lower, so that the central and side parts of his brain were reduced in size. His forebrain was also considerably smaller than a modern man's. Inferences about function from shape are exceedingly dangerous, but if we must speculate about them, we can hazard that *Homo erectus* could see at least as well as we can, but that his manipulative abilities with his fingers, his powers of speech and his ability to conceptualize were all inferior to ours. Nevertheless, there was still a good deal of room in an *erectus* skull. He may not have been able to think very complicated thoughts, but he certainly could think.

We can draw further indirect and somewhat more accurate inferences about his brain from our knowledge of the things he could do. For one thing, he became a much better toolmaker and tool user than *Australopithecus* was, and in time progressed from the extremely primitive chopping tool stage to one of making a more efficient, if still rather crude, kind of hand-axe. With his improved weapons he was a far more advanced and able hunter than *Australopithecus*, and had reached the point of being able to kill very large animals. To do this required a marked degree of planning and cooperation, which in turn meant that he must have lived in bands attached to a "home base" that was sometimes a cave, sometimes out in the open. By this time he had mastered the use of fire, and it must be assumed that he had some powers of speech; the ability to talk would appear to be a requisite in teaching the young how to make his kind of tool, and it certainly would be necessary in planning and executing an animal drive—particularly one that involved setting grass fires to stampede a herd into a bog or over a cliff.

To suggest that *Homo erectus* lit fires to engage in animal drives may seem wildly speculative, but the suspicion that he did is strong, based on research done in a dry valley in the rolling country of north-central Spain. About 80 years ago a water pipe was put through this valley, and the trench that was dug for it revealed the presence of numerous very large animal bones. This was a local curiosity for a number of years until an amateur archeologist, the Marqués de Cerralbo, began more serious excavations there. He published a paper about his findings and in due course this fell into the hands of the author of this book, who went to the valley, decided that it was worth study and began site work there in 1961.

What was intriguing about the site was that, unlike the great cave at Choukoutien, it promised to be an open-air residence of extreme antiquity. Because of the climatological vagaries of the Pleistocene, human fossils of a pre-Neanderthal nature are virtually nonexistent in Europe, and the only good evidence that pre-Neanderthal men lived there at all is the occurrence of their stone tools, which are scattered widely. The only trouble with them is that they usually find their way into beds of river gravels and thus say nothing at all about the living sites or the habits of the people who used them. This Spanish site was quite different. Detailed stratigraphic studies of the area, plus an analysis of a great deal of fossil pollen, revealed that about 300,000 years ago the climate was going through periods of both warmer and colder weather than at present, with annual mean variations of temperature running as much as six degrees either way. During the warmer times the landscape was more heavily wooded than it is now, but it was during one of the cooler, moister periods that human occupation was first found. Then, the valley where the farming villages of Torralba and Ambrona now lie was probably a migration route for herds of large mammals. These ranged from deer, horses and aurochs up to elephants.

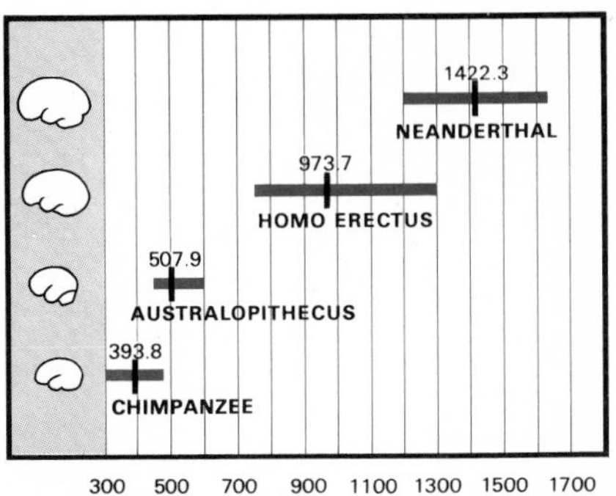

THE BRAIN GETS BIGGER

The evolution of the human brain from the time it was ape-sized to the point where it can be called modern is traced on this chart. The colored bands show the range in size, as measured in cubic centimeters, of the brains of chimpanzees, australopithecines, Homo erectus and Neanderthal men—with black bars indicating the average size for each group. The brain outlines show the marked development of the frontal lobes (at left). Thus Homo erectus, the first true man, had a brain which in total size overlapped Neanderthal's, but in which the frontal region lacked the complex lobes of intelligent modern man.

What made the fossil sites at Torralba and Ambrona interesting was the enormous number of elephant bones that they contained. These belonged to a straight-tusked species now extinct and somewhat larger than the African elephant of today. They were far and away too numerous to be explained away as having gotten there by accident. Furthermore, their condition and their position in the ground were extremely unusual. Many of the bones of the smaller animals, even some of the enormously heavy bones of the elephants, had been smashed open, presumably to get at the marrow. A large elephant skull had its entire top broken away. Most suggestive, these bones were all mixed up. It was almost impossible to reconstruct a complete skeleton of any animal. The more these sites were developed, the clearer it became that somebody had been cutting up animals and dragging their bones around. There was even a huge male elephant skeleton, only half of whose bones could be found. These were intact, all in one place, but the other half of this animal had been taken away.

Mixed in with the bones were many signs of ancient human presence. Stone tools, of a type associated with *Homo erectus* in Africa, were abundant. There were even pieces of wood, pointed or vaguely spatulate at one end—an extraordinary occurrence at a site of this age, considering the perishability of wood.

There was also a quantity of material that shows different degrees of burning, some of it charcoal, some of it carbon. These materials were not so concentrated in any one place as to suggest the presence of hearths and continuous fires over a long period of time. Rather they were thinly and very widely scattered. Whoever had been lighting these fires was apparently burning grass and brush over large areas. This evidence, plus that of the elephant bones concentrated in what was once a bog, suggests that the setting of those fires had been purposeful—to drive the unwieldy elephants into the mud. Deep mud, even to modern elephants, is usually fatal, and if the early men who came and went in the Ambrona Valley could have driven a herd of elephants into this bog, they would have been relatively easy to dispatch. Otherwise, it is difficult to see how such large numbers of animals as formidable as these could have been killed all in one place. Nobody, it might be added, kills elephants and *then* drags them to that one place.

The frustrating thing about Torralba and Ambrona is that not a single human fossil has been found at either dig. It is certain that men moved in and out of these places. The time they did so can be determined with substantial accuracy. And this dating, plus the evidence of their tools, points strongly to *Homo erectus*. Still, it would be nice to nail all this down with just one skull.

In general, *Homo erectus* might be labeled as a kind of migratory worker within a fairly diverse habitat, a fellow who returned to certain sites with some regularity. He probably made his rounds according to season, living on game and fruits as they became abundant in his territory. But that is about as far as our knowledge of his life habits goes. We do not know if he wore clothes, whether he spoke a definable language, had any form of dwelling or shelter other than natural caves and rock overhangs. We know nothing about his social structure other than the dim picture we have of a loose hunting band. We have no evidence of art, religion or any kinship system. We do not even know what became of him. His culture changed, and in another couple of hundred thousand years more modern kinds of men appeared. But what went on during this period and where it took place—except for the evidence of two peculiar skulls that will be described in the next chapter—is still hopelessly vague.

AMIDST WHEAT FIELDS OF SPAIN'S AMBRONA VALLEY, WORKMEN UNCOVER AN ANCIENT BOG WHERE ELEPHANTS WERE TRAPPED AND KILLED.

The First Men of Spain

Three hundred thousand years or more ago, small bands of hunters roamed Europe—probably members of the species Homo erectus, which at that time was widely distributed in Asia and Africa. Stone tools and animal bones found at two sites excavated by the author of this book show that they reached Spain. How such a hunting band lived is reconstructed in the five paintings that follow.

Digging in Ambrona Valley

The place in Spain where a *Homo erectus* band once appears to have lived is in dry, deeply valleyed country almost a hundred miles east and north of Madrid. Its existence as a fossil locality had been known for nearly 80 years and it was first worked by a Spanish nobleman, an amateur archeologist, who began digging up animal bones and stone tools there about 50 years ago. Clark Howell happened upon a paper by this man, and in 1961 began serious excavation there himself. Soon he found a second site about a mile from the first one.

So far, no human fossil has been found at either site, but the careful mapping *(next page)* of every other object reveals much about the people who once lived there. They hunted elephants, lit large fires, made distinctive stone tools that link them to *Homo erectus* in other places. Good stratigraphy and much fossil pollen date this site with remarkable accuracy.

ON PEDESTALS OF MARL, broken bones and stone tools have been left in place until they can be mapped, drawn and photographed. Later, each piece will be removed and catalogued.

SQUARE SECTIONS are methodically excavated, one by one. The water pipe running through this section, laid down in 1888, led to the discovery that the place was full of fossils.

ELEPHANT BONES, hardened with preservative, are jacketed in plaster and reinforced with rods to protect them during removal and shipment to a museum laboratory for study.

Blueprint of a Bog

What Clark Howell found at Ambrona is shown in this ground plan of the site, the heavy white lines representing one-meter squares. Vacant areas like that at right are still to be excavated; but where work has been done, everything encountered—bones, tools, stones, wood *(see key below)*—is recorded so that relative positions and associations may be studied and evaluated later. Red objects are man-made. Everything not otherwise keyed is a piece of animal bone.

The central concentration of bones, with the exception of two smaller tusks, all belong to a huge male straight-tusked elephant—the extinct *Elephas antiquus*. It roamed southern Europe during the Pleistocene. Above, to the right and left, are parts of smaller elephants and other animals—deer, horses and aurochs—all scattered haphazardly. From this it is evident that after they were killed these smaller individuals were dismembered, whereas such a huge beast as the bull elephant was stripped of meat but otherwise left more or less intact.

The production of a detailed ground plan like this distinguishes the work of present-day paleoanthropologists. Whereas earlier investigators were often content merely to catalogue their finds, such a meticulous blueprint of a site makes it possible for experts to build solid theories about the activities of early man.

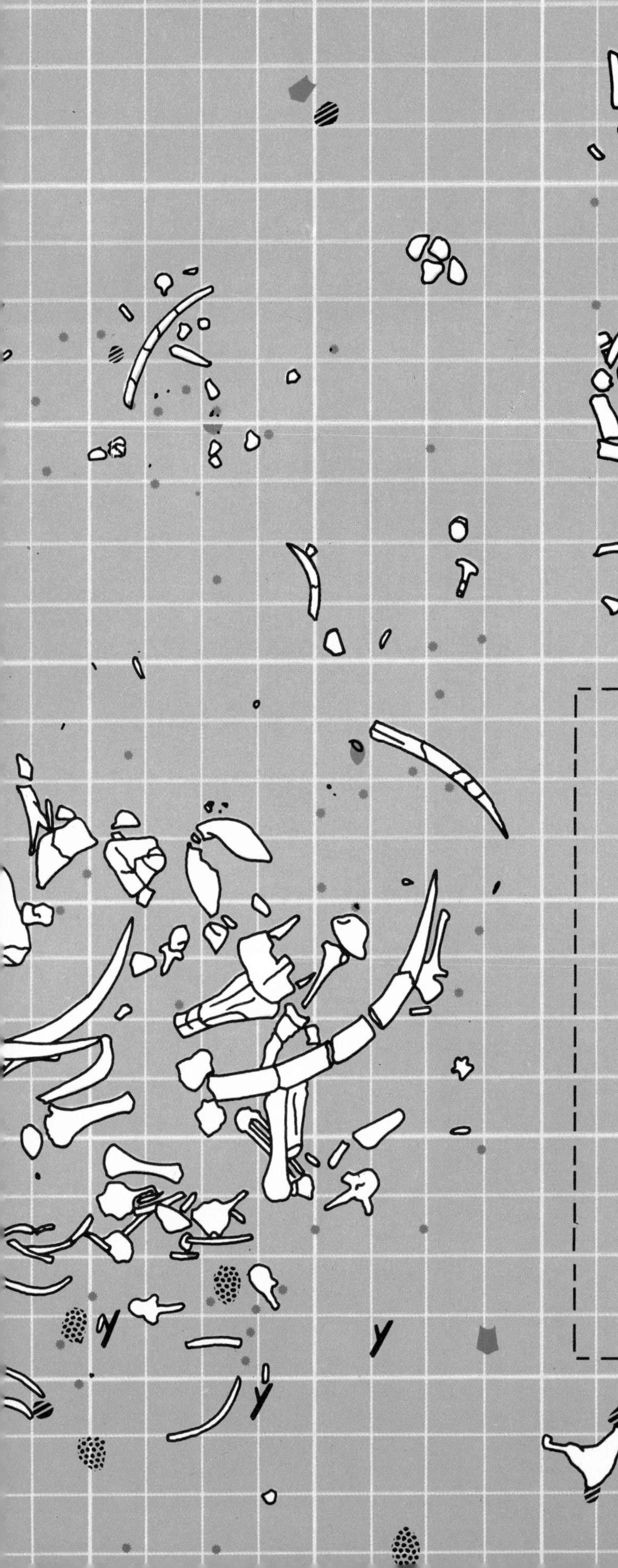

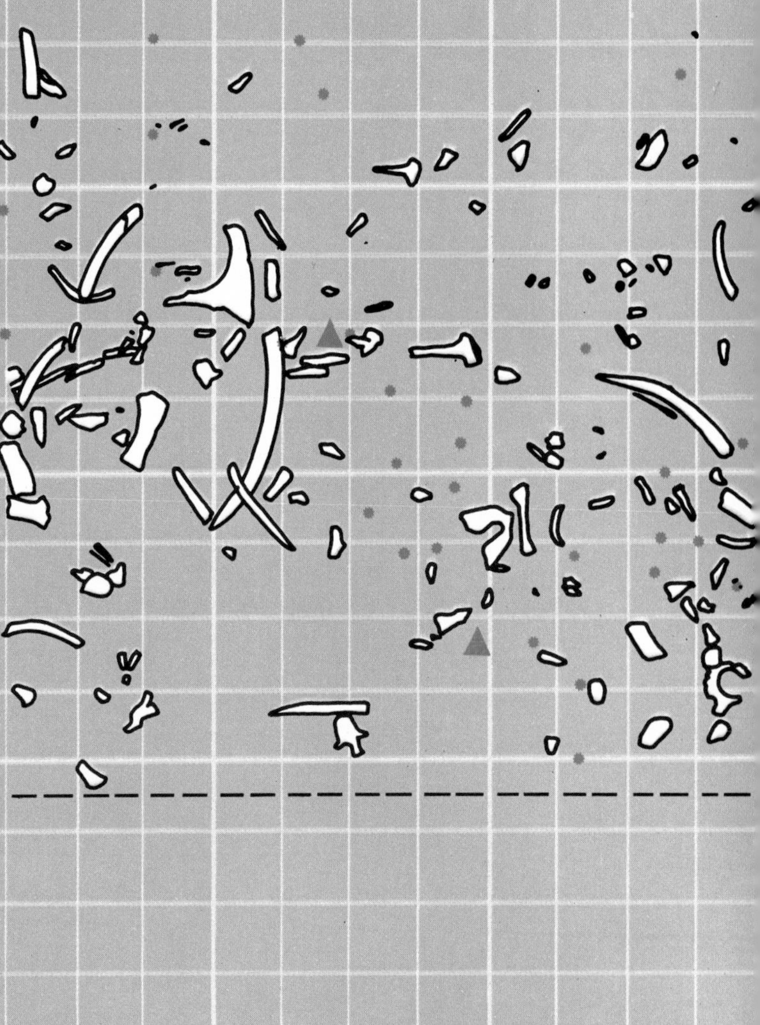

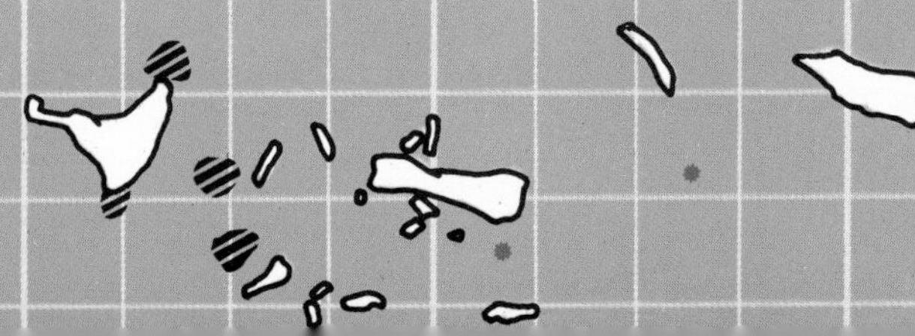

Area Not Yet
Excavated

STONE HAND-AXES found at Ambrona resemble those made by *Homo erectus* in Africa, and are strong evidence that his kind also lived in Spain.

A HOMO ERECTUS BAND PREPARES FOR A HUNT

Without human fossils for proof, it is impossible to say definitely that the men who visited the Ambrona Valley were *Homo erectus*. But the evidence of their tools is compelling. Here artist Stanley Meltzoff has reconstructed in five paintings some scenes from the life of that time, drawing on the information and inferences that three years of digging by Clark Howell have produced.

The season in this first painting is autumn, when the migratory grazing animals will be moving south through such natural funnels as the Ambrona Valley to the warmer lowlands. It is early morning, and while the mist still blankets the valley floor, a band of *Homo erectus* gathers on the steep slopes and makes ready for the hunt. In the center of the painting, a grizzled man sharpens his hand-axe with a hammer fashioned from a deer antler. At his knee a juvenile absorbs the lesson. The man by the fire holding a wooden spear matches the tools against his fingers, a sort of rudimentary counting.

Most tools found in the valley were made of alien stone, which means they were carried there in anticipation of the hunt. These early hunters had some understanding of place and season and could visualize events in the future. The stones were probably carried in skins like the one shown in the lower left-hand corner. In the background, standing like a sentinel, one of the band waits for more men to arrive and join them in the hunt.

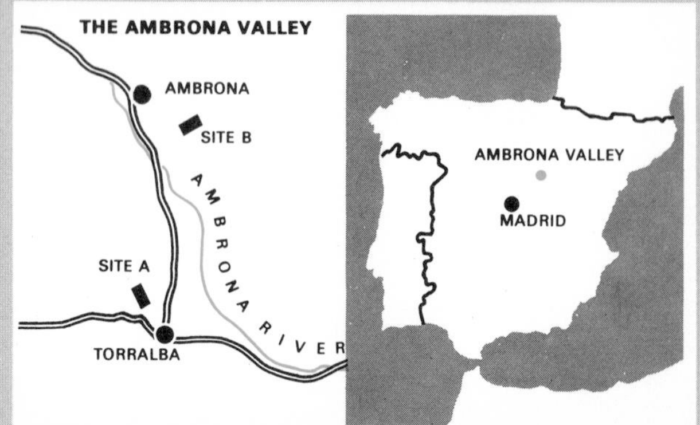

TWO BANDS JOIN FORCES

As the hunters get ready, a second band of *Homo erectus* approaches up the slope. The young children and adults hang back watchfully, but two adolescent females have run ahead to meet a young male belonging to the band already on the hillside. Such encounters may have provoked situations of momentary tension as well as attraction, even though these two bands have doubtless met and cooperated in the past. Perhaps they last saw each other the previous season; these adolescents could even be cousins, since by this time in man's development the exchange of mates between different bands might well have been a common practice.

That some sort of meeting took place before the hunt is cer-

tain; the sheer size of the job ahead demanded it. Judging from the composition of bands of apes and primitive hunter-gatherer tribes still living in remote parts of the world today, *Homo erectus* bands most likely consisted of a few adult males and a half-dozen or so adult females, with the rest adolescents, children and babies—a total of 30 or more. This would not be nearly enough able-bodied hands to conduct a successful drive of large, wild animals. Thus some form of cooperation must have been essential to successful hunting, and it may be assumed that many such bands as these joined forces.

Behind the approaching group the mist has risen from the valley floor revealing a boggy marshland and patches of the narrow Ambrona River—the same stream that meanders through the valley in north-central Spain today *(see maps)*. This will be the scene of the kill—but first the elephant prey must be driven there. For this the hunters need fire. We know they used it from the many bits of charred wood found at Torralba and Ambrona, and some of these early bands probably even knew how to make it when needed. But others may have been able to obtain it only from natural sources such as forest fires and then carefully nursed it along, taking it with them wherever they went. That is what the old female near the rear of the approaching party is doing, carrying the precious burning coals cupped in a ball of clay.

THE HUNT IS ON

A northwest wind is blowing, and fires set by the hunters far up the valley are sweeping the migratory herds before them. Already a number of straight-tusked elephants have been caught in the bog. On the left, wildly shouting hunters have fired the dry grass to keep the game from crossing the stream to solid ground. To the right the elephants are hemmed in by the steep sides of the valley, up which may be seen escaping a herd of more nimble-footed wild horses. Some of the mired elephants may yet break loose, but once so heavy an animal becomes stuck in mud up to its knees it is virtually helpless. The female in the center, trying so desperately to free herself and at the same time give her young a helping prod, is doomed. The hunters have only to wait: when she is exhausted, she will be dispatched with wooden spears and stones.

This painting shows the excavation site at Torralba at the very moment of receiving part of its ancient burden of bones. One unusual arrangement found there by Howell is that of the bones of the right side—and only the right side—of a male elephant *(right)*. Since an elephant would not normally be split like a lobster, the logical explanation is that it died half-buried, like the spent male in the foreground, and that only the parts above the surface of the bog were carried off.

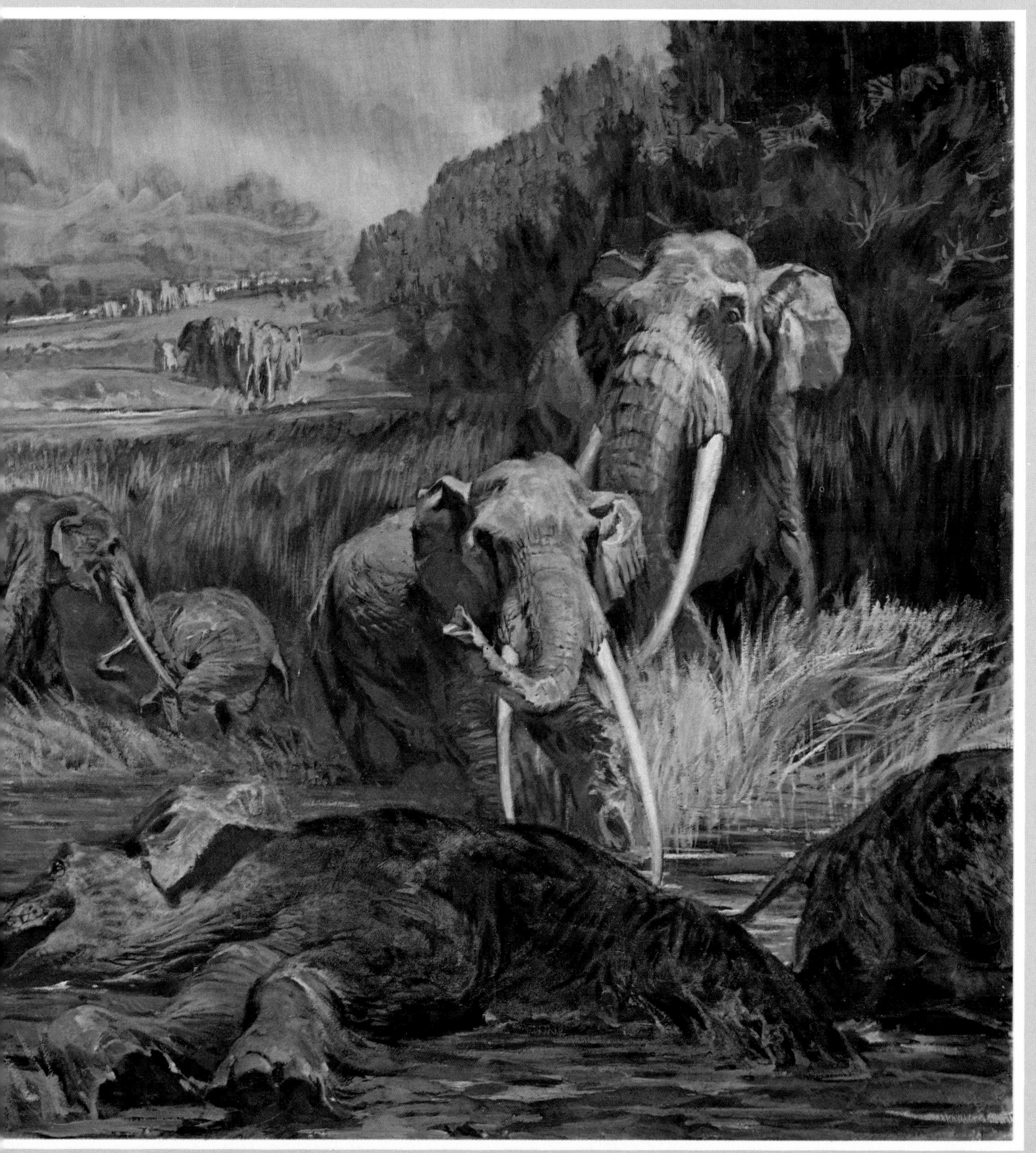

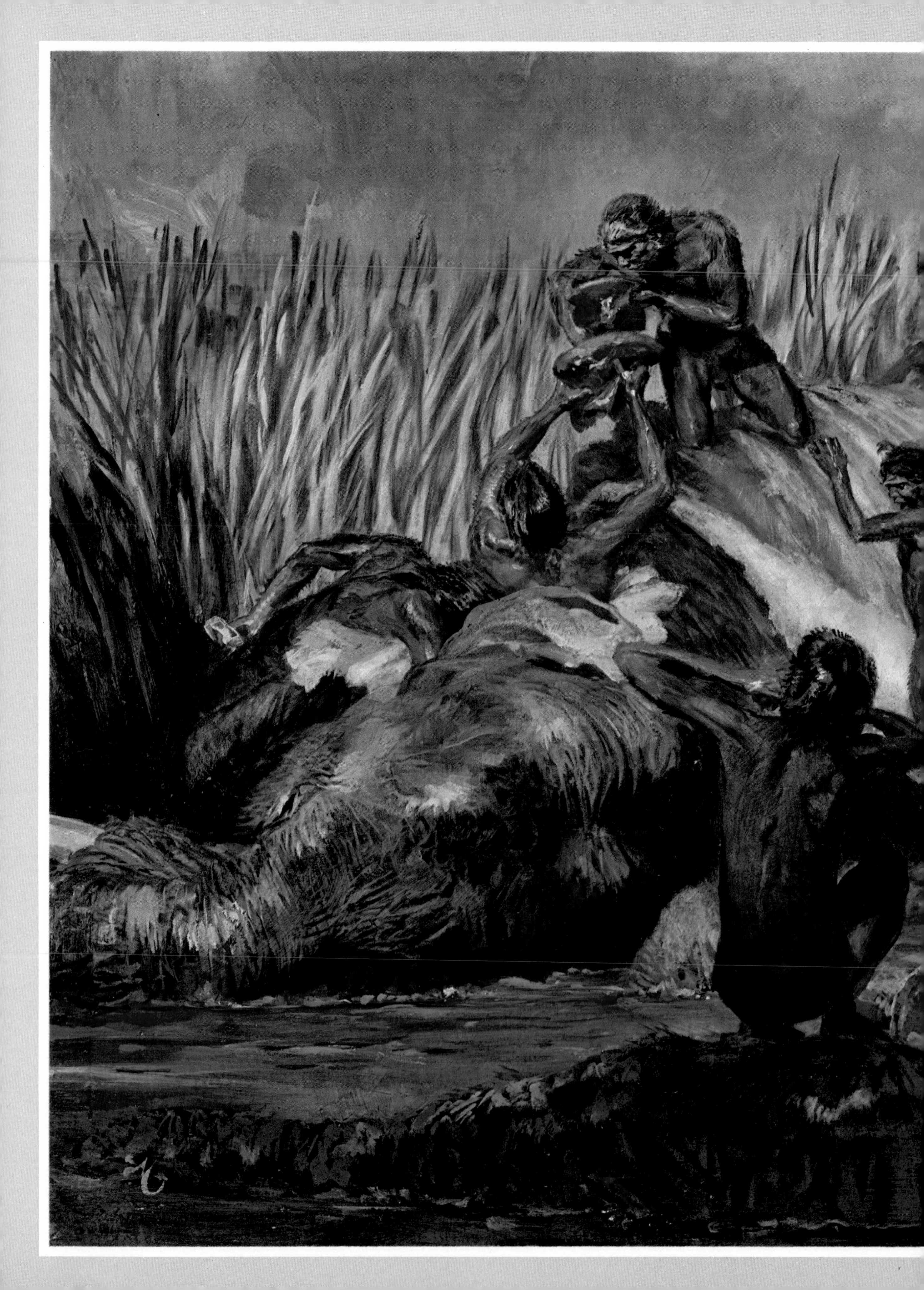

A LINEAR ARRANGEMENT of tusk and leg bones suggests that it was man who laid them that way.

THE KILL IS CUT UP

At dusk, in the smoking aftermath of the drive, hunters are butchering one of their kill. Already they have hacked through the thick hide to reach their prime target, the soft organs like the heart and liver, which were so much easier for them to eat than the tougher outer flesh. Squatting in the foreground, a man is greedily helping himself to brains scooped from a severed head; a crushed elephant skull was found in just this position. Walking away from the carcass, an adolescent with a slab of flesh on a stick over his shoulder balances on a crude bridge of disjointed leg bones.

In the summer of 1963, digging at Ambrona, Clark Howell came upon just such a linear pattern of elephant bones *(see photograph)*. Since chance would not deposit things in this way, particularly when the things are a tusk, two disjointed femurs and two tibias belonging to a single large elephant, Howell suspected—as he had with the half skeleton on the previous page—that the hand of man was responsible. Why was this done? It seems unlikely that the bones were laid thus as part of a ceremony since no evidence of such behavior by *Homo erectus* exists from other sites. One possible explanation is suggested by the deep mud in which the elephants were mired. Such terrain would be nearly impossible for a burdened man to cross. The leg joints, then, after having been cut from the carcass, might well have served as a causeway to firmer ground.

THE HUNT IS RE-ENACTED

The great glut is over. The two bands of *Homo erectus*, enjoying the rare double sensation of a full stomach and the stimulus of strange company, have gathered for warmth around the dwindling cooking fires. Within a circle of coals symbolizing the fire drive, a hunter prances about, draped in the gory skin of an infant elephant. Under his arms he clutches its mother's tusks. The sight of these trophies has inspired others to re-enact the hunt—leaping, shouting and thrusting with wooden

spears. For the children squatting in the foreground this is a kind of schooling. Here they will absorb the tradition of the hunt. For the adolescents it may also be a way of courting, with the males showing off their bravery to impress prospective mates. When the bands part to struggle through the winter ahead, certain females of one band will follow the males of another. Though there is no concrete evidence for this scene from the sites, it is enough to remember that these were human beings after all, and the kinds of activities that their descendants would—and still do—engage in, must have begun somewhere.

AN ACHEULIAN CLEAVER, about 10 inches long, is from Isimila, Tanzania, a rich open-air occupation site. Made from mylonite, it was probably used by a Paleolithic hunter to dismember large animals.

5

The Tools of Stone Age Man

Lying row on row, neatly sorted, neatly labeled, in the drawers of museum and university collections around the world, are enormous numbers of prehistoric stone tools—hundreds of thousands, possibly millions of them. This abundance may seem amazing when we consider the extreme scarcity of fossils of the men who made them, and yet it is entirely logical. Stone is one of the most enduring substances on earth. And tools were almost invariably made of the hardest kinds of stone. Once made, they were virtually indestructible. Too small to be affected by the ponderous upheavals of the earth's crust, which ripple and fracture larger sections of rock with ease, a stone tool—so long as it is not being rattled about on the surface of the ground, usually by water—can survive unchanged almost indefinitely. Thus, if it should happen to fall into the mud of a swamp or be slowly covered by rubbish in the floor of a cave, it could lie inert for a hundred million years or more before being accidentally spewed out and subjected once again to the hazards of life on the surface.

Since the oldest stone implements that could possibly be recognized as such today are only about two million years old, we must assume that practically all of the ones that have ever been made are still lying around somewhere or other. It is not surprising that a good many of them have been found, any more than it would be surprising for some archeologist of the future to stumble over a quantity of Coca-Cola bottles sleeping quietly where they had been dropped, one by one, into the ooze beneath the pier of a waterside pavilion. Every culture leaves some odds and ends behind, some of them very long-lived.

Another reason for the abundance of stone tools is that while early man had only one skull to bequeath to the clay bank, he had a whole lifetime in which to make implements. He made them quickly and easily. As fast as he broke them or lost them or blunted them, he made new ones. He started when he was a boy and continued throughout his life. So, even among the australopithecines, who were the clumsiest of beginners in the tool business, one man might have made anywhere from dozens to hundreds before he died. Those figures may be a ridiculous underestimate—we simply don't know anything definite about the rate of tool production at that early date, or even what proportion of the members of an australopithecine band made tools. It may be that only a few of the most able ones did, although the likelihood is that if toolmaking had become a characteristic of australopithecines, it was common to them all.

Certainly by the time of *Homo erectus* it was universal. Not only had man become much more dependent on tools by then but he was also making better ones, which, of course, changed his way of life and tended to further increase his dependence on them. Another important point: there were no specialists in those days. Everybody had to know how to do everything; all the cultural skills of an entire society were carried about in every human head, and it meant that every man was a toolmaker.

So far in this book we have covered between a million and a half and two million years in time, and have seen the emergence of two kinds of tool users. What impresses most during this immensely long period is a sense of almost utter cultural stagnation. Life was hopelessly conservative; it crept on for millennium after millennium without the slightest apparent change. Men, in fact, may well have changed more than their culture did. *Homo erectus* was still using the same kinds of crude tools in China that his australopithecine kin in Africa did up to a half a million years earlier, and yet he had evolved physically to a considerable degree.

THE earliest recognizable man-made, man-used implement is often called a pebble tool. This name has now fallen into disfavor, and the proper word is chopping tool, or, simply, chopper. Some choppers were as small as Ping-pong balls, others as large as billiard balls. Most were fashioned from roundish stones collected from stream beds or beaches and worn smooth by the action of sand and water. Such a water-rounded stone could be firmly gripped in the hand without hurting the palm when it was used. To turn it into a tool, two or three chips were knocked off one end with another stone. This gave it an edge of sorts or perhaps a point—an extremely primitive and rough one but better than nothing. Such an implement is readily recognized by an expert but might not be by a layman. Anything more primitive might not be recognized as a tool by anybody since it would be indistinguishable from a stone that had been pointed or edged by nature.

Nevertheless, the ancient tool kit does have more primitive implements and with luck and skill they can still be recognized. For one thing, the presence of large numbers of chips or flakes in one spot is an indication that toolmaking once took place there. A stone that bears the marks of a great deal of banging and battering may have been used as a hammer or as an anvil. Finally, the presence of "foreign" stones of a kind that do not normally occur at a site can be regarded as indicative of tool use, even though the stones themselves have not been chipped. In actual fact, choppers are by no means the commonest kinds of tools found in these earliest sites. Much more numerous are the smaller chips and naturally shaped stones. These latter, of course, were the principal source of tools for man for millions of years before it occurred to anyone to try and sharpen one himself. They are identifiable today only by the context in which they are found. As one French prehistorian has remarked, "Man made one, God made ten thousand. God help the man who can distinguish the one in the ten thousand."

A CHOPPER presumably was held as one would hold a rock while banging downward at something with a direct hammering or chopping motion. Using a chopper in this way, *Australopithecus* was probably able to hack his way through animal flesh and sinews, although considering the bluntness of his implement, mashing might be a better word than hacking to describe its action. The small chips that were knocked off during the manufacture of choppers are known as flakes. Sharper than choppers, they were probably used for slicing and cutting. They undoubtedly became dull very quickly, for although stone is hard, its edges break easily.

It should be clearly understood that a name like chopper describes a use that can only be guessed at by the archeologist. His guess may appear overwhelmingly logical, but it is still a guess. Considerable attention is being paid at this very moment to the whole question of tool use, and some extremely sophisticated experiments are being conducted by several paleoanthropologists, among them J. Desmond Clark, Louis Leakey and S. A. Semenov, in an effort to see if some scientific basis for determining how tools were employed can be worked out. Their method is to make several duplicates of a specific tool, use each one in a different way—chopping wood, cutting flesh, skinning animals, scraping hides, digging roots—and then examine their edges under a microscope to see if different uses produce different kinds of wear and tear. As a by-product of this study, Leakey has also gained a great deal of practical knowledge about what kinds of tools are best for what kinds of jobs.

In addition to being named according to their presumed use, stone tools are classified according to their workmanship to indicate what "industry" they belong to. Thus, chopping tools, which were first found by Leakey in East Africa, constitute the so-called Oldowan industry, getting their name from Oldoway, an alternate spelling of Olduvai. Similarly worked tools bear that name no matter what part of the world they are found in.

All in all, the Oldowan industry lasted for at least a million and a half years, perhaps much longer. How it got out of Africa is unknown; who carried it is equally unknown. No positively identified australopithecine fossils have ever been found outside of Africa and, until they are, we cannot assume that *Australopithecus* was the exporter of the chopping tool. It seems more likely that *Homo erectus* was, or perhaps an intermediate form between the two species.

The only possible route for the exportation of the Oldowan industry was through the Middle East, from where it could have branched out into both Europe and Asia. However, the chances of reconstructing this spread are dim indeed because of the onslaughts of cold that have disrupted so much of the face of Europe and Asia on six occasions during the last two million years.

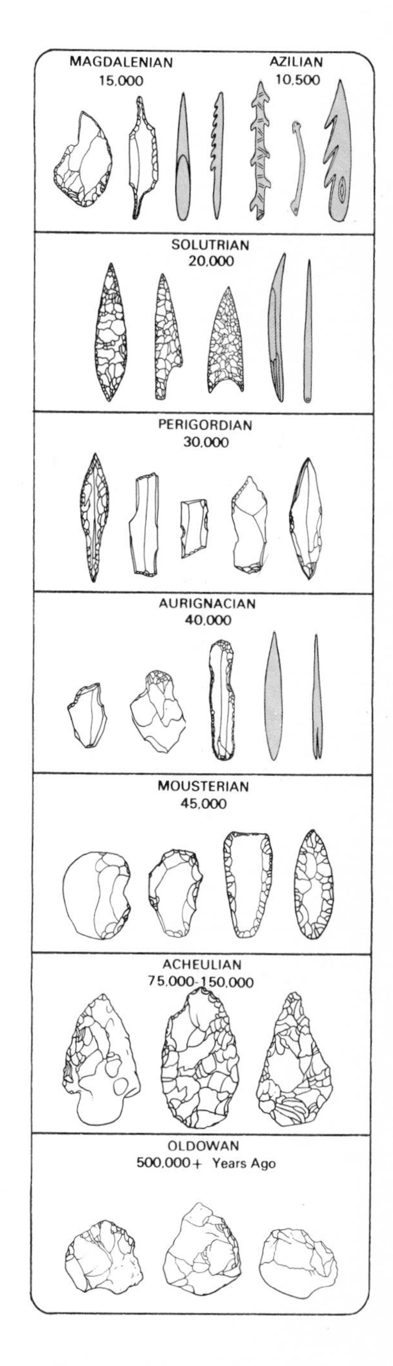

THE EVOLUTION OF TOOLS

This column shows the seven major tool cultures of Europe. Beginning with three Oldowan choppers from Hungary, it progresses to Acheulian hand-axes, to Mousterian sidescrapers of Neanderthal man and ends with a variety of burins, needles, points and harpoons of the Cro-Magnon peoples in France. Representative bone implements are shown in color.

It was not until 1963 that a relatively clean and undamaged Oldowan site was opened up in Europe. This is Vértesszöllös in Hungary, and it promises to be an extremely important one. Four different occupation levels have already been detected. They are thin, suggesting only the briefest kind of tenancy, probably by small groups. Some layers, in fact, are mere scatterings of debris, but the debris is significant. It contains a number of burned objects indicating the use of fire, tools in considerable abundance and the smashed bones of some 15 different species of small animals. The tools include many flakes and choppers, simply chipped on one or two edges and primitive enough to qualify as Oldowan. However, they do begin to show slight signs of refinement, and there is strong hope that further work at Vértesszöllös will throw some light on the evolution and distribution of the Oldowan industry, about which almost nothing is presently known.

Since the types of tools found at Vértesszöllös are much the same as those found at Choukoutien and East Africa, we can assume that *Homo erectus* was the man who made them although no human fossils have yet been found there. As far as dating goes, the site may very well be older than Choukoutien, and probably was inhabited some half million years ago. It is certainly the oldest known tool site in Europe since virtually all the others that we now associate with *Homo erectus* are characterized by a different kind of tool industry developed later on by him.

THE new style in toolmaking that these later men pioneered made its appearance about half a million years ago. In its earliest forms it bears several names like Chellean and Abbevillian but, for simplicity's sake, let us settle on the principal style and the principal name that covers it through most of the world and for several hundred thousand years—the Acheulian industry. The name comes from the small town of Saint Acheul in the Somme Valley in France. The Acheulian was a clear step forward. It spread rapidly, from Africa into Europe and eastward as far as India. To understand what made the new style "new," it is necessary to learn something about the various ways in which stone can be shaped.

The ideal stone, from the point of view of the toolmaker, is one that is hard, tough and of a smooth, fine-grained consistency. Stone of this type behaves somewhat like glass; it shatters rather than crumbles, and chips can be knocked off it that are razor-sharp, just like the edges of glass splinters. The best ones were flint, chert and similar rocks. Flint was the most common in Western Europe, and the typical Acheulian implement was a flint hand-axe. In many places where flint was unobtainable, quartz, quartzite and other rocks were used. Rocks of a coarse granular consistency, like granite, are almost useless for making chipped tools; they do not fracture along smooth clean edges but tend, instead, to crumble. Others, like common feldspar, tend to break only along certain fracture lines and hence cannot be controlled by the toolmaker.

In a very real sense the presence of good tool-stone helped determine the distribution of peoples during much of the Paleolithic, and that is one reason why so many of their artifacts are found in or near rivers. Rivers are an almost endless source of pebbles and pieces of rock, and emphasis should be on the word "pieces," for the best tool-stone in the world was of no use to an early Stone Age man if it existed in a solid cliff from which he was unable to detach small hunks that could be shaped by him.

Just as there are various kinds of stone, there are various ways of working it, and the combination of these two variables produces a surprising variety of results. The more fine-grained the stone, the flatter and more leaflike the flakes that can be chipped loose from it. The size and shape of these flakes can be further controlled by the ways in which they are separated from the parent stone. They may be knocked loose by a hammer or they may be pried loose by a pointed stick or bone. The angle at which the hammer blow is struck can be changed to produce either a small thick flake or a large thin one. Also, different kinds of hammers produce different kinds of flakes. "Soft" hammers of wood or bone produce one kind, hard stone ones another and a wooden point pressed against the edge of the tool will produce a still different kind. Even the way a tool is held while it is being made will affect the kind of flakes that can be struck from it. When it is held in the hand the results are not the same as when it is balanced on a rock.

Truly, stone is a much more subtle and flexible material than it appears to be. If some of these statements about it seem a little extreme, the reader is invited to test them by experimenting with rocks himself. If he lives in a neighborhood that is blessed with flint or chert, he will quickly discover that these substances are extraordinarily workable once some skill has been developed in handling them. The principles involved are all described and illustrated in the picture essay that follows this chapter; with considerable practice, almost anybody should be able to learn how to make simple tools. He will not make very good ones. He will not make them with the speed and virtuosity of François Bordes, the French prehistorian who has made a specialty of this craft and who can knock out a hand-axe in a few minutes. And he will certainly make nothing that *Homo erectus* would have been proud of. In fact, today's would-be toolmaker can only be impressed by the enormous skill that every ancestral craftsman must have had. This, of course, was based on dire necessity, on years of practice and on an intimate knowledge of the natures of different stones. For each has its own qualities, and these may vary further depending on whether the stone is hot or cold—even on whether it is wet or not. But these are the postgraduate frills in toolmaking. The basic principles are fairly simple. One may be surprised at how hard a blow it takes to crack or flake a stone, but if it is done right, the stone actually will—amazingly enough—behave just as this book says it should.

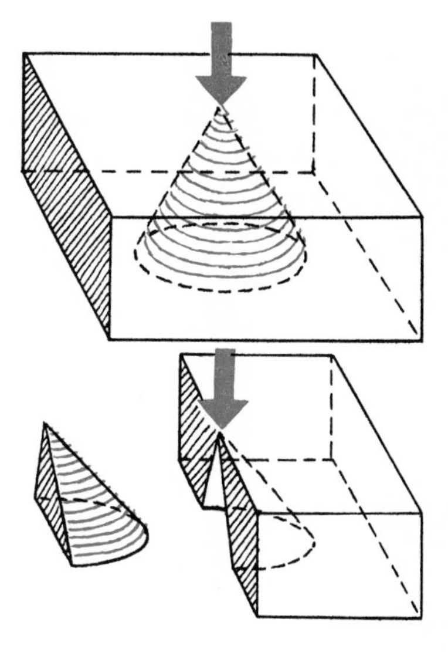

HOW STONE FRACTURES

These two simplified drawings illustrate the basic principles of fracturing, by which all stone tools were made. The top one shows how a cone of percussion is formed in flinty rock when a blow is struck. The impact (arrow) sends a widening wave rippling through the stone. A flake is chipped out when the stone fractures along the edges of the ripple. The commonest example of this can be found in window glass which has been hit by a flying pebble—the cone-shaped flake scar is always opposite the point of impact, where only a tiny nick may be visible. The fact that a cone of percussion is produced even when a rock is hit on an edge is shown in the bottom drawing. Here the waves move only through a half-cone, producing a flake of a different shape. In toolmaking, sharp-edged flakes are always struck from the edges of stone, never from the middle.

GIVEN all these variations in technique and material, there are still only two basic categories of tools: the so-called "core" tools, and the "flake" tools. To make a core tool, one takes a lump of stone and knocks chips from it until it is the desired size and shape; the core of stone that remains is the tool. A flake tool, as its name implies, is a chip struck from a core. It may be large or small and its shape may vary, depending on the shape of the core from which it is struck. It may be used as is or it may be further worked by having smaller flakes pried or chipped from it. In any event, the flake itself, and not the core from which it is struck, is the tool.

In the earliest days of toolmaking, flakes were very simple. One took whatever happened to fly off a core and did the best one could with it. In general, flakes were used as cutters because their edges were sharper than anything that could be produced on a chopper, which was more useful for heavy hacking. As time went on, more and more skills were developed in the manufacture of flakes, and eventually this became a much more sophisticated method of toolmaking than the core technique. It was discovered that every flake struck from a core of a certain shape would produce a long bladelike flake with a straight, smooth cutting edge. Much skill went into the preparation of special cores from which such tools could be made. A typical "blade" core would be trimmed to a shape something like that of a very large strawberry, held point down and with a prepared flat surface uppermost where the stem would ordinarily be. When a core of this shape was struck on its flat top, near the edge, a long knifelike splinter would fly off the side. Then the core could be rotated slightly and given another blow—and another perfectly formed knife blade could be produced. In this way the core could be worked down like an artichoke, producing smaller and smaller blades until it was thrown away. This technique was still being used up into historical times by Aztec Indians in Mexico, where a fine quality of obsidian was available from the local volcanoes. One observer watched a workman produce a hundred usable blades in a little under an hour from obsidian cores.

ALTHOUGH, as the Acheulian progressed, the emphasis was on flakes, core tools also underwent a great deal of refinement from the primitive Oldowan chopper, which was simply a roundish stone with several chips knocked off the end to make it sharp. The great forward step of the Acheulian core-toolmaker was to chip it all over instead of only at one end or one side. This may seem like an awfully small improvement, but it was a fundamental one and it made possible much more efficient tools. The purpose of the two-sided, or bifacial, technique was to change the shape of the core from that of an essentially round stone to a flattish one, for only with a flat stone can one get a decent cutting edge. A round one is too plump and tapers too abruptly. Thus the first step in making an Acheulian hand-axe was to rough out the core until it had somewhat the shape of a turtle shell, thickest in the middle and thinning to a coarse edge all around. This edge could then be trimmed with more delicate little scallops of flaking. The cutting surfaces thus produced were longer, straighter and considerably keener than any Oldowan chopper could offer.

Acheulian hand-axes ran somewhat larger than chopping tools and were usually pear-shaped or pointed. Some have been recovered that were more than two feet long and weighed upwards of 25 pounds. Obviously they were far too heavy and cumbersome to have been used for the kind of cutting and scraping that the smaller ones were designed for, and the thought is that they may have been fitted to boomlike handles and poised over traps, set to fall and split the skulls of animals that triggered them off. Another type of implement that appears for the first time in the Acheulian is the cleaver. A cleaver had a straight cutting edge at one end, and actually looked much more like a modern axehead than the ancient hand-axes did. It was probably used for heavy chopping or for hacking through the joints of large animals.

As the Acheulian craftsman developed his techniques, he gradually learned to exploit different kinds of hammers. In earlier times he knocked flakes from his stone core with another piece of stone, and the hard shock of rock on rock tended to leave deep irregular scars and wavy cutting edges. But a wood or bone hammer, being softer, enabled its user to control his flaking to a much greater degree. Such implements left shallower, cleaner scars on a core, and produced sharper and straighter cutting edges. In time, the use of stone on stone was pretty much restricted to the preliminary rough shaping out of a hand-axe, and all the fine work around the edges was done with wood and bone.

But the big advance during the late Acheulian was the development of the prepared core—a core from which each splinter struck was a complete tool in itself. This technique could only have been mastered by men with considerable mental ability. It is one thing to make a core tool, to visualize a shape and then chip away at a piece of rock until that shape is achieved. It is quite another to have the foresight and imagination to carefully prepare a core *that does not look like a tool at all* and then strike complete tools from it.

With all these advances in toolmaking, it is hard not to visualize people who were also advancing. Here we encounter another of those frustrating blank pages in the history of early man. The Acheulian industry, introduced by *Homo erectus*, lasted from about 500,000 to 75,000 years ago, but *Homo erectus* did not. The last we see of him is more than 300,000 years ago, which means that there is a stretch of nearly 200,000 years from which no definite *Homo erectus* fossils are known, and at the end of which an entirely different type of man appears on the scene—Neanderthal man.

Actually that 200,000-year period is not an utter blank. It contains two kinds of evidence. The first is a scattering of individual teeth and jaw fragments from a number of sites in Morocco and France, some of these associated definitely with Acheulian tools. The teeth themselves look generally like those of *Homo erectus*, but the recoveries are too meager and scattered, the jawbones too incomplete or hopelessly smashed, the bits too small for the evidence to give anything more than a vague idea of the men they were attached to.

It is tempting to say, "Well, we know that *Homo erectus* came before this; if teeth like his persist, why not assume that they are his teeth and that he persisted too?" It would be perfectly proper to deduce something like this if only the second bit of evidence from this blank period did not appear to contradict the first. Exhibit number two is a skull, actually two skulls, one from Swanscombe, England, the other from Steinheim, Germany. Both were discovered back in the 1930s and they have been bothering paleoanthropologists ever since.

The Swanscombe skull turned up in the Thames River valley, not far from London. Its age has been carefully calculated from the detailed geological knowledge that exists about that part of England—also from the animal fossils associated with it, above it and below it in a number of ancient terraces along the river. Together they place it between 200,000 and 300,000 years ago. What is so bothersome about it is that it consists only of three bones from the roof and the back of the head, and these fall within the range of variation of *Homo sapiens*. That is, their size, their proportions and particularly their curves are much the same as modern man's; they are definitely not those of *Homo erectus*. This is absolutely astonishing. What on earth was a modern-looking skull like that doing way back there?

THERE is no good answer to the question if one looks at the Swanscombe skull alone, for it seems to indicate a kind of precocious modern man sneaking into the picture along with, or even before, Neanderthal man. Inasmuch as science for many years regarded Neanderthal man as more primitive than ourselves, this was obviously a puzzle. However, a fascinating solution begins to suggest itself if we now turn to the other skull, that of Steinheim man in Germany. This, too, has been dated with great care and its age appears to be approximately the same as Swanscombe man's. The shape of the back of its head is also similar. What Steinheim man adds to the picture is a face, for the front of his skull has been preserved. And it is not modern. It has heavy brow ridges and a low forehead that are not quite primitive enough to fall within the range of variation of *Homo erectus* or advanced enough to fall within the range of variation of

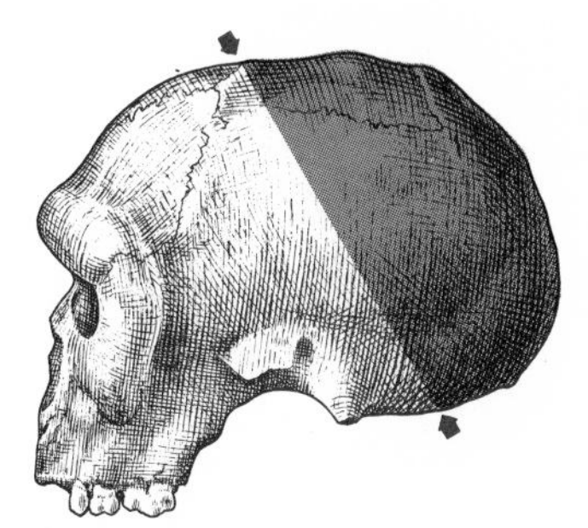

STEINHEIM

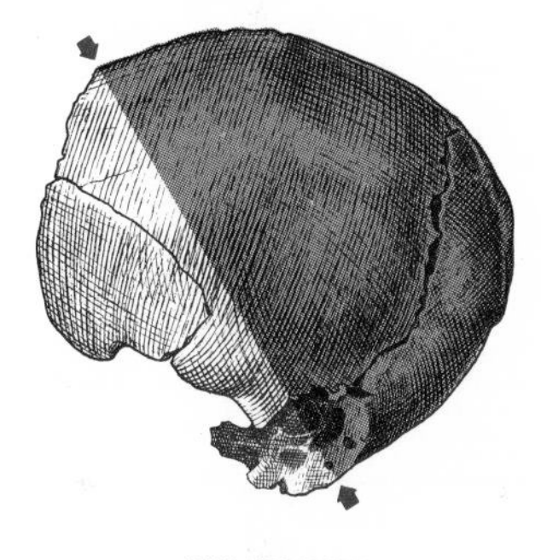

SWANSCOMBE

TRANSITIONAL SKULLS

These skull fragments are the only major links known between Homo erectus and Neanderthal man in Europe. The Swanscombe fossil consists only of bones from the top and back of a head, corresponding to the area marked in color on the Steinheim specimen in which the face is preserved. Both are similar enough to be classed in the same species. But they are different from Homo erectus, who had a smaller average brain capacity and larger brow ridges—and from Neanderthal man, with a larger brain and smaller brow ridges. Although more fossil evidence is needed, these skulls probably represent a widely spread European population of proto-modern men.

modern *Homo sapiens*. Clearly it is an intermediate type. Taken with Swanscombe man, the inference must be that the evolutionary processes that led to the emergence of more modern individuals from *Homo erectus* were working more swiftly on the back of the head than on the face.

The evidence from Swanscombe man and Steinheim man is painfully thin, but it is extremely suggestive, and as pieces are added to the puzzle, it all begins to hang together better and better. For one thing, Acheulian tools have been found in association with Swanscombe man. Once again, the imperishable evidence of stone artifacts as reliable indicators of time enters and gives substance to the picture.

Further matching-up of tools with fossil evidence from this confused period will undoubtedly take place and lead to further clarification. For the cultural evidence from the mid-Pleistocene is varied and rich. It reveals the development of a large number of subcultures during the long span of the Acheulian. These have many names, each usually identifying a peculiar local way of toolmaking. Man was obviously moving in many directions in his culture by this time, and as these different threads met, crossed, tangled, disappeared and re-emerged again, the fabric of human society began to become increasingly complex and increasingly widespread. Acheulian tools of one type or another are found in all major river valleys of western Europe and Africa.

One thing that should be borne in mind is that the more developed a culture is, the more quickly and the more obviously it will be able to respond to local conditions. By the mid-Acheulian, the sophisticated toolmakers of that time were capable of living almost anywhere—on the seashore, in the forest, on the tundra or the subtropical savanna. Whatever specialized tool kits they needed for a successful life in these places, they made.

THE threads become even more numerous—and more tangled—during the days of Neanderthal man, from 110,000 to 35,000 years ago. The tool kit grows steadily larger, until at the end we are confronted with literally dozens of different styles of axes, borers, choppers, knives, scrapers, notched instruments with sawlike blades, chisels and planes—not to mention the really increasing evidence of the importance of antler and bone as weapon and tool materials. It is almost certain that man used wood and bone from the very beginning, perhaps even before stone. However, these substances are much less durable than stone, and almost all the surviving fragments that we have go back only to the latest days of the Neanderthal period. There is an astonishing exception: some bits of wood from the Torralba site in Spain show that much earlier peoples used wood 300,000 years ago. And there is a wooden spear from Germany, presumably Neanderthal, that was found stuck right through the ribs of a straight-tusked elephant. Beyond these, however, there is not much else. The first evidence of any worked bone or ivory is also late Neanderthal, although both are plentiful in the culture of the Cro-Magnon people.

The culture of the Cro-Magnons lasted from 35,000 to 10,000 B.C. After that a revolutionary new technique appeared: stone tools were ground to shape instead of being flaked. With this innovation the Old Stone Age—the Paleolithic—was over. It had served man for upwards of two million years and had brought him from a state almost indistinguishable from that of apes to a remarkable level of intelligence and cultural achievement. His days as a hunter were also about over. Just ahead lay the "inventions" of crops and domesticated animals, and the discovery of metals. Written history was about to begin.

FROM A CATWALK AT THE OLORGESAILIE SITE IN KENYA, TOURISTS SEE STONE TOOLS PRESERVED IN PLACE FOR AS LONG AS 150,000 YEARS

The Decisive Implements

For almost two million years, man's ability to make stone tools enabled him to exploit and finally dominate his environment. With tools he fought enemies, hunted food, made clothing, built shelters and fashioned art. Because stone implements are so durable, they are often the evidence most found by paleoanthropologists and are essential in re-creating the activities of prehistoric peoples.

How Stone Tools Are Made

Throughout the Paleolithic period—the Old Stone Age, characterized by chipped stone tools—three basic techniques of manufacture were used. With them, prehistoric peoples fashioned implements of increasing sophistication and complexity, from the crude chopping tools made by the australopithecines two million years ago to the delicate leaf points and burins of Cro-Magnon men only 25,000 years ago.

The two earlier methods of toolmaking are based on percussion—a stone or bone hammer is struck against the surface of a suitable rock to remove a chip, leaving a sharp jagged edge. The third technique, a much later innovation, is the pressure method, in which a flake is literally pushed from the tool's surface with a pointed instrument—resulting in a finer chip and consequently a sharper edge. All three are based on the maker's knowledge that certain rocks will fracture in a more or less predictable manner—and Stone Age man developed a remarkable ability to recognize these rocks wherever they were in the world. The study of those materials and the methods used to shape them into tools is one of the paleoanthropologist's chief present concerns.

STONE-ON-STONE TECHNIQUES

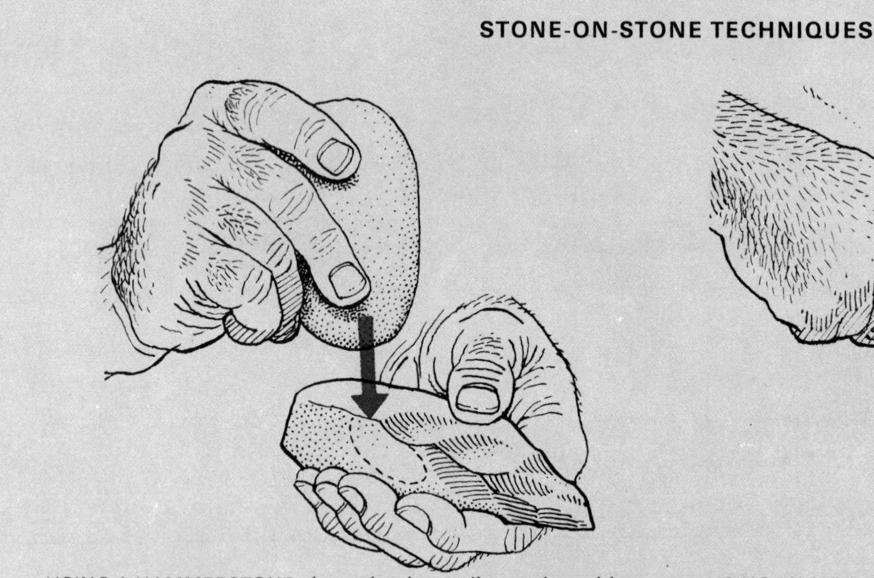

USING A HAMMERSTONE, the toolmaker strikes a sharp blow just behind the edge of his tool core. The impact fractures a large chip from the underside, leaving a deep flake scar.

USING AN ANVIL STONE, the craftsman hits the tool core against a stationary rock, driving a flake from the upper surface. This method is quite difficult to control but was sometimes used.

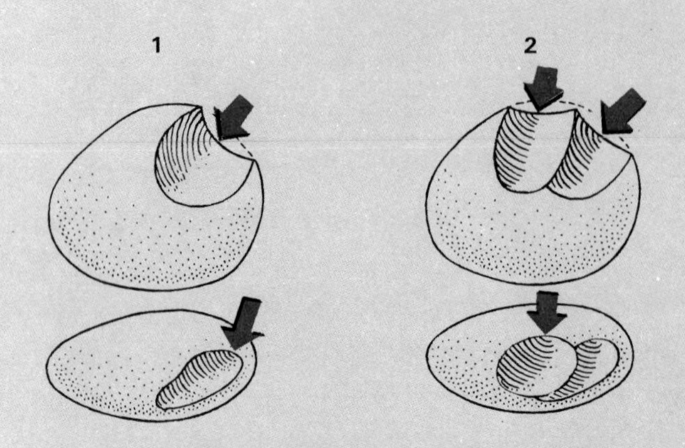

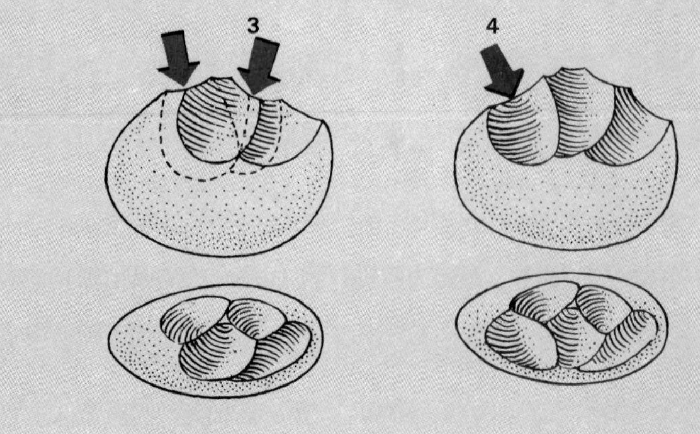

A CHOPPING TOOL emerges from a round pebble. Side view *(top)* shows how two flakes are first struck off with a hammerstone (1 and 2); then the tool is turned over and the process is repeated (3). When another flake is struck off (4), the tool gets a short, irregular, quite sharp edge. From above *(bottom row)*, a ragged edge is visible where the flake scars converge.

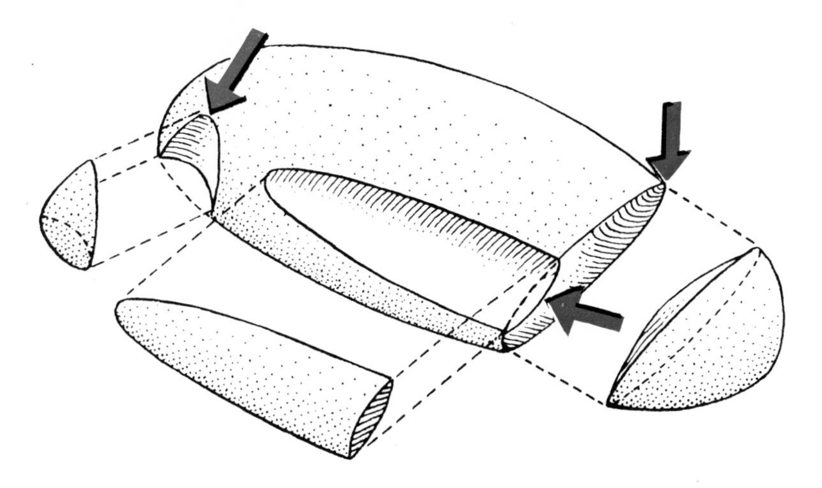

VARIOUSLY SHAPED FLAKES may be struck off fine-grained rocks by varying the angle and force of the blow and using different hammers. The principle is simple: radiating waves of force, like ripples in a pond, crack out chips.

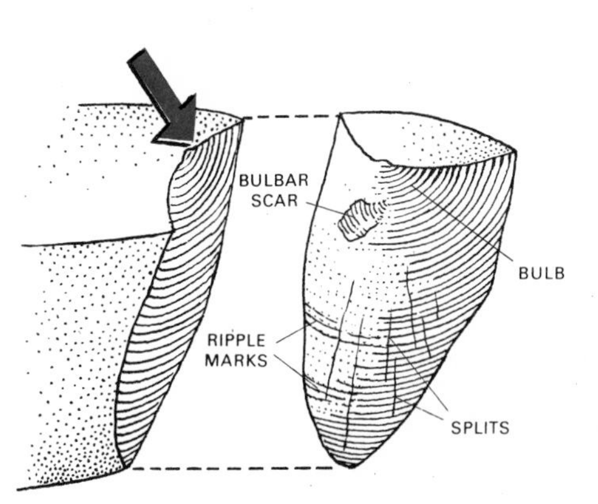

TELLTALE SIGNS exist on flakes which have been produced by man; they never occur on naturally broken stones.

BATON TECHNIQUE

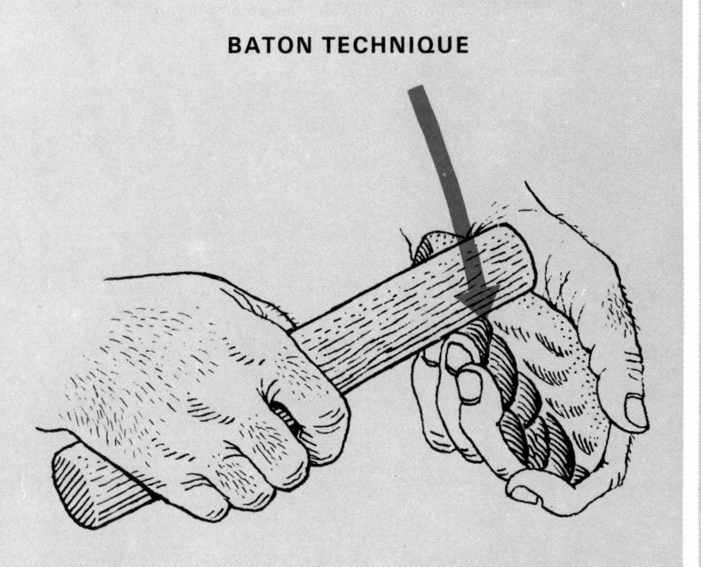

USING A WOOD OR BONE HAMMER in the finishing stages, the maker repeatedly taps the edges of his tool, striking off thin chips. Rough shaping was first done with a hammerstone.

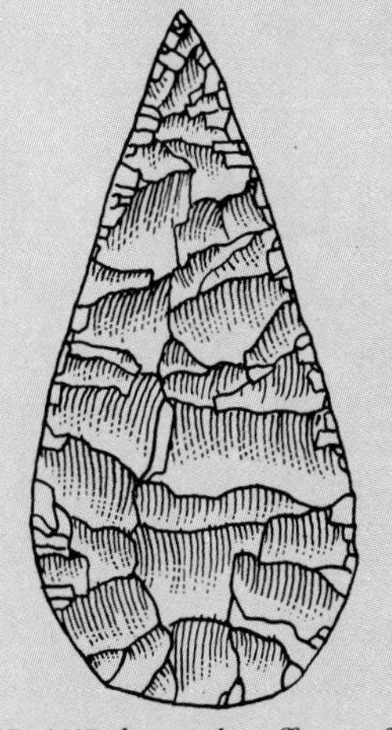

AN ACHEULIAN HAND-AXE shows the effects of delicate edge retouching by the baton method. With this technique, toolmakers fashioned especially sharp, straight-edged cutting tools.

PRESSURE-FLAKING

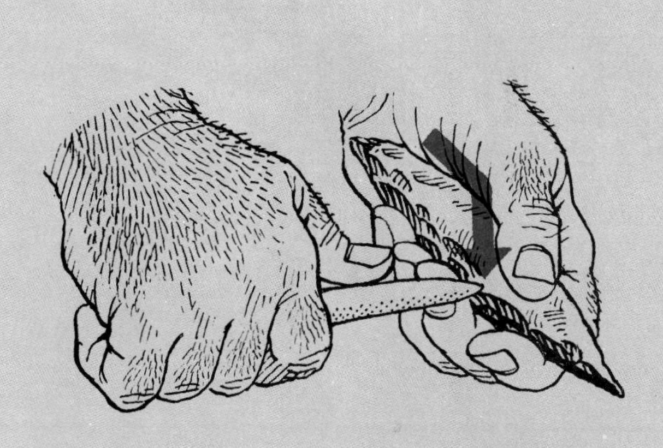

USING A POINTED IMPLEMENT of wood, bone or stone, the artisan forces a flat flake from the lower surface of the tool by pressing against the edge in a slightly downward movement.

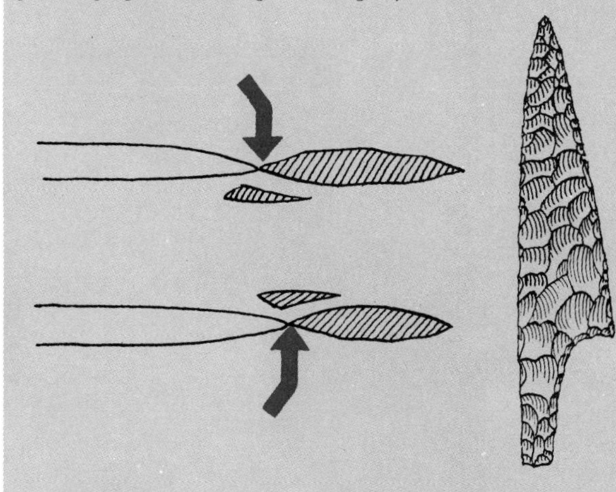

END-ON VIEWS of pressure-flaking show how force is applied to the tool edge itself. Controlled fracturing with this method results in finer flakes and finer tools, like the leaf point at right.

Techniques Improve as Man Evolves

About 150,000 years ago, the first of several dramatic advances in tool technology took place. With their increasing brain capacities, early *Homo sapiens* acquired the foresight and ability to perceive in a raw lump of stone a finished tool of a complex nature. To produce such implements required a long series of preparatory steps, but with new methods, developed from the old techniques of percussion and, later, pressure flaking, early men produced tools of increasing sharpness, delicacy and beauty.

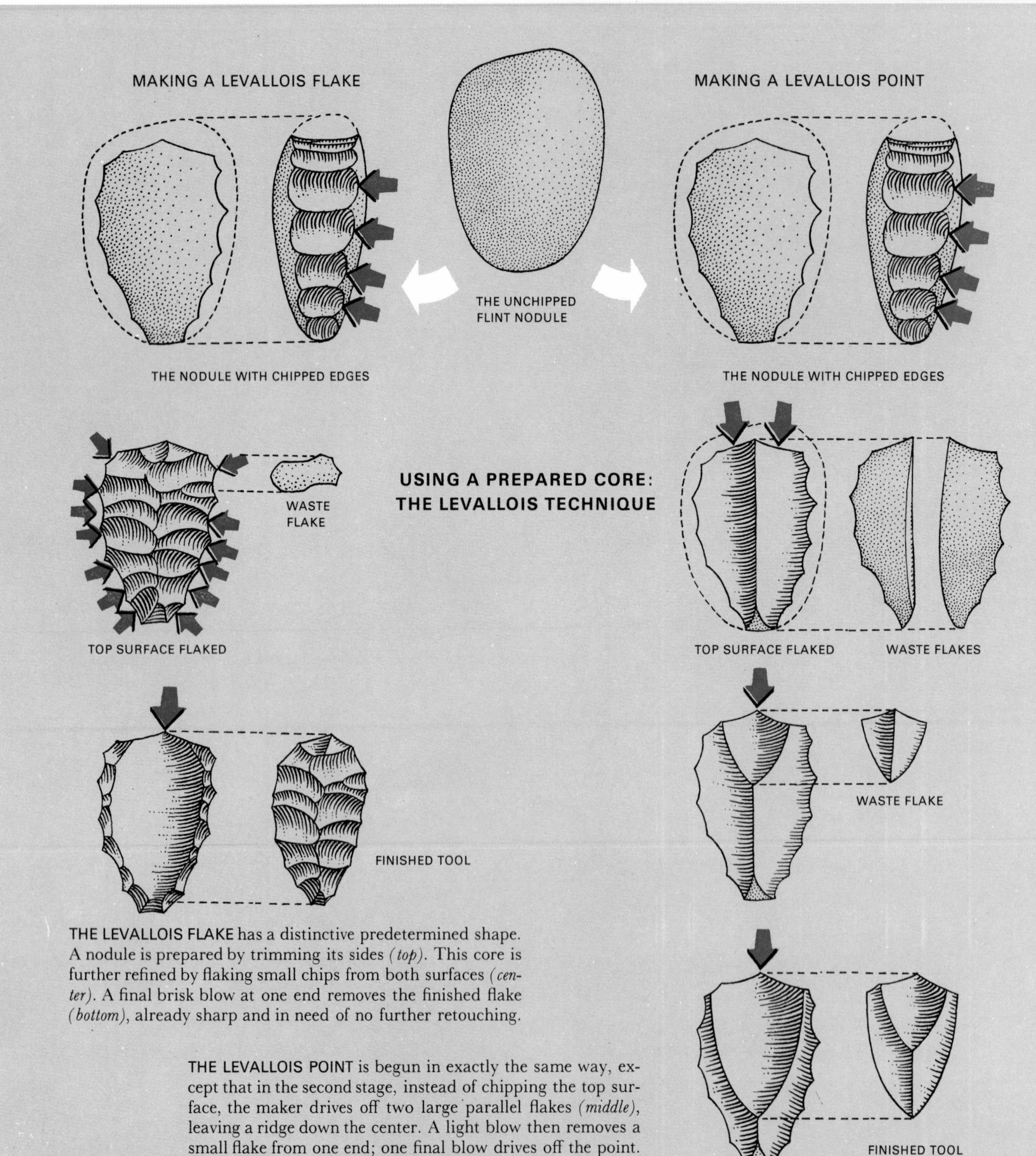

THE LEVALLOIS FLAKE has a distinctive predetermined shape. A nodule is prepared by trimming its sides *(top)*. This core is further refined by flaking small chips from both surfaces *(center)*. A final brisk blow at one end removes the finished flake *(bottom)*, already sharp and in need of no further retouching.

THE LEVALLOIS POINT is begun in exactly the same way, except that in the second stage, instead of chipping the top surface, the maker drives off two large parallel flakes *(middle)*, leaving a ridge down the center. A light blow then removes a small flake from one end; one final blow drives off the point.

BLADE CORE TECHNIQUE

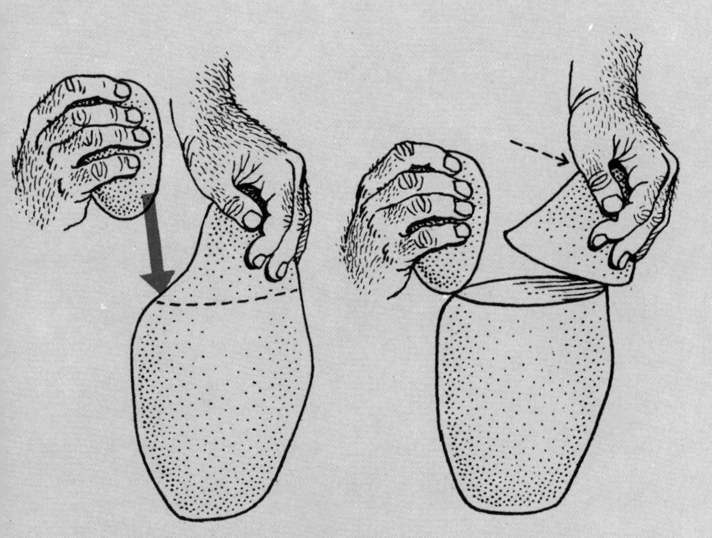

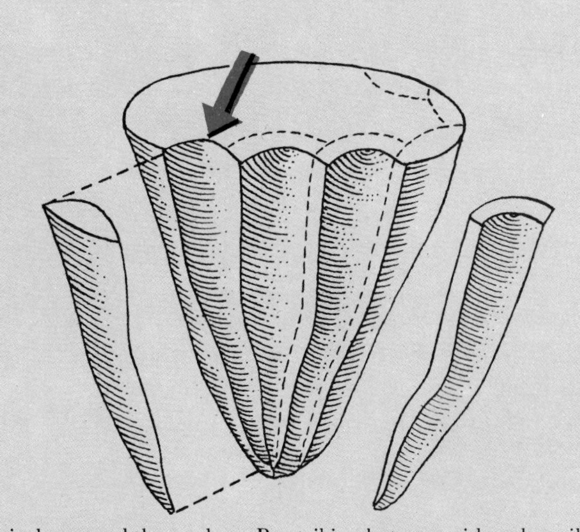

A CORE FOR MANY BLADES is prepared by breaking a large flint nodule in two with a hammerstone. Using either piece, the maker then knocks long, thin flakes from the outside rim leaving a tapering fluted core. From this he produces a whole series of finished blades, striking them off one by one as he spirals around the nucleus. By striking between ridges he will get a hollowed blade *(top right)*. It has been estimated that a two-pound nucleus, flaked in this fashion, will yield some 25 yards of working edge, whereas a hand-axe shaped from the same stone would yield about four inches of effective edge.

MAKING A BURIN FROM A BLADE

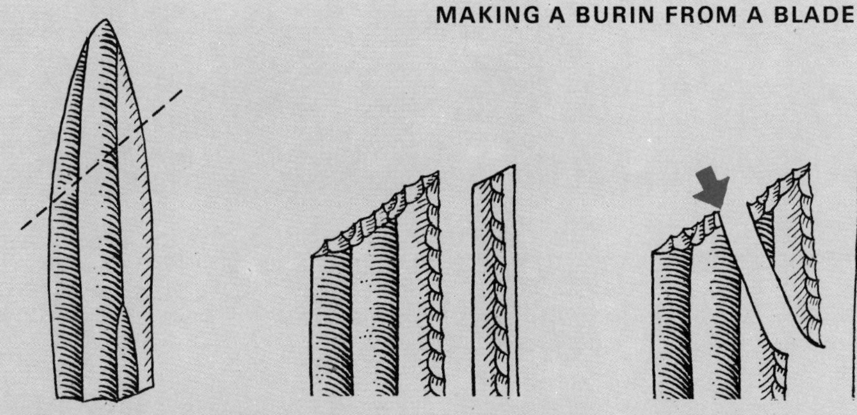

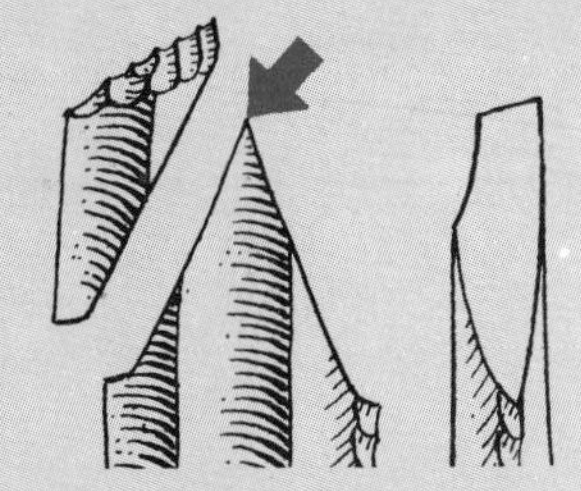

STARTING WITH A FLUTED BLADE, the toolmaker first snaps off the pointed end *(left)*. Next, using a wood or antler hammer, he chips the broken end to make a striking platform, then dulls one edge (two views, second drawing). He may now make either a single or double beveled edge (third and fourth drawings) with one of the methods described in detail below.

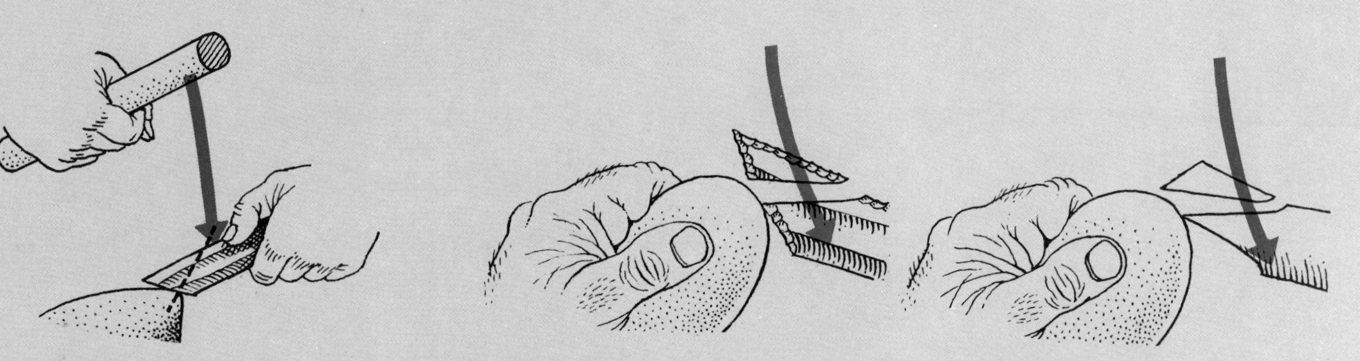

TIPPING A BURIN can be done in two ways. In the first, the blade is rested on an anvil stone and struck with a wood or bone baton, causing the tip to fly off at an angle determined by how the blade is held. In the second method, the blade is pressed sharply against a stone to remove the tip. If a double bevel is desired, the blade is turned over and flaked again.

How Tools Were Used

When the first ancient tools were dug out of the ground they were assigned names based on the function it was believed they served. No one knew for certain, of course, but their resemblance to modern implements and the presumed needs of a simple, hunting way of life made the naming quite logical. Some tools for which no function could be imagined were described simply on the basis of their shape, such as the polyhedral stone *(right)*. Today, most of the names applied years ago still stand.

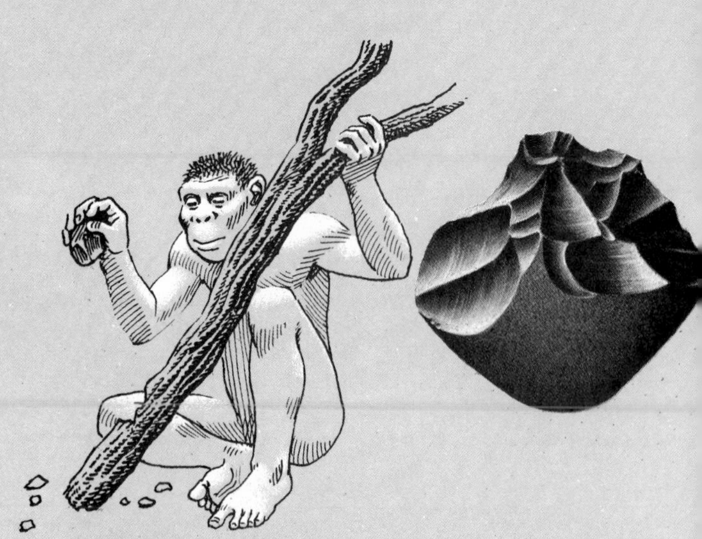

A CHOPPING TOOL, usually fashioned from a fist-sized rock, was an early, all-purpose implement. It might have been used for hacking wood, cracking bone or as a weapon in fighting.

A LATER HAND-AXE shows the more finely finished edge made possible by the baton technique. These tools of various sizes were probably widely used in skinning and cutting up game.

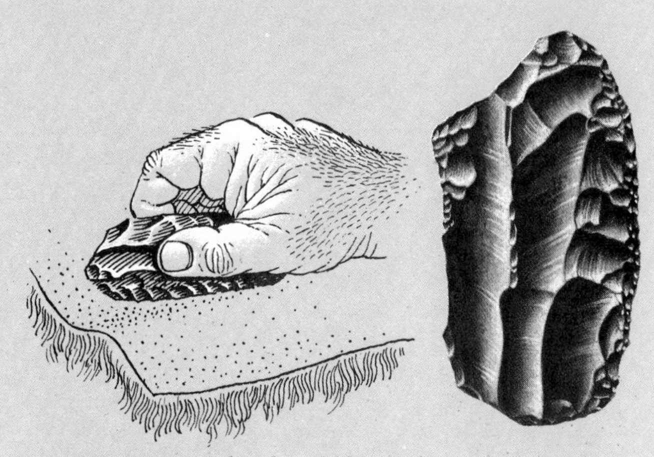

A SIDESCRAPER, used to dress hides, is the typical tool of the advanced Mousterian industry always found at Neanderthal sites. These easily made flakes had strong retouched edges.

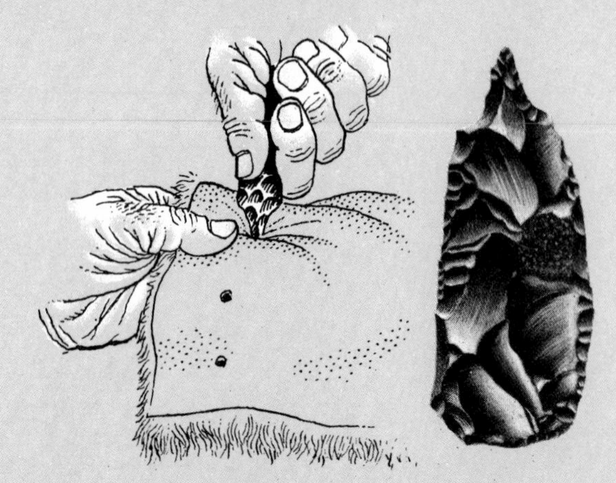

A BORER, formed on a retouched flake, was probably used as an awl to punch holes in animal skins. If so, the appearance of borers may possibly mark the first preparation of clothing.

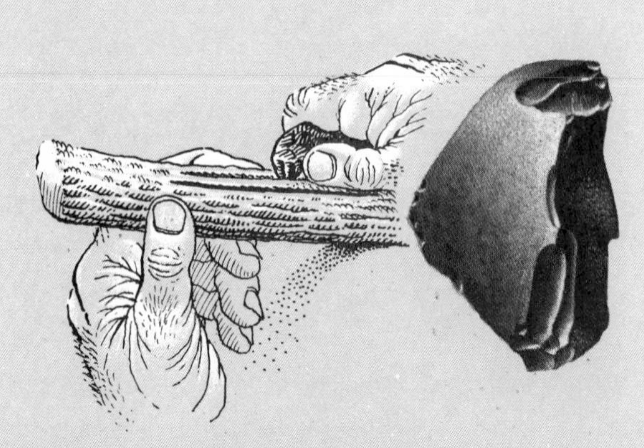

A BURIN, the characteristic tool of the Upper Paleolithic, occurred in many varieties. Its chisel blade could gouge two parallel cracks in antlers and then break out slender needles.

A POLYHEDRAL STONE, so called because of its many battered faces, was probably used to smash and split bones, and as a thrown missile to bring down animals and perhaps enemies.

A PRIMITIVE HAND-AXE was a picklike tool, rather crudely worked on both surfaces and with a fairly sharp point. It may have been used to dig edible roots and tubers from the ground.

A LEVALLOIS POINT with its sharp edges and prepared surface was well suited to mounting on a lance. Used for attack and for defense, it was probably thrust rather than thrown.

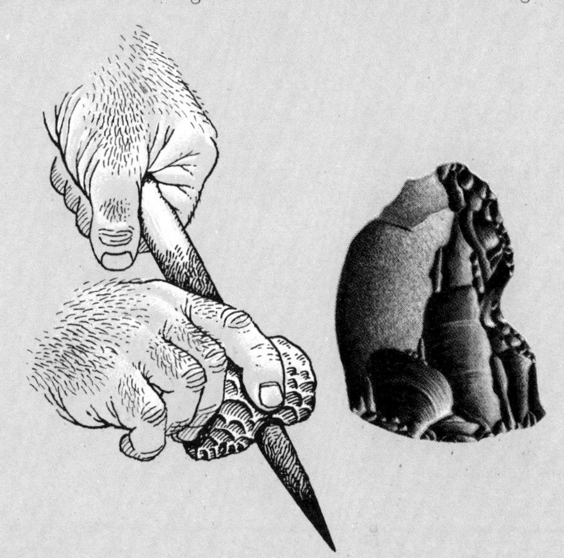

A DENTICULATE TOOL, or notched piece, may have been used like a spokeshave to shape wood. This may have been the first tool which, not directly useful, served in the making of others.

A BACKED FLAKE, so called because it has a dulled back edge like a pocket knife, was an all-purpose cutting tool made on long, core-struck blades. It could cut flesh quite easily.

A GRAVETTE POINT, one of many knifelike backed blades of the Upper Paleolithic, may have been hafted onto a spear for throwing. This tool is only found at certain Cro-Magnon sites.

AN ACHEULIAN TOOL KIT from Torralba, Spain, includes a 10-inch quartzite cleaver, a small flint cleaver *(lower right)*, a screwdriver-ended piece in chalcedony *(upper center)*, and a double-edged side scraper made of jasper *(upper right)*. Such a diversity of raw materials at one site is unusual, indicating that some of these tools were made elsewhere and brought in.

The Raw Materials for Stone Age Tools

Early men used a great variety of raw materials in fashioning their tools. Wood was probably used very early, even before the knack of working stone into diverse shapes was learned. Unfortunately, it is seldom preserved and little is known of very old wooden tools. Flint was the most abundant material used by Paleolithic hunters in Europe, where even today good-sized flint pieces are easy to find. Elsewhere more common local rocks were utilized: among them, quartzite, quartz, lavas, chert and obsidian—probably the best material of all, although it is rare. Much later, when they learned to make sharper and better-pointed stone instruments, men began to carve tools of antler and bone.

A PALEOLITHIC POTPOURRI illustrates the remarkable variety of tools made from three abundant materials: flint, bone and antler. At the top is an early hand-axe, followed by more delicate flint implements from later periods and, at the bottom, eyed needles of bone and antler, barbed harpoon heads and bone awls—highly specialized tools of the late Old Stone Age.

A Master Toolmaker

François Bordes, professor of prehistory at the University of Bordeaux in France, is the outstanding authority on Paleolithic tools. At the age of 14 he became fascinated with the ancient artifacts he found near his home, and he set out to learn all he could about how they were made and used. After studying geology and prehistory in Paris, Bordes returned to southwestern France, where he now teaches. Each summer he spends six to eight weeks excavating several important early man sites in the Dordogne valley, where he continues to experiment with flint toolmaking techniques. Bordes is able to make, within a few minutes, all of the known varieties of Paleolithic implements. He practices almost constantly on a large supply of fresh flint nodules which he keeps in the backyard of his home and at a farm near his favorite site.

MAKING A CHOPPING TOOL

Bordes begins with a rounded quartzite lump and a smaller hammerstone. With

MAKING AN ACHEULIAN HAND-AXE

Having knocked the end off a large flint nodule, Bordes has prepared a striking

platform from which, using a hammerstone, he proceeds to strike off several

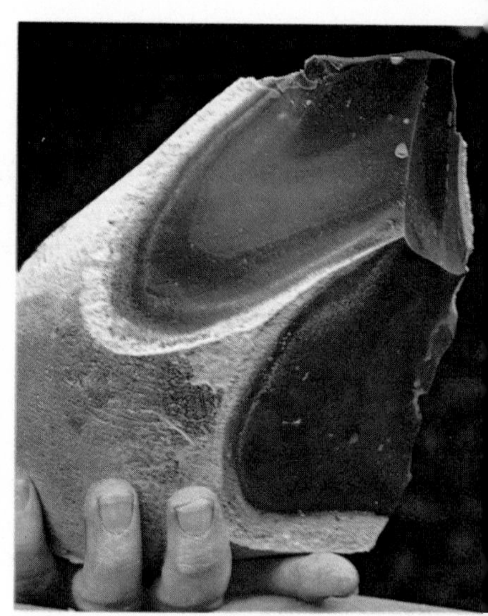

large flakes, roughing out the general shape. He then switches to an antler

MAKING A LAUREL LEAF POINT

Taking a large flake, a by-product of his hand-axe, Bordes starts finishing it

with the antler hammer. Resting the flake on his knee for support, he strikes

off shallow flakes, turning the tool over and over, working both surfaces and all

two or three blows he can produce a rough but serviceable cutting edge. Such tools as this were early man's basic weapon and hunting implement for over a million years. They have been found in Africa, the Middle East and in Asia.

hammer (fifth picture), working both sides of the tool to thin out and retouch the edge. The final product, with its long, straight, sharp edges, is one of the tools used for several hundred thousand years by early *Homo sapiens* hunters.

the edges. Having roughed out the shape, he sharpens the tool by driving tiny chips from the edges (fifth picture). He ends up with an exact duplicate of the beautiful leaf points used by Stone Age hunters as spear heads and daggers.

USED AS AN ADZE to sharpen a digging stick, this stone axe has been hafted on a handle with rattan and tree sap. Although it showed little wear, a crack developed from a hard blow.

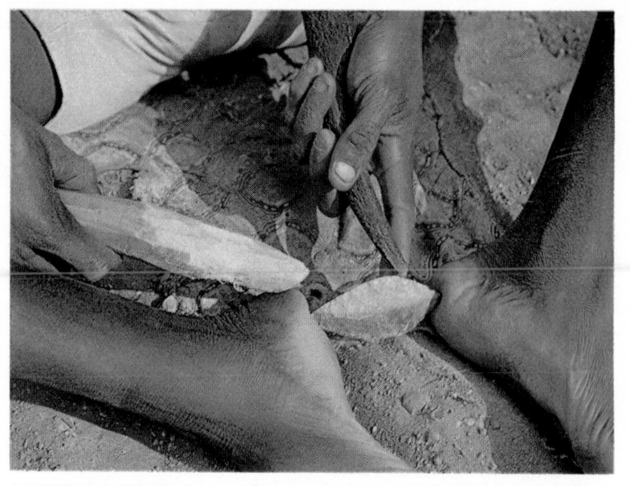

MAKING A COPY, this craftsman imitates Paleolithic technique to shape a leaf point. By striking a horn punch with a wooden hammer he will flake the tool just as ancient hunters did.

MOUNTED FOR DIGGING, a newly made core-axe is used to open up an old termite mound to extract edible yam tubers. The tool's edge acquired a smooth polish.

SKINNING AN ANTELOPE, cooperative Bushmen experiment with authentic stone cleavers dug from an African site. They were able to skin and dismember it easily.

The Lessons of Wear

How were Paleolithic implements actually used? J. Desmond Clark, a specialist in African prehistory, has attempted to find out. Like Bordes, he made copies of ancient tools, and then had them systematically used for different tasks on a variety of materials so that he could study the wear patterns which resulted. By comparing those patterns with ones found on Stone Age tools, Clark has been able to infer what function the tool served. Those with light scratches, for example, may have been used for digging; those with deep chips, perhaps for cutting or chopping hard materials like wood or bone.

HACKING AT BARK, an experimenter uses an authentic Middle Stone Age axe to cut a rectangular section from which a dish can be made. Even this quite heavy usage left the tool unworn.

OVERHANGING CLIFFS, like this one in southwestern France, provided early man with one of his favorite homesites. This cave-studded region has yielded copious evidence about the Neanderthal epoch.

6

Just Who Was Neanderthal?

Of all the different kinds of prehistoric peoples, certainly the one who projects the clearest image is Neanderthal man. For most of us he *is* Stone Age man, the squat, shaggy, beetle-browed fellow that inevitably comes to mind when we think of our ancient relatives. We see him standing in the mouth of a cave—stone axe in hand, a few rough furs over his shoulder, some mammoth bones piled in the background—staring out over a snow-choked landscape as he ponders the ever-present problems of the ice age and the giant cave bear.

The reason that this image is so persistent is that there is some truth in it. Neanderthalers were more primitive than we are (in some ways), they did live in cold climates (sometimes), they dressed in skins (sometimes) and they lived in caves (sometimes). That is the way they were first pictured to us and that is the way they are remembered. The first fossil skull ever to be positively identified as belonging to ancient man was that of a Neanderthaler. Having nothing else to compare it with except the skull of a modern man, scientists of the time were more struck by the differences between the two than by their similarities. Today the reverse is true. Compared to an early australopithecine, who was little better than a two-legged ape, a Neanderthaler is a model of evolutionary refinement. Put him in a Brooks Brothers suit and send him down to the supermarket for some groceries and he might pass completely unnoticed. He might run a little shorter than the clerk serving him, but he would not necessarily be the shortest man in the place. He might be heavier-featured, squatter and more muscular than most, but again he might be no more so than the porter handling the beer cases back in the stockroom.

In other words, Neanderthal man's and modern man's ranges of variation overlap. Indeed, the more we learn about the former, the more overlapping there appears to be. And this eventually forces a question that has been bubbling up in the minds of anthropologists with increasing pressure in the last decade or two: is Neanderthal man actually a different kind of man than *Homo sapiens?* Fifty years ago anybody rash enough to raise such an obvious question would have been laughed out of the room. Today a good many anthropologists would probably say that they were members of the same species.

This does not mean that there are not differences between the two. There are plenty. To understand and evaluate both the differences and similarities, it will be necessary to consider for a moment some of the most modern ideas about how speciation takes place and what makes a species.

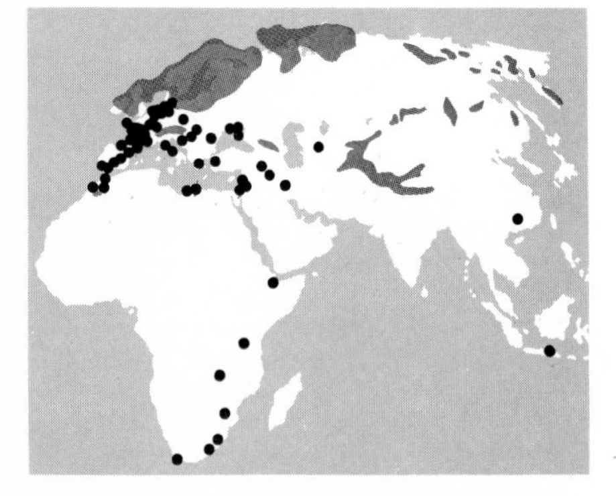

NEANDERTHAL MAN AND HIS CONTEMPORARIES

Between 110,000 and 35,000 years ago, Homo sapiens was widely distributed in the Old World. One type, Neanderthal man, ranged throughout Europe and the Mediterranean. He had relatives in Southeast Asia and Africa who are represented by Solo man and Rhodesian man respectively. Western Europe, however, has yielded the greatest number of early types of Homo sapiens. This map shows where their fossils have been found (black dots) and outlines the maximum extent of the last glaciers (grayish areas).

THE classic definition of a species is: one or more groups of individual organisms that actually interbreed with one another or are enough alike in structure and behavior so that they could interbreed if they had access to one another. This classic concept goes on to recognize that some groups do not always stay together. For various reasons—often because of climate or geography—they become separated. If that separation goes on for a long time, the different populations may become so changed by evolution that if they should come together again they might no longer interbreed. At that point it would be correct to say that the original single species had been split into two.

This is an extremely simplified statement of what is actually a very complex and subtle process. For one thing, separation is often behavioral: if one animal acts in a way that makes it impossible for it to breed with another, the separation between the two is as real as if they were kept apart by a mountain range. What would we say, for example, of the various races of song sparrows that inhabit North America? There are song sparrows that habitually migrate north to Alaska every year, and there are others that go only as far north as the Gulf Coast during the breeding season. Theoretically both populations could interbreed, but their habits as migrants do not give them a chance to. And they show the results of this separation. Natural selection has already made the northern race measurably larger than the average for all song sparrows. It has also made the southern race smaller and darker-plumaged than the average. What tends to hold them together as a single species is the existence of a large number of intermediate sparrows that live in between. Through them the individuals on the northern and southern fringes keep in genetic touch, as it were, by doing their breeding and scattering their genes inward from the edges of an enormous pool of genes that represents all the traits of every bird in the entire species. At the same time, they keep receiving genes that are passed out toward them from the center of the pool, which keeps any tendency toward extreme differentiation along the edges from running away with itself. In other words, genetic contact with the main body of birds tends to ensure that the outlying members of the group will continue to look and act pretty much like all the others as long as the contact is maintained. It is these two opposing influences—one environmental and selective, tending to create differences; the other genetic and connective, tending to distribute the same traits through a population—that determine the course of speciation in any group of organisms.

If we were collecting sparrow fossils and had only a couple of Alaska specimens and half a dozen Gulf Coast specimens to study, how would we relate them—particularly if we had no knowledge of any sparrows living anywhere else? Would we recognize the obvious differences between them and assign them to different species, or would we still consider them the same kind of bird? It is that problem that continually confronts the paleoanthropologist. His sample of human specimens is often so small that it is next to impossible for him to learn enough about the distribution of the men he is studying to tell whether his samples are from opposite fringes of a single, rather varied population or whether they are truly different.

The latest views about speciation make it possible to deal with this problem by looking at it in a slightly different way. Current species theory emphasizes whole populations, not individuals. Its concern is with the entire gene pool. It recognizes that differences exist among individuals or groups of individuals, and acknowledges the importance of these differences. What is equally important, however, although largely overlooked in the past, is that such differences continue to have a chance, through interbreeding, to be reabsorbed into the gene pool as a whole, and so continue to be able to express themselves. Thus, whereas older theory tended to look at an evolving species as a tree trunk with distinct limbs branching off it from time to time as new species were created, the newer theory visualizes a species as a tangle of interlocking strands, a maze of vine tendrils that separate and join again in no orderly pattern. How they join is not so important as that they do join. These constant joinings represent the individual mating decisions of countless members of the species. If one part of the gene pool should drift away from the main body to a point that these rejoinings no longer take place, then it would become a separate gene pool and eventually, perhaps, a separate species.

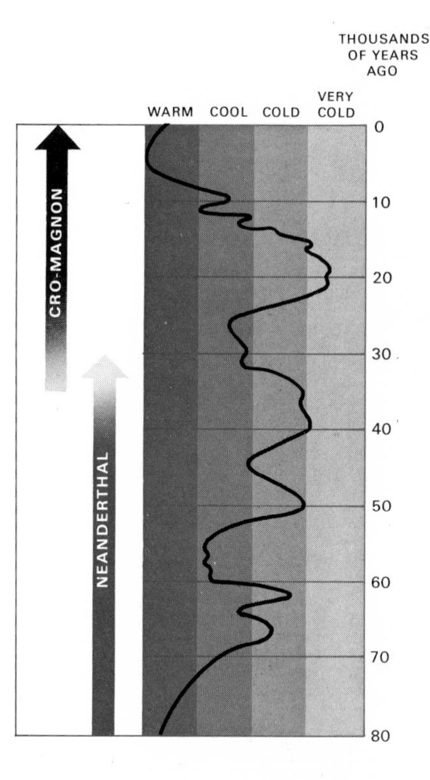

TEMPERATURES OF THE PAST

Early men in western Europe endured great changes in temperature during the last 80,000 years, as the above graph shows. The arrows represent the time-spans of Neanderthal and Cro-Magnon peoples who lived during the period; the scale at right is divided into intervals of 10,000 years, and the undulating black line indicates the relative temperature at any particular time. During most of this time it was much colder than it is today. For instance, about 20,000 years ago the annual mean temperature of Paris was probably 11° F. lower than it is now.

THIS flexible model of a species fits what we know about *Homo erectus* rather neatly. It emphasizes the similarities that exist among the various known specimens and acknowledges their differences by assuming that a good deal of variety will inevitably manifest itself in any widely distributed species. Let us now apply the same model to Neanderthal peoples, who present us with a problem of a different sort. Their fossils are—compared with *Homo erectus'*—very numerous; the difficulty is not so much with rarity as it is with how to interpret a rather embarrassing and perplexing abundance.

The first Neanderthal finds came from western Europe. Most of the field work of the last century and the early part of this one was done by Europeans, and much of it was concentrated in their own countries. They had little reason to look farther afield; as discovery followed discovery, it became increasingly clear that toward the end of the Third Interglacial Period, about 75,000 years ago, Neanderthal peoples were already well established in Europe. Moreover, they always appeared in conjunction with a new tool industry, the Mousterian. Tools of this kind are extremely abundant, and wherever they are found, we can assume with some confidence that Neanderthalers also were once found. As to where they came from, we must assume rather less confidently that they are the descendants of people like Swanscombe and Steinheim man.

This western European Neanderthal, now called the "classic," variety is not

THE CAVE BEAR CULT

Why Neanderthal man began hunting the cave bear is not certain. It was a formidable animal, standing more than eight feet tall when reared in anger (above), and must have been a dangerous foe. It also lived in much more inaccessible places than most of the other game. Nevertheless, it was hunted—perhaps to fulfill an early hunting ritual. Discovery of bear skulls stacked in a stone chest in Drachenloch, Switzerland, supports this idea. Such skulls (below) may have been man's first hunting trophies.

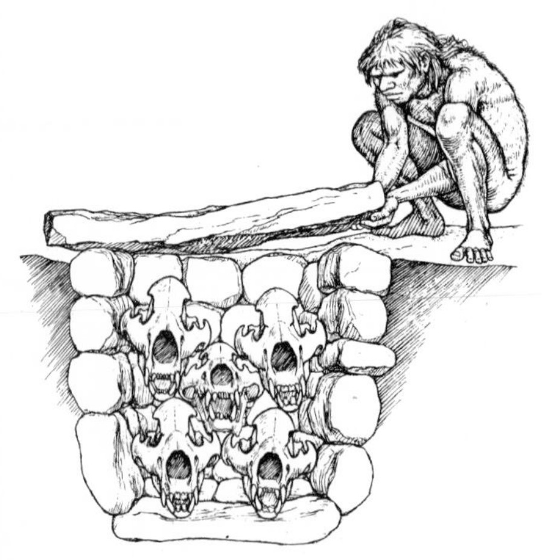

hard to recognize. Even a nonanthropologist would quickly note its special characteristics. Although the cranium is commodious and could accommodate a brain just as large as modern man's, it is differently shaped. It has a lower, flatter crown, and achieves its interior space by being longer and by bulging more at the back and sides. The face has three distinctions, a definitely receding chin, larger cheeks and extremely prominent brow ridges curving over each eye and connected across the bridge of the nose. It is this continuous ridge of bone that gives the classic Neanderthaler his famous beetle-browed look.

The rest of the skeleton marks a short man, but a powerfully built one. The Neanderthaler stood just over five feet. His extremities were short and their long bones robust and slightly curved—which may have given him a somewhat bandy-legged appearance. His hands and fingers were short and stubby. So were his feet, which is borne out not only by the bones themselves but by the astonishing preservation of actual Neanderthal footprints, one of which is shown on page 8. Such footprints are the only direct evidence known to exist about any soft part of any prehistoric man. All in all, the Neanderthaler was heavily muscled and appears to have been immensely strong. No doubt he would have been a formidable opponent in a college wrestling tournament.

WHEN the Third Interglacial ended and the ice spread down over northern Europe once again, Neanderthal peoples still hung on there, managing to adapt themselves to the changes in their environment. Whereas they had often lived out in the open in warmer times, they now increasingly sought out caves and rock shelters. They made their own clothing of skins and tied their way of life more and more closely to the huge herds of reindeer and other kinds of cold-weather animals that swarmed in the land. On the whole, on the evidence of the cultural debris that they left behind, they managed very well. The earlier part of the last glacial period was an irregular one, with intervals of somewhat warmer climate scattered through it. Neanderthal man endured both cold and mild cycles with apparently equal success. He continued to exist in western Europe right up to about 35,000 years ago, and then he abruptly disappeared. The evolutionary tendencies that he exhibited during this period are extremely puzzling. For he seems to have gotten more "primitive," not less so. The last fossils we have from western Europe are even squatter, bulkier and more beetle-browed than their predecessors.

If we had only the evidence of Europe to go by, Neanderthal man would certainly seem to follow the classic pattern of speciation. He was noticeably different from modern man and became more so as time went on. Is this not a good example of species-splitting somewhere farther back in the human line? If so, should we not look elsewhere than to Neanderthalers for our own ancestors? These questions seem particularly pertinent when the various levels of certain caves in western Europe are examined. In addition to stopping abruptly, the classic Neanderthaler is replaced with equal abruptness by people like ourselves. There is no blending, no gradual shading from one type to the other. It is as if modern men came storming in and dispossessed the Neanderthalers—perhaps even killed them.

This certainly suggests two species overlapping in time, with the more advanced one exterminating the more primitive one. However, the classic variety is not the only Neanderthaler in the fossil stew. Other populations with different characteristics existed, it is now known, in a great many places besides western Europe. Traces of them have been found along the Mediterranean, in eastern Europe, in Asia Minor and in northern Africa. Significantly, in these latter places they do not exhibit nearly as extreme traits as the western European classic type. They tend to be less massive, taller and more finely made. Their forearms and legs are not as stumpy and not as curved. Their skulls are a bit more lofty and their faces a trifle smaller.

The first Neanderthaler with any of these more modern traits was found in a cave at Mount Carmel in Palestine in 1932. This was the skeleton of a woman. A proper Neanderthaler in most other respects, she had peculiar eyebrow ridges. They were less massive than they should have been. In addition, the back of her skull was more rounded than that of any previously discovered Neanderthaler. Considering that all Neanderthalers known up to that time were of the classic western European type, and considering that a good deal of scientific opinion then held that modern man and Neanderthal man were not directly related, this mixture of a Neanderthal body and a rounded, more modern skull was somehow "wrong." This fossil, given the name of the Tabūn woman after the place in which she was found, was a great puzzlement. At the same time in a nearby rock shelter—at Skhūl—an entire cemetery full of skeletons was discovered. These people, 10 of them, revealed an astonishing variety. They ranged from almost classic Neanderthal to scarcely Neanderthal at all. Some of them had longer, straighter limbs, more lofty skulls, smaller faces and more pronounced chins. They were different enough from the Tabūn woman to raise considerable doubts as to the nature of the relationship between them.

Then in 1957 a complete skeleton of a Neanderthal hunter, precisely dated at 44,000 years of age, was dug out of a cave at Shanidar in the mountains of northern Iraq. This man had been a victim of a hazard peculiar to cave dwellers; he had been crushed by a massive fall of rock from his own ceiling. At the time of his death he was about 40 years old and had bad teeth. He was five feet three inches tall, barrel-chested like his western cousins, but—like the Tabūn woman—his eyebrow ridge was less thick and heavy, giving the whole upper part of his face a more modern look. Further search in the Shanidar cave yielded five more adults; together with a baby previously found, they totaled seven almost complete skeletons, all showing this curious hint of modernity in the upper face, some of them with traces of other characteristics that hinted at a departure from the strict classic Neanderthal model. The Tabūn woman fitted very comfortably among them; she too was a Neanderthaler with a vague suggestion of modernity. Despite their differences, Shanidar and Tabūn are now taken to be the same kind of people—both of them representatives of a Middle Eastern variant of the Neanderthalers on the verge of transition. The individuals from the Skhūl cemetery represent a further stage in the transition process; they are actually closer to Cro-Magnon than to Neanderthal man.

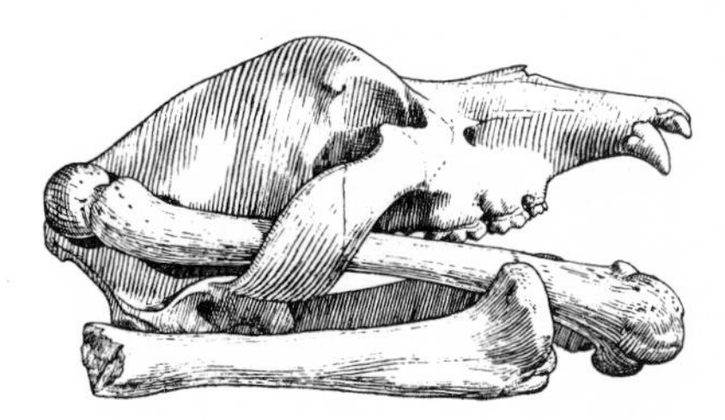

A SYMBOL OF THE CULT

Another piece of evidence that the cave bear had symbolic meaning for the Neanderthal hunter is this skull-and-bone complex found in Drachenloch. The skull is that of a three-year-old cave bear; the leg bone piercing its cheek belongs to a younger bear. These are resting on two bones from still two other bears, an arrangement that could hardly have happened by chance. A more detailed discussion of the mysterious bear cult will be found in the next chapter.

THIS provocative evidence from the Middle East tells an entirely different story from that told in western Europe. It suggests an extremely varied gene pool capable of producing all kinds of individuals—some with this more primitive characteristic, others with that—but a gene pool that was unmistakably moving in the general direction of modern man.

However, we cannot simply ignore those squat men from the icy caves of western Europe. Somehow we must fit them into our species model. Perhaps the best way to do this is to regard them as Alaskan song sparrows, fringe dwellers, representatives of a population living under drastically different environmental conditions and subject to different selection pressures than the main group of their kind—and possibly even separated from them toward the end.

Isolated for periods of a good many thousand years at a time, one or many localized inbreeding populations could have been created and could have evolved in what now appears to have been a primitive direction. But is this really primitive or is it simply adaptive? Some scientists believe that in a very cold climate the stockiest man with the shortest limbs will be the most efficient conserver of body heat. If this is true, he, and not the slender "more advanced" man, would have the survival advantage.

So, pending further knowledge, let us say that the Neanderthalers were a widespread and widely varied group, not all of whom exhibited the extreme characteristics of the classic type. Their gene pool evolved out of that bequeathed to them by *Homo erectus*, presumably via people like Steinheim man in a way that can only be nailed down by the disclosure of more evidence. Some of them in turn bequeathed their gene pool to modern man. They did it gradually in the Middle East and not at all in western Europe. As for their disappearance in western Europe, this may or may not have been an actual extermination. If it was, it was a Cain and Abel affair. They were killed by members of their own family, by a mixture of brothers and first cousins—not by strangers.

Looking at human evolution in this way, we begin to get a picture of a world that may never have held more than one species of man at any one time. The vine stems may have been extremely tangled, and a few creepers may have strayed, like the classic Neanderthaler, far enough from the central cluster to have withered and died. If we wish to begin thinking about species, we would do well to examine the cluster "vertically," not "horizontally" as many past students have done. The element of time must be taken into account. When it is, the idea of a vine becomes more compelling, with *Homo erectus* occupying one section of it and Neanderthal man another section, higher up and later in time. To find out where one stops and the other starts, we will have to select a point in time and slice through the vine at that point to see what we get. Since evolution does not proceed in all places at the same rate or even in the same way, wherever we slice will reveal some inconsistencies. And if the slice is wide enough to include places like South Africa and Java, where other races lived contemporaneously with Neanderthal man and shared some—but not all—of his traits, the inconsistencies become very plain. Nevertheless, the general indications of species relationship persist. They become more meaningful the more one thinks about the gene pool as a whole, and not about individuals.

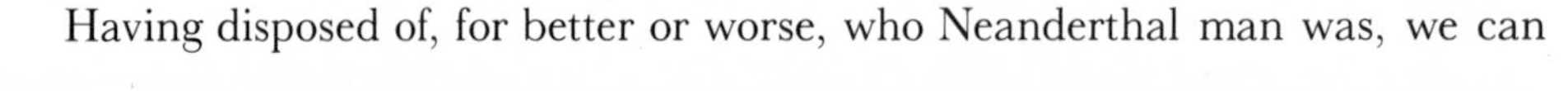

Having disposed of, for better or worse, who Neanderthal man was, we can

A NEANDERTHAL FAMILY'S PREHISTORIC CEMETERY

The solicitude that Neanderthalers lavished upon their dead is made abundantly clear at La Ferrassie, France. Here anthropologists discovered what appears to be a 40,000-year-old family cemetery containing the skeletons of two adults and four children. The presumed parents (1 and 2) were buried head to head; two skeletons (3 and 4), possibly those of their children, each about five years old, were neatly interred near their mother's feet. The graves of two other children buried in this plot (5 and 6) are described in detail on the opposite page.

turn now to what he did. Here the evidence is less speculative. The Mousterian industry that he developed and that he seems to have taken with him wherever he went, is an outgrowth of the Acheulian. It first appears toward the end of the Third Interglacial and reveals a man living much the same kind of life that the Acheulian toolmakers lived before him. The climate was still mild, and he hunted and gathered what he could. He had a great diversity of stone tools, bone points and spearlike sharpened animal ribs. He utilized both core-tool and flake-tool techniques of implement making.

His prey, from the fossil animal remains he left behind him, varied from mice to mammoths. He ate a great many horses and deer, and as the weather gradually got colder and colder in Europe, he moved into caves and switched more and more to reindeer, ibex and chamois as food sources. Neanderthal sites in Europe tell this story over and over again. Unfortunately, not many have been studied carefully enough to tell all they might. Rarely do we have sufficiently detailed statistics on the numbers of species or the numbers of individuals, or their ages, to tell us what we will someday undoubtedly learn about Neanderthal's seasonal hunting habits and whether he migrated with the game. In a few places we know that he did not. He stayed put the year round and lived on deer and reindeer of all ages—from fawns to adults.

WE have learned that during his stay on earth he did develop certain distinct groupings of tool types. These are known as tool kits. They show up at various levels in the caves that he dwelt in off and on—some of them inhabited intermittently for thousands of years. Opinions are divided on the significance of the differences in tool groupings at different levels. One idea is that they simply represent different groups of people moving in and out, each with its own local preference in toolmaking. Another is that the tools reflect differences in living habits, in jobs to be done—as a carpenter's tool kit will differ from a machinist's. At one level a great abundance of scrapers may occur. Was this a woman's tool kit used for scraping, dressing and preparing hides? At another level, borers and knives may predominate, again suggesting a woman's kit, this time with more emphasis on the cutting and sewing together of animal skins. At still another, saw-edged and notched tools will appear. Could this have been a man's kit oriented toward woodworking, to the making of spears and tent props? Such questions will only be answered by the analysis of great quantities of data—as yet uncollected and probably requiring the help of computers.

Neanderthal man had a sure control of fire. He used it regularly, presumably could create it when he needed it, and had progressed to the point of digging hearths in the floors of his caves. He was also a home builder as well as a cave

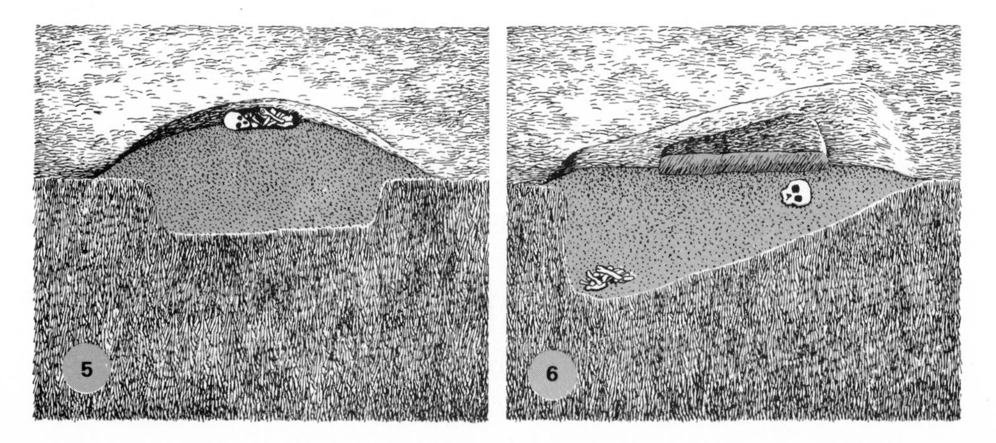

WHAT TWO GRAVES HELD

Grave 5, from the cemetery shown opposite, contains bones so small that they may be those of a stillborn baby. The tiny body and three beautiful flints were buried in the top of one of nine mysterious hillocks, all the same size and height, arranged in rows of three. This is the only one of the hillocks that contained any bones or flints; either the others were looted by a prehistoric vandal, or the pattern has some ritual significance not yet understood.

Grave 6, containing the skeleton of a six-year-old child, was covered by a triangular slab that had been hollowed out on its bottom surface. With the body were found two flint scrapers and a point.

dweller. There are several sites in Russia that give evidence of their having served as dwellings of Neanderthal man. One such is marked by a rough ring of hearths; outside that is a large circle of heavy elephant bones and tusks which may have served—along with wood, which is no longer preserved—as a framework to support animal skins. Aside from this, Neanderthalers undoubtedly made other kinds of more perishable shelters, just as hunter-gatherers like Australian aborigines and African Bushmen still do. These are simple affairs of sticks and grasses, some of them mere windbreaks which quickly disintegrate and vanish after their builders move away.

In keeping with the growing complexity of his life and the greater variety of his possessions and his talents, Neanderthal man also apparently stood on the edge of becoming both an esthete and a mystic. For the first time in human experience, faint signs of decoration and artistic appreciation appear. He began scratching designs on bones. Two interesting objects emerge from a dig at Tata in Hungary, neither having any apparent utilitarian purpose. Rather, they seem to have been fashioned for esthetic or ceremonial reasons. One is a piece of mammoth tooth trimmed to an oval shape and then carefully smoothed and polished. Another is a numilite, a marine invertebrate already fossilized for several hundred million years before it caught the eye of the Neanderthaler who would shape and polish it to his fancy and then perhaps wear it as an amulet.

PERHAPS the most important of Neanderthal man's cultural accomplishments was his registering of the first stirrings of a social and religious sense. He buried his dead, which suggests an awareness of the transitoriness of life, concern over the future, and also a willingness to care for the aged. A number of Neanderthal burial sites have been discovered, both in western and eastern Europe, and they reveal a good deal. At Le Moustier in southern France (from which place the Mousterian tool industry gets its name) the grave of an 18-year-old youth was discovered in 1908. He had been carefully and reverently buried on his side, his legs bent, his head cushioned on a pile of flaked flints and resting on his right arm as it might in sleep. Buried with the body were several stone implements and a number of animal bones. Other Neanderthal burials excavated since then show a similar careful laying out of the body and a thoughtful addition of tools and bones. In a cave at La Ferrassie, also in southern France, a family of two adults and four children was discovered lying buried in the floor. All six had been placed with their bodies lined up in an east-west position. Evidence of this sort clearly indicates that Neanderthal man believed in some kind of a life after death and that it was probably not unlike the life he lived on earth, since he seemed to be trying to help his corpses along on their journeys with tools and food. Death itself appears to have been regarded as a kind of sleep, since corpses were carefully arranged in sleeplike positions.

Beyond these suppositions, and it must be remembered that they are only suppositions, it is impossible to go. However, some kind of intellectual and fantasy life was not only possible for Neanderthal man, considering his intellectual potential, but is also overwhelmingly logical. Like physical evolution, the evolution of behavior does not proceed in large jumps. It is a gradual process. Looking ahead, beyond Neanderthal for only a short distance, we will find it impossible to account for the cultural advances that will soon appear, unless we make some allowance for their grounding in the thoughts and aspirations of the men from whom the later men will spring.

NEANDERTHALERS FASHION SPEARS FROM FIRE-CHARRED SAPLINGS THAT THEY HAVE SHARPENED WITH FINELY WORKED STONE SCRAPERS.

The Neanderthal Epoch

Neanderthal men, the first true Homo sapiens, were not the dim-witted brutes they traditionally have been pictured to be. Anything that their Homo erectus forebears could do, Neanderthalers could do better: they were excellent hunters and toolmakers who probably spoke a crude language. They had pondered the nature of death and probably had felt the first primitive stirrings of religion.

The Hardy Life of a Roving Band of Hunters

Neanderthal peoples, some phases of whose lives are painted here by the Czech artist Z. Burian, first appeared in Europe about 110,000 years ago, shortly before the last ice age.

At right, a small group, typical of the bands that ranged throughout Europe and around the Mediterranean, sets out in the spring for new hunting grounds. They are taking all their possessions with them: hides, weapons and a few stone tools like the hand-axe carried by the man in the center. At left a man is carrying small game for provisions—a rabbit and a waterfowl—indicating that Neanderthalers hunted other creatures besides cave bears and woolly rhinoceroses. Each adult male is armed with a heavy club to protect the band from marauding animals. The women look out for the small children—in the right background one is nursing an infant—and carry bundles of skins that the group can use as blankets at night, or as makeshift tents.

Although this scene represents life during a relatively warm period before the glaciers advanced, the ice age at its coldest probably did not impose intolerable hardships on Neanderthalers. In fact, ice age life, while very cold, may even have been easier, since animals were more plentiful. Like the modern Eskimo and Laplander, Neanderthal man was a resourceful fellow who could make the best of any environment, no matter how severe.

AN IBEX DRIVE provides a band of Neanderthalers with enough food for several days. The stronger animals clear the chasm but weaker ones plummet to the bottom where they are slain by waiting hunters.

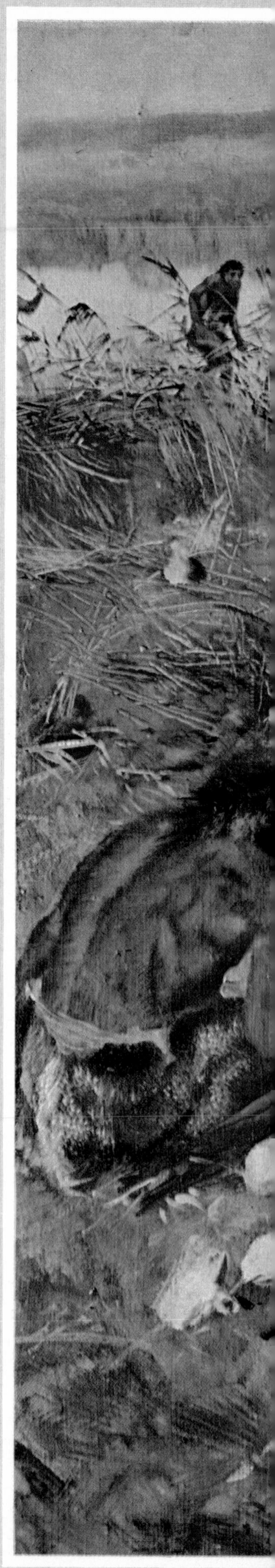

A CAMOUFLAGED PIT traps a woolly rhinoceros that was headed for a nearby water hole to drink. After killing the quarry with spears, the hunters butcher it and carry the flesh and hide back to their camp.

A CANNIBALISTIC FEAST is reconstructed from a site in Krapina, Yugoslavia, where human bones were discovered that had been cut, smashed and charred. Cannibalism probably had ritual significance.

THE CAVE MOUTH at Combe Grenal extended up to the wheelbarrow in the foreground during Neanderthal times. Since then, the roof has collapsed, pushing the entrance back to its present location. Excavators are exposing one of the 64 occupation levels in the cave. Markers in the left background divide the site into quadrants to facilitate the recording of discoveries.

PROFESSOR BORDES PROBES FOR FOSSILS

An 85,000-Year Diary

Combe Grenal, a huge site above the Dordogne valley in southwestern France, contains one of the most remarkable records of Neanderthal life ever discovered. No less than 64 layers of occupation, spanning some 85,000 years, provide a unique picture of the people who lived there.

Of particular interest are the types of tool groups, or "kits," associated with each layer. It can be assumed, for instance, that an occupation level with a predominance of spear points reflects a different way of life than a layer with a predominance of scrapers. Strangely, certain types of kits appear and disappear again and again throughout the 64 levels, sometimes at intervals of thousands of years. Whether this reflects fluctuation within a single people or whether it indicates entirely different tribes, each with its own specifically oriented culture, is a paleoanthropological puzzle.

François Bordes, professor of prehistory at the University of Bordeaux, has excavated Combe Grenal since 1953 and has made one major generalization: Neanderthalers were a highly complex people, much too diverse to be lumped in a single entity.

EXCAVATING, laborers and college students follow the meticulous methods set by Professor Bordes. At top, a worker plots a new find on a map of the site. In the center, a large chunk of stone that once was part of the cave roof is removed. At the bottom students carefully uncover a fossilized reindeer jaw.

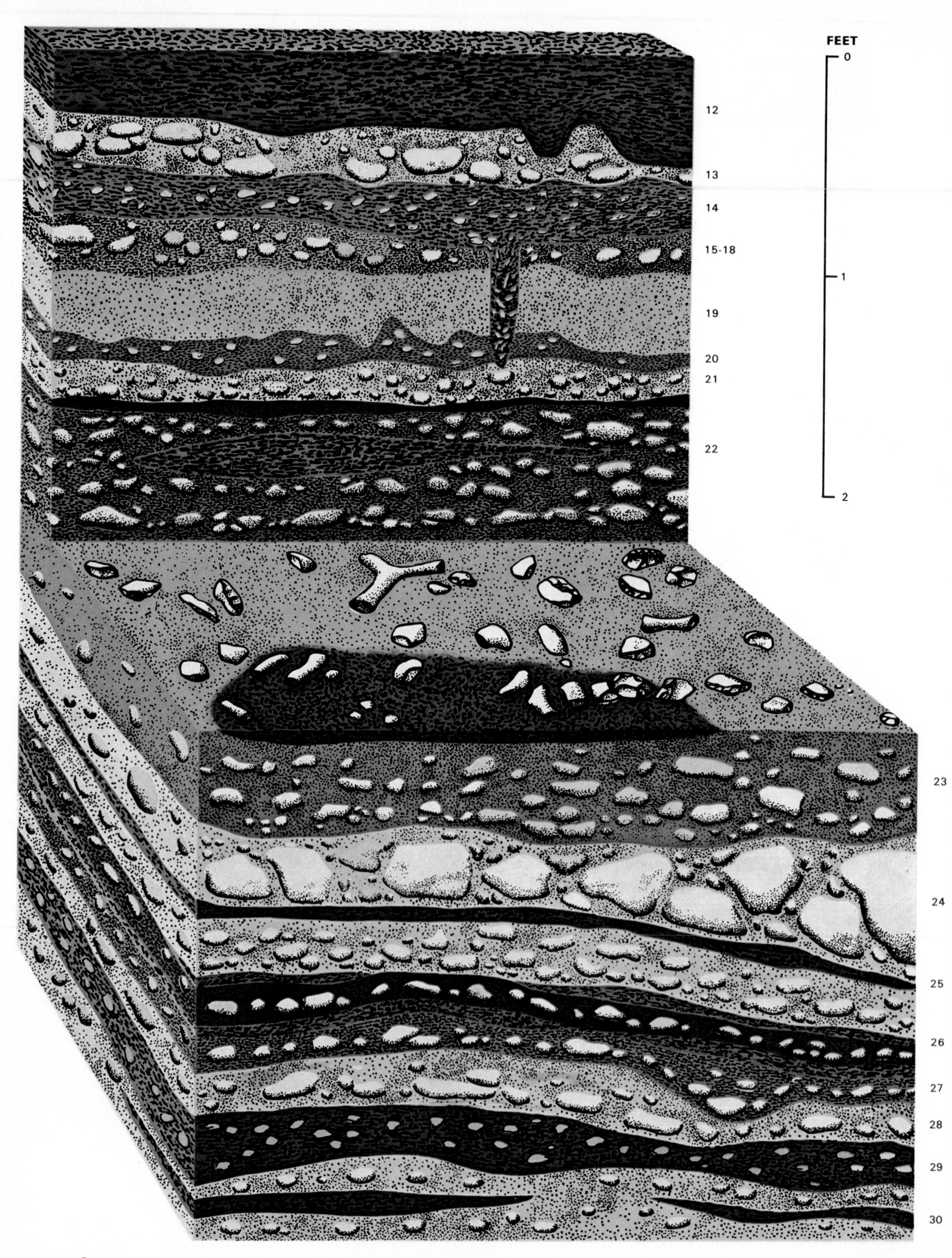
FEET
0
1
2
12
13
14
15-18
19
20
21
22
23
24
25
26
27
28
29
30

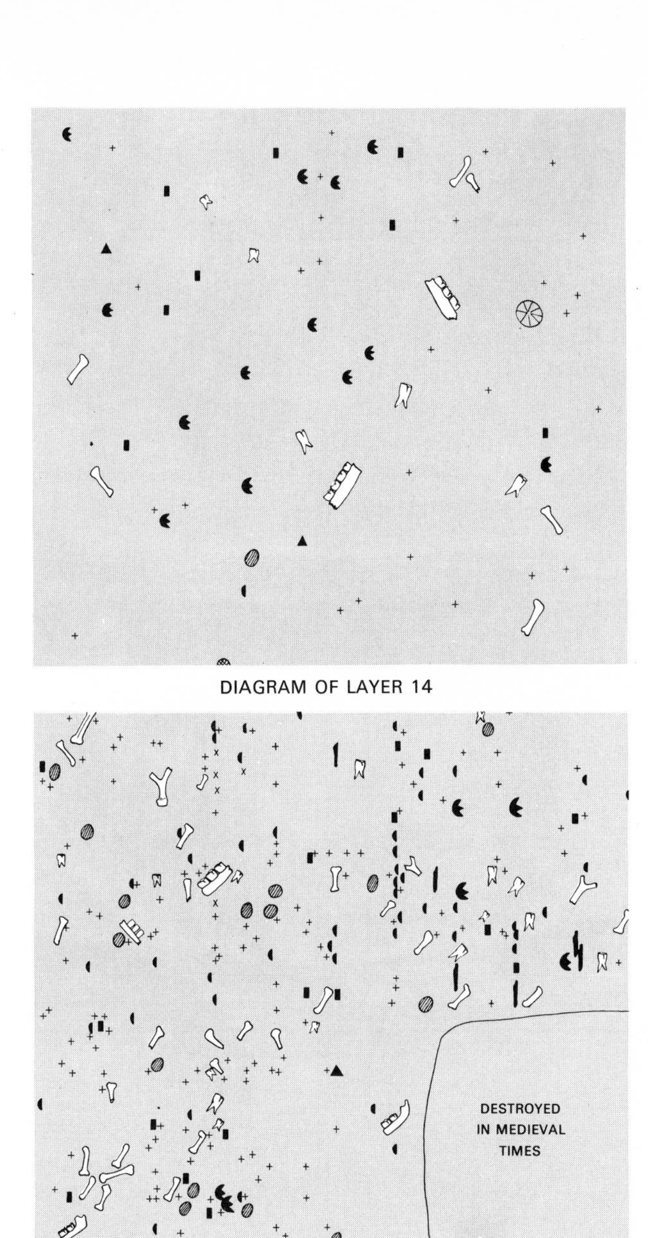

DIAGRAM OF LAYER 14

DIAGRAM OF LAYER 21

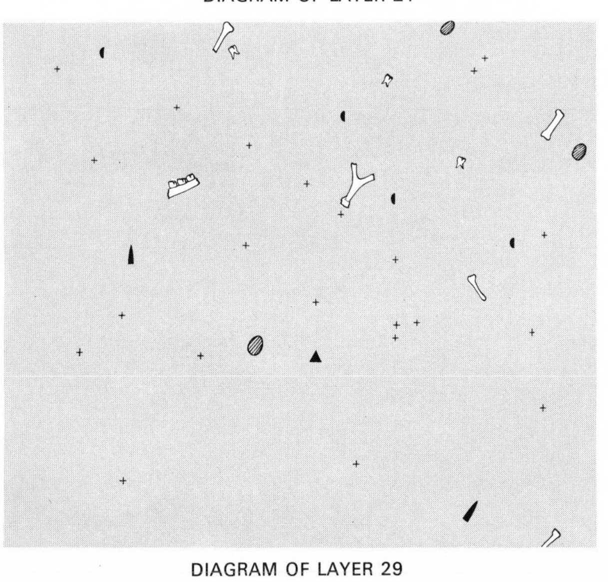

DIAGRAM OF LAYER 29

DIGGING AND RECORDING, Professor Bordes and his associates hunt for fossils and artifacts in their square-meter plots.

Combe Grenal in Detail

The scientists who excavated Combe Grenal *(previous page)* kept records in minute detail, as shown here. Each of the square-meter plots into which the site had been subdivided was mapped in three dimensions *(far left)* to reveal the interrelationship of the various layers. In addition, each layer was then mapped individually *(immediate left)* to show the quantity and relative positions of its fossils and artifacts. The different types of occupational debris were assigned symbols and counted, showing what type of fossil or artifact was most prevalent in that particular layer.

The cross-sectional plot is especially intriguing because it contains evidence of the oldest posthole ever discovered (it runs from layer 14 to 21), indicating some sort of crude construction at the site.

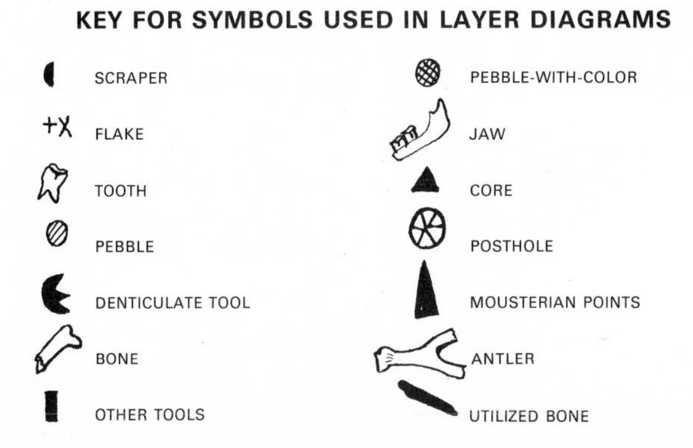

The Revelations of Shanidar

Until well into this century it was believed that Neanderthal man was strictly a European phenomenon. All the Neanderthal discoveries had been made in Europe, and many anthropologists were comfortably settled in the belief that Europe was the cradle of civilization. Then came a shattering series of Neanderthal finds in Africa, Asia and the Middle East, which were climaxed in the 1950s by Ralph Solecki's discoveries of seven Neanderthalers in Shanidar cave in northern Iraq—the very area where modern civilization first arose. Shanidar had been inhabited by Neanderthalers for some 60,000 years, a span of about 2,000 generations.

Early anthropologists obviously had been mistaken; Neanderthal man had been very widespread indeed, inhabiting three continents over a long period of time and through a great variety of climatic conditions. He apparently was a highly adaptable creature who was by no means restricted merely to an icy existence at the edge of Europe's glaciers.

KURDISH SHEPHERDS, helping with the excavations at Shanidar, still use the cave to shelter themselves and their flocks in cold winter months, much as Neanderthalers did thousands of years before.

SHANIDAR I, the first adult Neanderthaler found in the cave, was buried in cave earth for at least 44,000 years. He was a 40-year-old arthritic who had a withered arm and was killed in a rock fall.

A BUCKET BRIGADE and a makeshift cable car haul debris to the surface where it is discarded. Deep inside the cave, Solecki and his associates comb the debris for bones and artifacts.

BURIED IN LIMESTONE, this Neanderthal jaw was only 100 yards from a much more recent Cro-Magnon site at Lascaux.

A Story in Skulls

Neanderthal men lived over a considerable period of time—about 100,000 years—and over a great expanse of territory throughout Europe and the Middle East. Through the millennia they underwent important changes, especially in the shape of their skulls. These changes apparently differed from place to place: for instance, while some Middle Eastern Neanderthalers were becoming more like modern man, the European Neanderthalers were evolving toward the "classic" Neanderthal type—long, low and narrow skulls with jutting brows. The reasons for this are not known, but it is theorized that the European Neanderthalers were isolated from the main genetic pool by glaciations and could not share in evolutionary gains made by Middle East cousins.

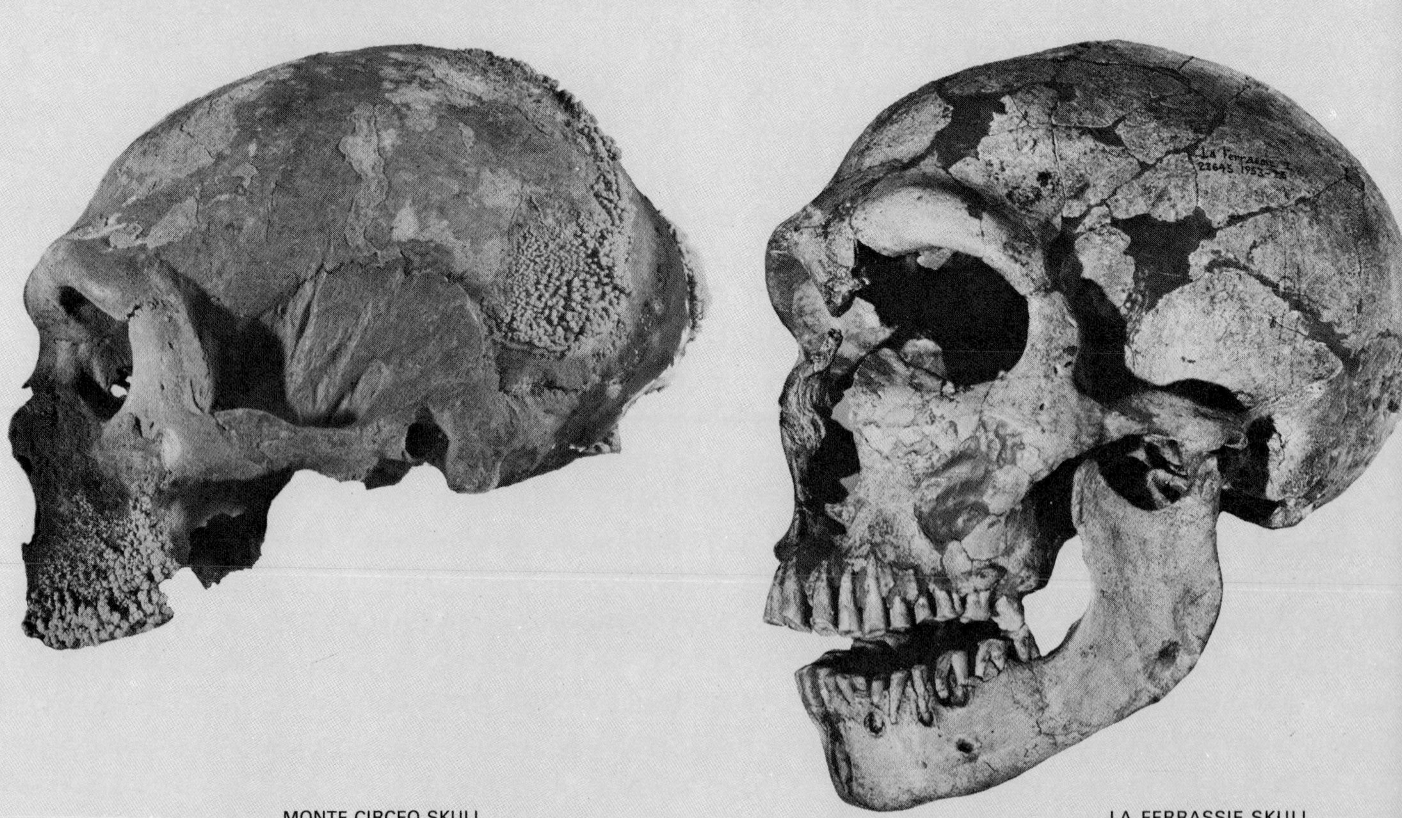

MONTE CIRCEO SKULL

LA FERRASSIE SKULL

MONTE CIRCEO MAN was a classic Neanderthaler found in an Italian cave that had been sealed for some 40,000 years. He was about 40 years old—a senior citizen by Neanderthal standards—and had been murdered. His temple was smashed, and a hole was cut in the base of his skull, probably for plucking out the brain. He seems to have been a victim of ritual cannibalism: his skull had been carefully centered in a ring of stones.

LA FERRASSIE MAN, discovered in fossil-rich southwestern France, is particularly interesting for two reasons: first, he was found buried with five other skeletons (described in the margin on page 128); second, his front teeth show a unique type of extreme wear that is found today among some Eskimo tribes and other hunting peoples. This could well have been caused by years of chewing animal skins to soften them for clothing.

EVOLUTIONARY RETROGRESSION is seen by the comparison of the quarter-million-year-old Swanscombe skull, almost indistinguishable from modern man's, to the thick-browed, low-domed skull of the Spy man, a classic Neanderthaler.

SWANSCOMBE SKULL

SPY SKULL

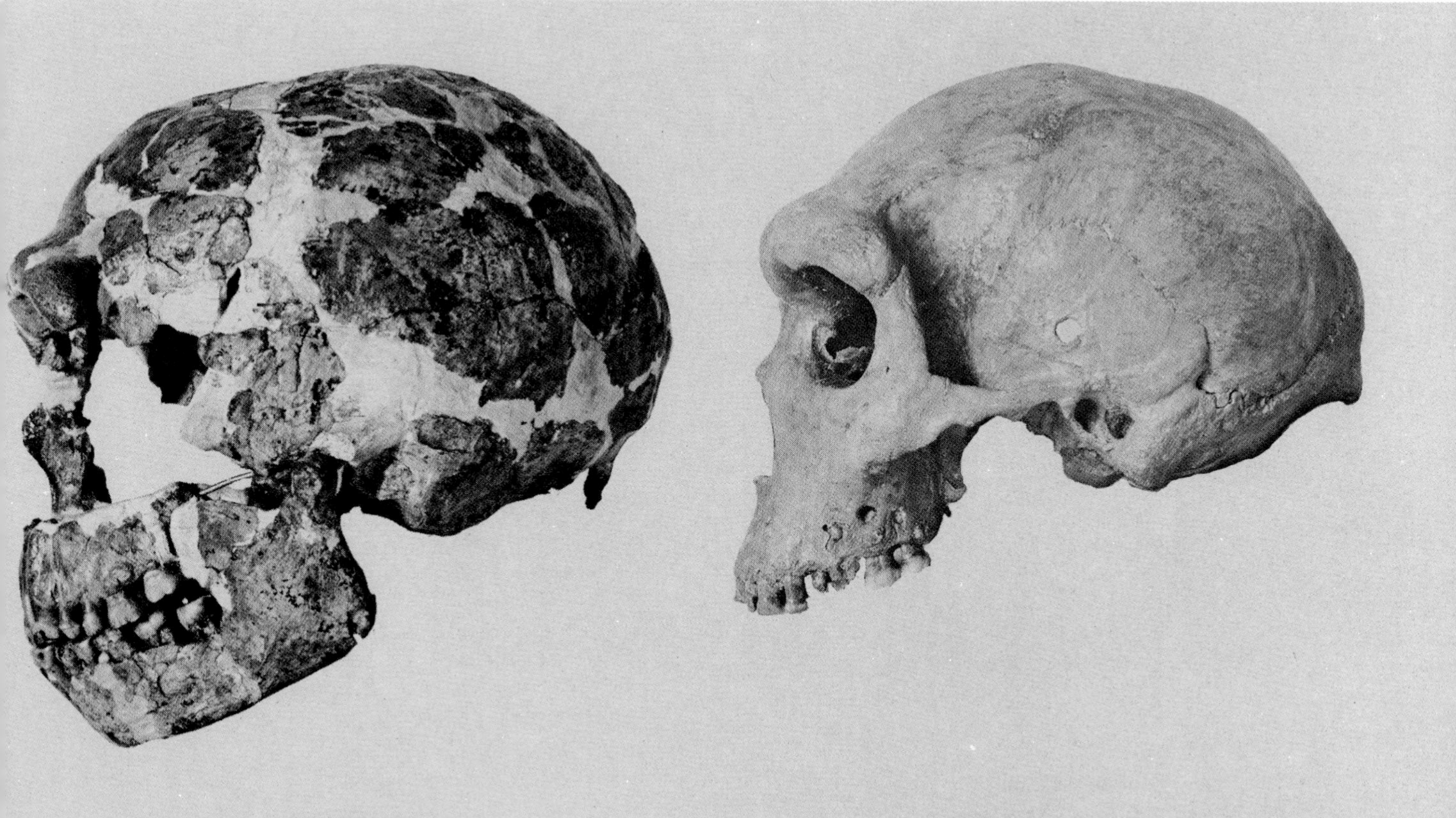

TABŪN SKULL

BROKEN HILL SKULL

TABŪN WOMAN, found on Mount Carmel in Israel, was the Middle Eastern counterpart to the European Neanderthalers. Like most non-European Neanderthalers she never quite achieved classic Neanderthal features: although she had heavy brows and a large face, her forehead was much higher. The evolutionary range of skulls found in the Middle East is great: from near-classic to ones very much like modern man's.

BROKEN HILL MAN, found in Rhodesia, was the equivalent to Neanderthal man in sub-Saharan Africa. He has an enormous face and huge brow ridges, but there are some subtle evolutionary advances around his nose and ears. The small hole in the side of his head intrigues scientists; it was carefully cut while he was still alive—the bone shows signs of healing. It may have been a prehistoric "operation" to release evil spirits.

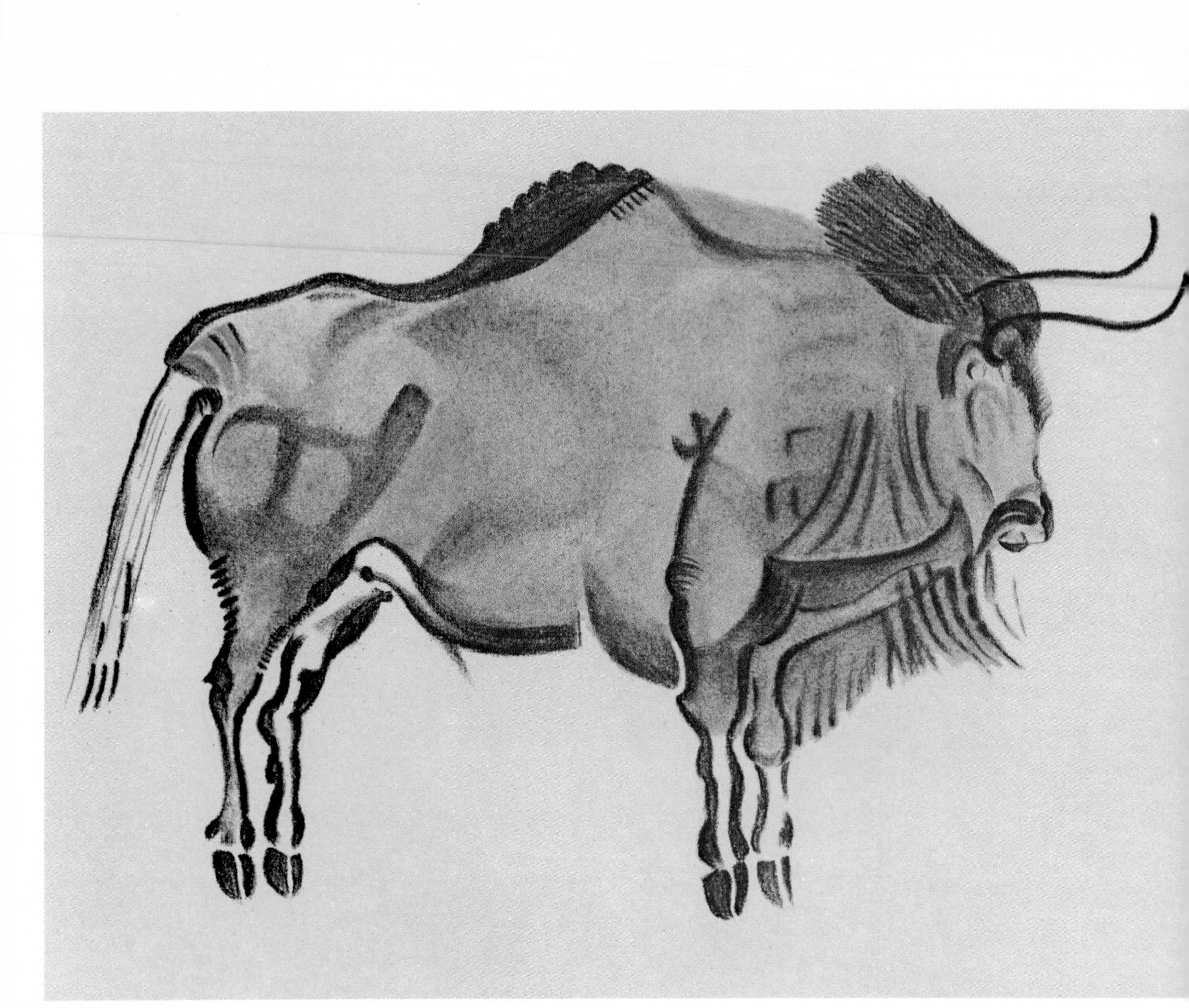

CHARGED WITH ENERGY, A BISON IN SPAIN'S ALTAMIRA CAVES SHOWS HOW MUCH KNOWLEDGE OF ANIMAL ANATOMY EARLY ARTISTS HAD.

7 The Dawn of Modern Man

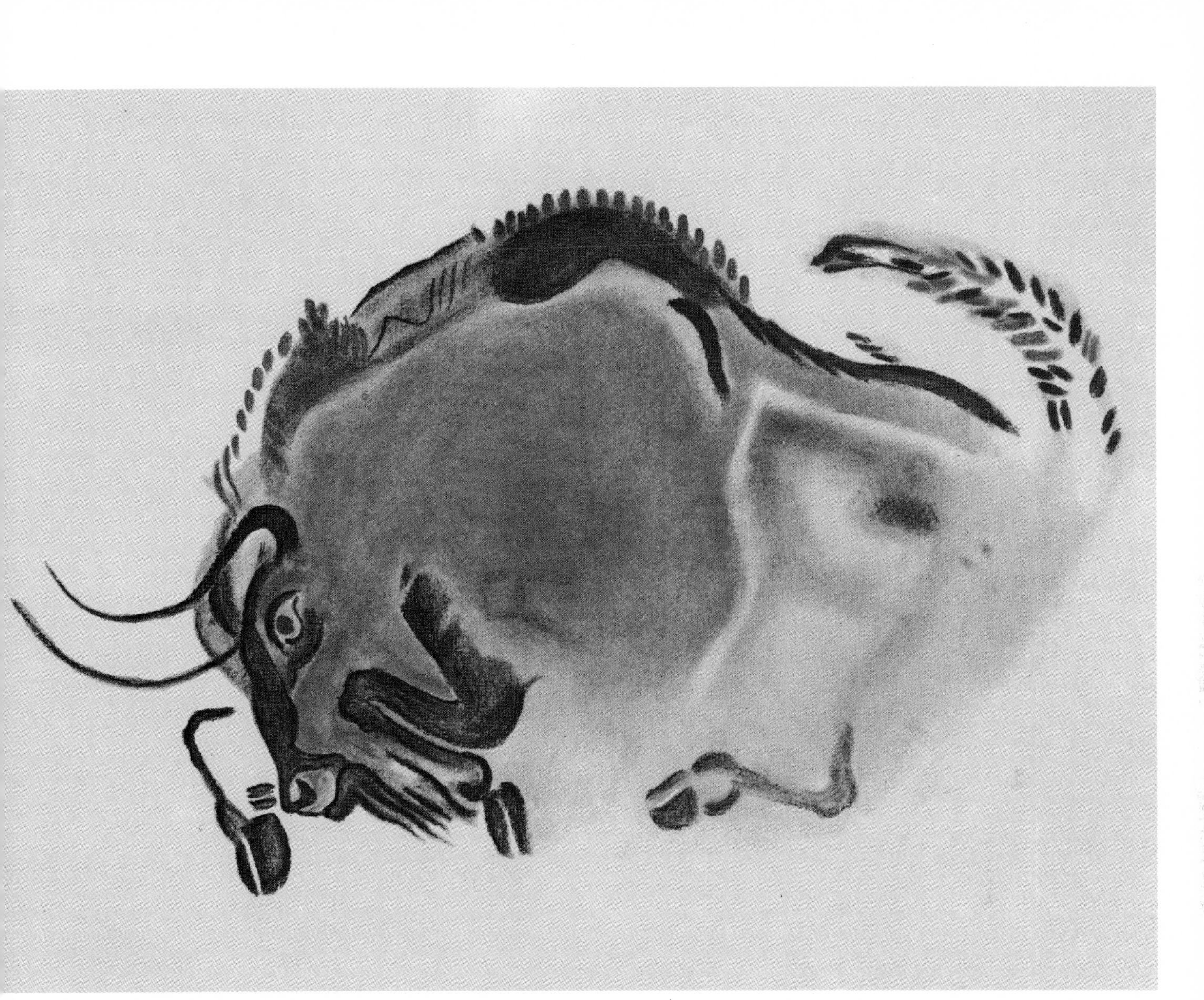

THE SKILL OF CAVE ARTISTS IS FURTHER REVEALED BY THE OUTLINING OF THE MUSCULATURE AND THE DEFT SHADING OF THE BODY MASSES.

Although, as the last two chapters revealed, traces of modern man may go back as far as a couple of hundred thousand years, he cannot be said to have emerged in his present form until about 35,000 years ago. At that point people made their appearance who were virtually indistinguishable from those of today. They did this gradually and unevenly, and the modern men who emerged were not all alike, any more than they are alike now. But this date of 35,000 B.C. may be taken as a handy one for marking the establishment of the present model of *Homo sapiens*—after that, earlier forms are no longer seen.

As usual, the evidence is lopsided and incomplete. Again, a principal reason is that most of the paleoanthropological work that deals with the period 35,000 to 10,000 B.C. is concentrated in Europe. As a result we know a good deal about one group of men who lived there during those years and much less about those who lived in other places. That the rest of the world was occupied, we know very well. Africa was full of people, the ancestors of today's Bushmen. But the modern Negro was not there, as far as is known. Who he was and where he came from remains to be discovered, as does the ancestry of all the

Mongoloid peoples. In this same period Australia, North America and, later, South America were invaded by men for the first time. But we have nothing like the detailed investigation of them and their settlements that has been made in Europe, particularly in France in the region of the Dordogne.

The Dordogne is a land laced with several rivers that wind down through the Massif Central, joining and eventually emptying into the Atlantic at Bordeaux. Long ago these rivers scoured a series of narrow valleys with steep rock walls that rise for two or three hundred feet to the rolling upland plateau that covers that part of France. This is a world of limestone, and limestone being a porous rock, subject to the action of water, it is a veritable sponge of caves, grottoes and overhangs. Men of the classic Neanderthal type began appearing in considerable numbers in these sheltered places with the advent of the last ice age, and they have been inhabited intermittently ever since. It might even be said that they are still inhabited, for the back wall of many a modern house tucked in under a bulging overhang of rock is the rock itself. The present owners have dug horizontal grooves in the rock face overhead to divert dripping water that otherwise might flood their kitchens.

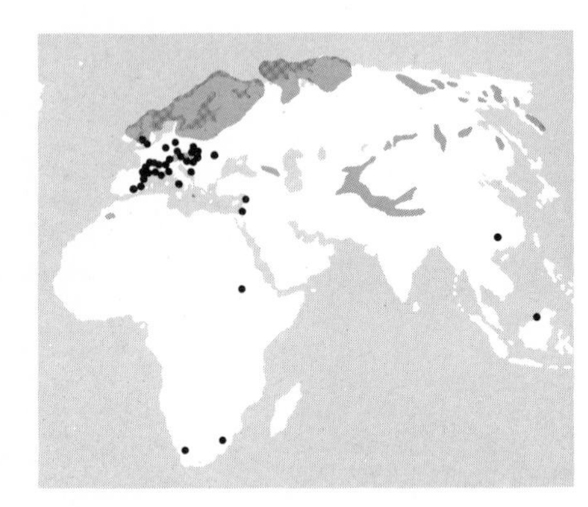

PRESERVATION IN CAVES

Most of the known sites where Upper Paleolithic man lived, shown here by black dots, are in Europe, particularly the Dordogne in southern France. The caves in which these European men sheltered themselves from the cold of the ice-age glaciers (gray) also protected and preserved their artifacts and bones for hundreds of centuries. Men in Africa and Asia at this time might also have had large populations, but in the milder climate their sites were built on open ground and their bones have not lasted.

The possibility of the Dordogne's antiquity as a living place for man first began to be seriously explored just a century ago when a lawyer-turned-anthropologist, Edouard Lartet, started looking into caves at Les Eyzies and other spots in the Vézère River valley. Traces of man were everywhere. As discovery followed discovery, the suspicion grew that the Dordogne had been densely populated for thousands of years. Today there are literally hundreds of known sites of prehistoric human occupation in the Dordogne, with many more awaiting discovery. Les Eyzies itself has come to be known as the prehistoric capital of the world.

To drive down into the Dordogne on the main road from Paris is to step back into the Stone Age. The road runs along the river almost underneath streaked limestone walls. All around are the silent habitations of the past, some open to the public as small museums, others closed because they are being excavated by scientists. Harvard University's Hallam L. Movius Jr. is making a detailed study of a site almost in the main street of Les Eyzies. Aside from these visible reminders, there are invisible ones. One feels them, hidden all around one, beneath their shallow shrouds of earth, behind the tangles of gorse and bracken, waiting for the blundering picnicker, the lost ball, the incautious foot to break through and reveal their existence. It was a dog that discovered the great cave at Lascaux. It fell into a crack in the earth. The boys with it dug the crack wider and slipped down into a cavern hundreds of feet long whose walls were covered with perfectly preserved colored paintings of horses, deer and bison. Lascaux is one of the most recently known (it was discovered in 1940) and the grandest of many such sites. No one knows when an even more dramatic one will be found.

Les Eyzies is the place where local contractors decided to widen the highway in 1868. In cutting into a roadside rock shelter known as Cro-Magnon (literally big-large, or great-big, in the old local dialect) they found some skeletons and stone implements carefully buried in the cave. It is this place and these skeletons that gave the name Cro-Magnon to the race of people who lived not only in southern France but in many parts of Europe at the end of the last ice age. On the evidence of their bones they were tall, strong people with large heads, wide faces and big eyes. They had prominent chins and high-bridged noses, and seem to have resembled today's Irish, Scandinavian and Anglo-Saxon types more closely than other living peoples. Harvard's William W. Howells goes so far as to say that their skins were undoubtedly white.

Cro-Magnon men may indeed be the ancestors of modern "Europeans," but this is not provable. We must be suspicious of being too eager to claim descent from them just because they seem to have been such upstanding fellows with features and proportions that suit present Western ideals of beauty. Nevertheless, it was during Cro-Magnon times that differentiation into the living races of man undoubtedly was taking place. Today there are slight skeletal differences between the indigenous people of Europe, Africa and Asia, just as there are different skin colors, different hair textures and different facial features, though no one knows for sure where they came from or when they appeared. We do not know if Cro-Magnon man had straight or curly hair, thick or thin lips, or even if he had the "slanted" eyes of a Mongoloid, for this is a fleshy attribute, not a bony one. Nevertheless, logic suggests that he probably looked most like the people his skeleton most closely resembles today.

The principal differences between Cro-Magnon man and a Stockholm bus driver, say, are that the former's head was a trifle longer, his brow ridges somewhat—and sometimes—more pronounced. These might be taken to be primitive features, but offsetting them was a brain capacity that was just as large as the average for modern Europeans as a whole.

What Cro-Magnon man did with this large brain was remarkable. He produced a culture that, in variety and elegance, far outstripped anything that Neanderthal man, in his most daring moments, had aspired to. He inherited many of the tool techniques of Neanderthal man, and while he continued with some of these, he was also responsible for some remarkable technological changes in working stone and particularly bone. Notable as these advances are, it is his intellectual and spiritual achievements that impress, particularly his fantastic artistic ability, a talent that seems to have sprung full-blown out of nowhere. There are more than 70 sites of Cro-Magnon cave art in France alone. These date from approximately 28,000 to 10,000 B.C. Cro-Magnon man was a close observer of the animals he hunted and a magnificent artist. More than that, he had a sufficiently sophisticated way of life to appreciate and encourage his own talents and to work them into his dreams and rituals. From all indications, his paintings and carvings are closely tied in with his spiritual life.

One strong indication of this is seen in the places he chose to put his wall paintings. It should be emphasized that there are basically two kinds of caves in the Dordogne. First there are the rock overhangs, more or less open and facing out over the valleys, which can be made more livable by the addition of stone walls in their fronts to keep out the wind and snow. These are the ones that Cro-Magnon man lived in. They are full of the signs of long occupancy. Tools lie in all strata in their floors. Buried skeletons occur. Hearths abound, tending to become bigger as we come closer to the present.

There is little or no decoration on the walls of these open cave homes. Nearly all the great Cro-Magnon wall art is restricted to true caves: deep underground fissures with long galleries and passages, the kind that spelunkers explore, that have their own subterranean pools and rivers, their festoons of stalactites. Such caves are dark and mysterious. They could only be entered by people holding fat-filled stone lamps or torches, and those used by Cro-Magnon man quite obviously served as shrines, since they were not only inappropriate as dwelling places but contain little or no evidence of having been lived in.

MAN'S FIRST NECKLACES

The custom of wearing body ornaments started with the imaginative Homo sapiens. Typical are the four necklaces shown here, all found in excavations in Czechoslovakia and all made from the most durable animal parts. The cylindrical beads of the top necklace are carved from the tusk of a mammoth. Next is a string of snail shells. Then come two necklaces made of the pointed teeth of predatory animals—foxes, wolves, bears.

Another interesting point about cave art has been brought out by the Abbé Henri Breuil, the French priest who devoted his life to the study of prehistory, and by Johannes Maringer, who has studied this art intensively. This is that the paintings or engravings were often made in the worst possible places for viewing —in narrow niches, behind bumps of rock, sometimes in areas that must have been not only difficult but actually dangerous for the artist to work in. "It is simply impossible," says Maringer, "that this art should have been intended, in these locations, to give pleasure to the eye of the beholder; the intention must always have been to veil it in mysterious secrecy."

What was its purpose then? According to Maringer and numerous other experts, it was a vehicle for magic—more specifically, what is known as sympathetic hunting magic. Cro-Magnon man was a hunter, perhaps as good as any the world has ever seen. He was strong, intelligent, well equipped with all kinds of weapons from spears and knives to slings. He knew how to make traps for small animals and pitfalls for large ones. He could ambush and stampede. And he has left impressive records of his skill behind him. In Předmost, Czechoslovakia, there are skeletons of 1,000 mammoths, and below the great cliff at Solutré the remains of more than 100,000 wild horses. Nevertheless, despite his formidable powers, he knew, as all primitive men do, that he walked always in the shadow of unpredictable and incomprehensible events, of malign forces. Doubtless he felt it necessary to try to forestall misfortune, injury and sometimes death—for some of the prey he hunted was extremely dangerous, notably the cave bear.

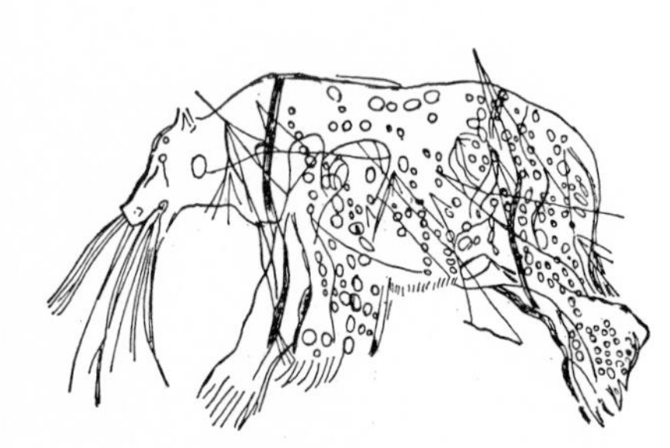

ART FOR THE HUNT

Tribal artists of the Upper Paleolithic hoped to insure the success of the hunt by depicting animals being destroyed through the efforts of hunters. The engraved bear (above), from Les Trois Frères cave in France, is dying, spewing out blood from its mouth and nose. The circles on it represent wounds inflicted by spears and stones. Below is a painting of a mammoth caught in a trap at Font-de-Gaume cave in France.

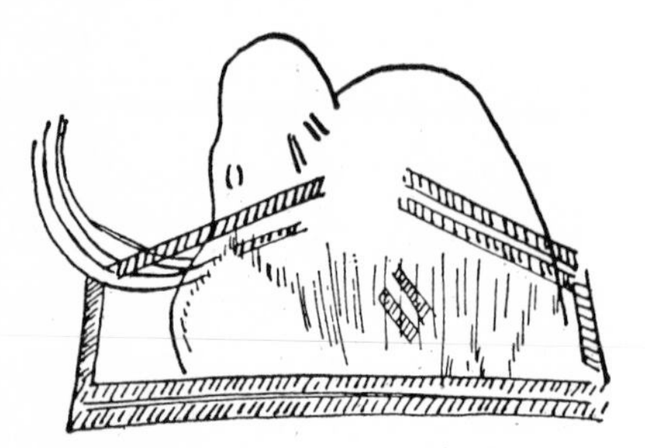

It was not enough merely to dodge misfortune. The hunter had to be positively fortunate too; he had to find an animal and he had to kill it. He improved his chances by painting a picture of the animal he wished to kill and then performing certain religious or magical rituals before the hunt to strengthen the power of his wish-picture.

This is not entirely guesswork; there is a variety of evidence to support it. First, and most direct, is the large number of animals painted with spears in them, or marked with the blows of clubs—clearly intended to show in painting what would, hopefully, occur in the chase. In a cave at Font-de-Gaume near Les Eyzies, there are several drawings of traps or enclosures with animals suggestively shown caught in them, including a magnificent picture of a mammoth in what seems to be a pitfall.

ANOTHER hint is found in the peculiar practice of superimposing one painting on another. This phenomenon may be observed over and over again in the caves. At Lascaux in one spot the paintings are four layers deep, suggesting that a new picture was made not so much for display as for new magic—for a future hunt involving a different kind of animal. If paintings were to be looked at and enjoyed esthetically, this would not have been done, particularly where there were empty wall spaces nearby. This concentration on certain spots in the caves suggests that they were favored for some magical reason. Good wall space, logically enough, would be the places where previous paintings had worked good magic by producing kills in the field. Since all ritual depends on duplicating as closely as possible a procedure that has proved successful in the past, certain "lucky" spots in the caves would probably have been more highly regarded than others.

In some instances, any wall space would seem to have been at a premium. Certain sites are extremely crowded, and Les Combarelles has nearly 300 animals painted on its rocks. Crowding of this kind, or perhaps the desire to find a less arduous way of working magic (for many of the cave paintings are 10 or 20 feet long and obviously took time and effort to execute) may have been responsible for still another phenomenon of Cro-Magnon wall art. This is the tendency to overpaint one animal's head on another's body, possibly a time-saving way of suggesting the new quarry by making the picture of the old one do. We can almost see a man contemplating a large and beautifully executed picture of a bison, and then deciding—rather than do the whole thing over—to simply substitute the head of a deer.

This kind of "short-cut" magic seems also to have spilled over to the still-easier practice of carving or scratching the image of a desired animal on a small magic stone instead of making a wall painting. Such stones are fairly common in living sites, and some experts think they were used as practice tablets.

A SORCERER FOR THE HUNT

Another type of cave picture done for the sake of hunting magic shows creatures that are part animal and part man. This painting, also from Les Trois Frères, has the ears and antlers of a stag, the tail of a wolf and the arms, legs, feet and beard of a man. Some scholars feel this figure is a hunting god who controlled the abundance of game and protected hunting expeditions. Others identify him as a tribal shaman, dressed in skins and headpiece for a hunting magic ceremony.

MAGIC, of course, requires magicians, and cave art supplies them too. There are more than 50 known pictures of strange-looking sorcerers or shamans —human figures clad in the skins of animals, sometimes depicted with animal heads or horns, often appearing to be engaged in some kind of dance. These may have been attempts, by illustrating it in advance, to guarantee successful stalking by hunters disguised as animals. Or they may have been more highly symbolized projections of the hunter's feeling that a ritual dance by a magician or spellbinder would work more potent magic on the game. Or they may even have been attempts to portray a superhuman figure, the spirit of the hunt or the deity of the animals.

We can only speculate about these tantalizing and long-lost rituals, but they have so many parallels in hunting societies of more modern times that there is no doubt at all that Cro-Magnon man was a ritualist too. Any society that lives by hunting spends most of its time thinking about the animals that it hunts, and many elaborate systems of totems and taboos are still known among hunting tribes today, telling them what they must and must not do. These range from propitiating the spirit of the animal, so that it will submit easily and gracefully to being killed, to attempts to disarm its spirit after death so that it will not come back to haunt or harm the killer. The cultures of Eskimos, American Indians and many of the primitive tribes of subarctic Siberia—all of them, like Cro-Magnon man, cold-weather followers of big game—were steeped in rituals of this kind.

Another thing that preoccupies hunting societies is the problem of fluctuations in the game supply. Cro-Magnon man apparently dealt with this in his magic system by emphasizing the fertility of many of the beasts he painted. Pairs of animals were often shown together, sometimes in the act of mating. Horses, does and cows were painted with the swollen bellies of advanced pregnancy. In others, the udders were enlarged, as if to emphasize the rich supply of milk that the mother would be capable of giving to any offspring that might be born. That scarcity of game was periodically a problem with Cro-Magnon man is likely. During the colder episodes of the last glacial period he probably did all right. Mammoths, woolly rhinoceroses, ibex, a cold-adapted shaggy little steppe horse and, particularly, reindeer flourished in large numbers in the tundra environment that came with the cold. As it warmed up from time to time he undoubtedly switched over to the deer, bison and wild cattle that replaced the cold-loving species. But increasing numbers of men, and the beginnings of a tendency toward a settled life (in winter, at least) hinted at by cave occupancy, may well have led to local depletion of the game in many areas and seriously complicated Cro-Magnon man's ability to make a comfortable living. If so, he must certainly have turned to sympathetic hunting magic to help him out.

Cro-Magnon man's paintings, although of stunning virtuosity, are rigidly limited in their scope. There are few scenes, and aside from the sorcerer-types described above, almost no people. This is natural, for anybody accustomed to practicing sympathetic magic by making pictures would not be likely to run the mortal risk of having it practiced on him by drawing a picture of himself. What late Stone Age man painted was mammals, and of these only about a dozen of the commonest species of large game mammals. Very occasionally something like a bird, a fish or a snake will be seen, but the preoccupation of the hunter with the one thing in life that fascinated him is obvious. His animals are individual portraits, always drawn in profile, and with sure, bold outlines. He used various colors which he obtained from natural clays and mineral oxides—blacks, reds, yellows and browns. These he mixed with charcoal and animal fat as a binder, and he applied them either by using a kind of crude crayon made of this material, or by blowing his colors directly onto the wall in powder form through a hollow bone.

Once applied to a wall, these colors were slowly absorbed by the limestone, which explains their phenomenal durability. Thanks to constant humidity in the caves, many of which were also protected against frost by being deep in the ground, much of Cro-Magnon art has retained its original brilliance for ten or twenty thousand years, some of it for even longer. A tragic exception to this is the great cave at Lascaux. After its discovery in 1940, nothing was done with it until the end of World War II, at which time it was taken over by the French Government and declared a historical monument. It was fitted with doors, electric lights and an air-conditioning system, and became one of the great tourist attractions of France. By the early 1950s those who knew the cave best were beginning to wonder if its paintings were not fading a little. By the 1960s this was no longer a wonder but a certainty. Furthermore, insidious green algae were beginning to creep over the walls, defacing some of the finest animal portraits. Some blamed this on the air conditioning and—for a cave—an unhealthy dryness. Others thought the opposite; they blamed it on excessive humidity raised beyond the natural dampness of a cave by the breathing of many visitors. Still others thought that the chemical toxicity of human breath was responsible. Whatever the reason, the algae continued to spread, and in 1963 the cave was closed. It is now being searchingly analyzed by a panel of experts. Whether or not this beautiful cave will ever be open again to the public remains to be seen.

In addition to painting, Cro-Magnon man showed considerable proficiency as a sculptor and engraver. He incised the outlines of animals on cave walls and went on to develop the more advanced technique of carving subjects in high relief. Cap Blanc, near Les Elyzies, has a marvelous set of horses done in this way, the bulging sides of their bodies accentuated by the natural curves of the rock which the artist incorporated with great skill.

Cro-Magnon artists also made complete statues in the round, and in doing so, left us a means of gaining further insights into Stone Age life and thought. These are statues of women—more properly statuettes, for most of them are only a few inches high. They are made of stone, bone and ivory, and some are a mixture of clay and ground bone, fired to make them hard. They have a very wide distribution in Stone Age sites over much of Europe and eastward as far as Siberia. Although they vary a good deal in appearance and artistic merit, they have some significant things in common. The most obvious of these is that the sculptor's interest was focused on the torso. Arms and legs are extremely small in proportion to the trunk, and in some cases merely suggested. The heads are also small and show little attempt to portray features, although the famous *Venus of Willendorf*, a four-inch figurine made of limestone, does have a wavy hairdo executed with considerable care. The emphasis is all in the bodies, with their female characteristics—breasts, belly and buttocks—greatly exaggerated in size. They look like tiny earth goddesses or fertility figures, and a good deal of informed speculations suggest that this is what they were.

Again there is evidence for this idea—slender, but still evidence, mostly having to do with where they are found and when they are believed to have been made. The majority of them come from the Upper Périgordian period, named for a late Paleolithic culture of western Europe that existed between 22,000 and 18,000 years ago. During this period, the weather ranged from cool to very cold. In the cold periods it was bitter in the extreme, especially on the eastern European plains; nevertheless many peoples continued to live there. They made their homes in shallow pits dug in the ground and then covered them with hides or other material for roofing. The vague outlines of the walls of many of these sunken huts may still be seen. The interesting thing about the female figurines is that some of their most abundant occurrences are in sites like these, and that they are often found lying right next to the walls. At one site in the Ukraine, seven figures were found actually standing on the walls. The figurines themselves often taper to a point at the bottom, as if they had been designed to be stuck in the earth or into a base of some sort.

On this evidence it is fairly clear that the figurines were closely associated with the daily life of the peoples who made them, and have a significance utterly unlike that of the wall art that was practiced in secret, deep in underground caves. To go on from here and speculate on how they were used is a little tenuous, but again Johannes Maringer has some interesting inferences to draw. He points out that the greatest occurrence of the statuettes is during the cool Upper Périgordian, when the hunting tribes were relatively sedentary. By contrast, in the cold and less sedentary Magdalenian, in which hunters were dependent on migratory herds of reindeer for a living, the carvings became increasingly rare. The Magdalenian period, from 15,000 to 10,000 B.C., was bitterly cold at the outset but warmed up later on. During it men are believed to have lived a life not unlike that led by extreme northern peoples right up to today. Magdalenian man dressed in furs. He perfected the eyed needle and for the first time was able to stitch his clothes to fit his body, particularly his arms and legs. All life during the bitter environment of the Magdalenian depended on success in the hunt, and society was strongly male-dominated. Women doubtlessly played a subordinate role, as they do among Eskimos.

When this kind of nomadic life is compared to that which was lived in the Upper Périgordian, it is possible to visualize a more important role for women during that earlier time. Women were not entirely dependent on men for survival since the gathering of fruits, roots and berries was an important seasonal occupation, and it fell to them. Also, if one is not completely dependent on herds of migrating animals, one can settle down in one place for considerable periods of time and have a home. Homemaking is also woman's work, and the

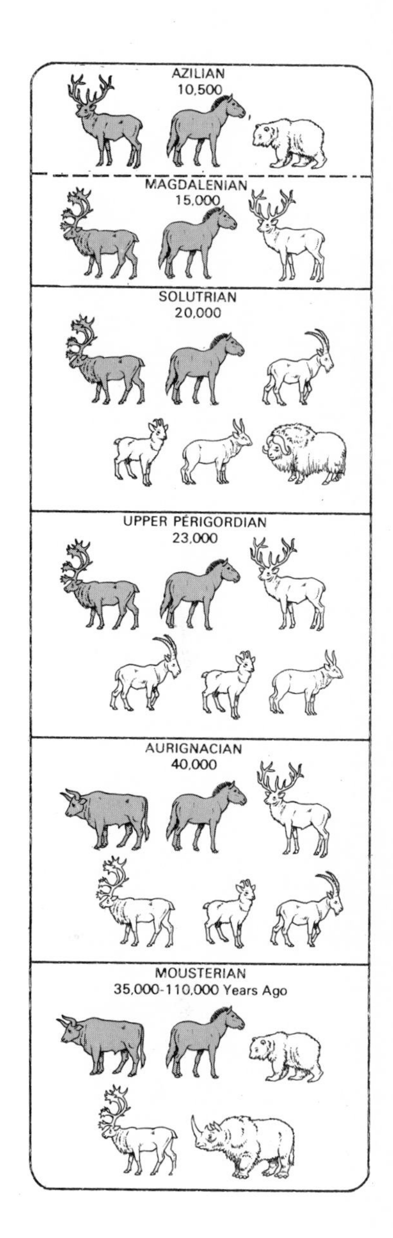

A CHANGING MENU

What men ate during six successive cultures in the Dordogne region of France is shown in this diagram. The most numerous and most hunted animals are indicated in color, lesser ones in decreasing order of importance in black and white. Thus, in the Mousterian, aurochs and horse were the mainstays of the hunting tribes. The next most abundant animals were bear, reindeer and woolly rhinoceros. In the Aurignacian, red deer replaced the bear; then came the reindeer, chamois and ibex. In the three subsequent cultures herds of reindeer provided up to 90 per cent of the meat supply. But in the Azilian, the reindeer moved away and red deer became the principal food. Horses were heavily hunted in every period.

eastern societies at the time of the Upper Périgordian are believed to have been considerably more sedentary than the later Magdalenian ones, which had to be always on the move to keep up with the reindeer herds that meant the difference between affluence and starvation.

This is not to say that the winters were not severe. They were dreadfully so, particularly on the windswept eastern steppe. But here again, in the dawning sedentariness of the Upper Périgordian, women probably proved important. They had the job of planning, rationing, utilizing and storing supplies so that the tribes could get through the winter. Much of their meat came from mammoths, and one mammoth frugally put in natural cold storage by a strong-minded housewife would certainly have lasted a group of people for weeks, perhaps for months. Storage pits were found in many sites, some with animal remains.

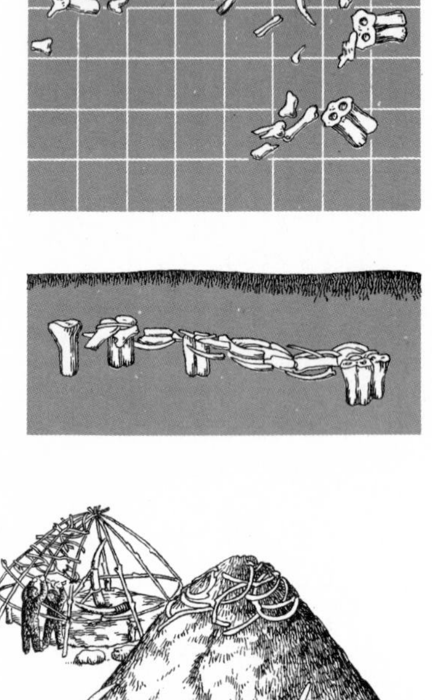

A HOUSE OF BONES

What were the dwellings of Upper Paleolithic peoples like? Careful mapping of a site in the Ukraine has revealed how mammoth bones were found lying in a semicircle (top diagram), suggesting that they were part of a round structure. The second diagram, a side view, shows how the large bones with holes in them were partially buried around the outer edge of the circle, possibly as anchors for poles. It has been assumed that the original dwelling was dome-shaped, probably covered over with hides and weighted down with other bones, as depicted in the reconstruction (bottom).

For these many reasons, it is not hard to imagine a position of considerable importance for women in Upper Périgordian society. This may well have stimulated enough interest in, and veneration for, the mysteries of fertility and birth to explain the great abundance of those little fertility figures. But whether they were merely household good-luck charms or tiny goddesses to be worshiped or something else entirely, is not known. They whisper to us about late Paleolithic life, but they say nothing about themselves.

Cro-Magnon man's treatment of his dead was careful and thoughtful. Graves were protected with covering stones and often lined with hot ashes—not, it is believed, to cremate the body but to keep it warm for a little while. This touching concern for the deceased also expressed itself in the practice of smearing red ocher on a corpse in an effort to give the pallid skin a more lifelike look.

Not all the evidence from the late Stone Age is supplied by whole skeletons from graves. There are large numbers of scattered human bones here and there. In some instances leg bones have been cracked apart, as if somebody had been after the marrow in them; in others skulls have been smashed open from behind, to get at the brains. This raises the specter of cannibalism, which also has been hinted at among the remains of Peking man and Neanderthal man. However, any use that Cro-Magnon man or his predecessors may have made of human bones seems to have been largely of a ritualistic nature. Many primitive societies of today keep skulls, and even civilized people preserve the ashes of their ancestors in urns. Australian aborigines expose and dry some of the bones of their dead, and later carry them around in long packages. There are tantalizing bits of evidence that Cro-Magnon man also was a skull-and-bone man. One cave in France has yielded three human skulls placed with obvious forethought on a slab of rock. Another contained the skull of a woman with a quantity of shell ornaments carefully arranged around it. Elsewhere in this same cave were pieces of skulls arranged with equal care. Detailed examination of these by the Abbé Breuil, and by the German Hugo Obermaier, suggests that these pieces were actually used as shallow cups. Their position in the cave—at the end of a small tunnel, arranged in a row and lying open side up—was suggestive to begin with. When they were examined, they showed signs of actually having been made into cups. Each one bore marks on its surface indicating that the muscles and flesh that originally covered it had been hacked or scraped away with a stone implement and that the lower parts of the skull had then been chopped off and the rough edges smoothed all around, leaving a skull cap which actually made a shallow cup.

Whether the skull caps were those of relatives or ancestors and used out of affection and pride, or whether they were the skulls of enemies and used in triumph cannot be determined. Later history is crowded with instances of both usages, right up to the Middle Ages when the skulls of Christian saints were still employed as ceremonial drinking cups. Prior to that, many peoples like the Teutons and Scythians drank from the skulls of their fallen enemies, and set particular store by those of the bravest men.

Aside from his own remains, man of the late Stone Age also left behind many provocative assortments of animal bones and skulls. Some of these suggest animal worship, others appear to have been sacrificial offerings to ensure good hunting. The best-known and most durable brand of animal worship was the Cult of the Bear, which had its start back in Neanderthal times and persisted down into the late Paleolithic—covering a span of some 40,000 years. The bear in question was the cave bear, a now-extinct species that bore a close resemblance to the kodiak bear of Alaska. It was a formidable animal; a full-sized specimen measured eight feet or more from nose to tail and weighed as much as 1,500 pounds. At the time of the fourth glacial period, bears of this type were extremely numerous throughout the mountainous areas of Europe and western Asia, holing up in dens and cracks in the rock. One such in Austria —the Drachenhöhle, or Dragon's Lair—was mined for phosphates about 40 years ago and produced a staggering haul of bones. Estimates of the number of bears that lived and died in that one cave run as high as 50,000 and indicate a fairly steady occupancy by bears for at least 10,000 years.

THAT worship was involved in bear hunting seems logical, for other more prosaic reasons do not stand up too well. Bears could have been hunted for meat and skins, but this must have been a hazardous way of getting these commodities since the cave bear was an immensely powerful animal and other less dangerous prey would have served as well. It could have been for cave sites, but these were often high in the mountains and not really suitable for human occupancy. In fact, it took a good deal of cave excavation and the finding of stone tools to convince many skeptics that Paleolithic man went after cave bears at all. But the evidence is unmistakable that he did. Many bear skeletons found in caves carry the marks of healed wounds, and a cave in Czechoslovakia

A CAMP OF BONES

MAMMOTH BONES

SWAMP

HUTS AND HEARTHS

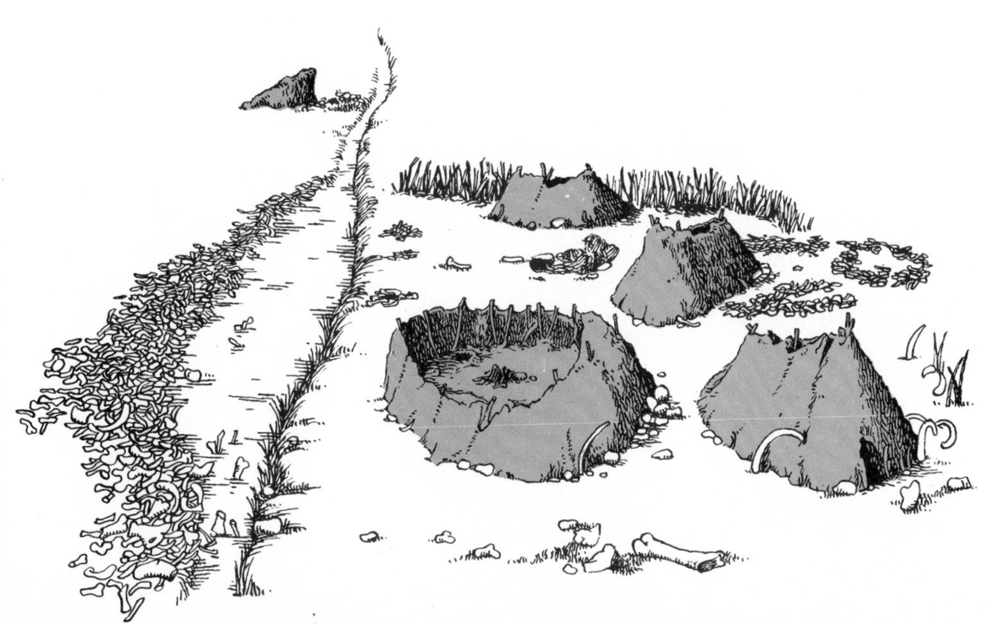

A 23,000-year-old site at Dolni Vestonice, Czechoslovakia, outlined in the top diagram, shows how Upper Paleolithic man placed his huts of bone and hide (color) and cooking hearths near a swamp. On the far edge of this swamp were piled hundreds of thousands of dried mammoth bones (key above). The picture at left reconstructs this settlement to show the different types of dwellings believed to have been built. The huge heap of bones at the left and other scattered bone piles in the camp itself demonstrate the heavy dependence on the mammoth by some East European tribes of this period.

yielded the skeleton of a bear whose skull had been severely damaged by a stone spear tip which broke off in the animal's head. Apparently it survived this wound, for the skull healed up. When the bear grew old and died and its flesh disintegrated, the spear tip fell out and was found thousands of years later lying beside it.

As for the bear cult itself, hints of it appear in another Dragon's Lair, the Drachenloch, in the Swiss Alps. This is a tunnel-like cave running back into the mountain for more than 200 feet. About halfway back is a chamber which was occupied intermittently by men over a considerable span of time. Buried in the floor of this chamber is some most unusual evidence suggesting that man had an interest in bears entirely apart from skinning and eating them. On one side of the cave investigators found what appeared to be a low rough wall made of flattish slabs of rock. Hidden behind this was a large pile of cave-bear bones and skulls. What suggested that they had been put there (aside from the evidence of the wall, which is disputed by some authorities) was that many of the skulls had holes in them. Could these holes have been made by falling rock? Possibly, except that pieces of bone to fit the holes were missing; searchers looked for them assiduously but could not find any. Also, if a dying bear had decided to crawl back there to spend its last moments, it would have left behind all its bones, not just some of them. This pile was peculiar in that it consisted mostly of skulls and leg bones, and the majority of the legs did not even belong with the skulls, but were from other bears entirely.

Further investigation of the cave turned up a group of seven skulls and leg bones stacked in a kind of rock "chest" buried in the floor with a large stone slab on top of it. All of these skulls were arranged so that they faced the mouth of the cave. In another spot a single skull was found with a leg bone stuck through it in a way that could not possibly have occurred in nature.

THE evidence from the Drachenloch is repeated, with minor variations, in literally dozens of other caves containing bear skulls that speak strongly of having been kept and cherished by their owners. Usually they turn up in dark out-of-the-way back corners of the caves. This circumstance, plus the way they are arranged, the peculiar assortments of leg bones that sometimes accompany them, and often the complete absence of other bones, all suggest a special regard, perhaps a ritualistic one, for bears. Maringer points out that a number of existing primitive societies, although not necessarily descended from Paleolithic bear worshipers, still have bear cults. These are concentrated among cold-weather peoples, among Siberian tribes and the Ainus of northern Japan. Many of these peoples keep captive bears (and evidence is growing that Paleolithic man may have done so also). Among the Ainus a captive bear is regarded as a protector of the settlement. When it has fulfilled this function for a season it is then killed in a sacrificial ceremony during the winter, and its spirit passes on to meet the over-all spirit of the forest, carrying to this forest god the wishes of the people for good health and good hunting until the following year.

The more we learn about the myths and rituals of existing primitive societies, and the more evidence we get from Paleolithic living sites, the narrower the gap will become between the Old Stone Age and ourselves. But it will never be entirely closed. The intimate details of social life, the games that children played, the gestures and courtesies that give a society its flavor—all these have vanished like smoke. We have absolutely no knowledge of how one Cro-Magnon man addressed another, or even the words he used. And we never will know.

ONE OF THE WORLD'S FIRST ARTISTS, A HUNTER IS PORTRAYED HERE KNEELING BEFORE THE PRODUCT OF HIS LABOR, A VENUS MADE OF CLAY.

A New Kind of Man

The men who replaced the Neanderthalers in Europe some 35,000 years ago are believed to have migrated from the Middle East. Intellectually and culturally superior to their predecessors, they gradually acquired sufficient leisure to produce the first art—sculptures, paintings and stone engravings so powerfully conceived and executed as to rank among mankind's great artistic achievements.

THE CEREMONIAL BURIAL of a mammoth hunter who lived during one of the earliest cultural phases of the Upper Paleolithic is re-created here by the Czech artist Z. Burian. Members of the dead man's tribe are shown paying their last respects—one places a tusk in the grave, another sprinkles the corpse with red ocher to restore to it the blush of life, while two others

wait to cover it with the shoulder blade of a mammoth. The artist took his inspiration from the discovery in Czechoslovakia in 1891 of the actual grave, 15 feet under the city of Brno.

CRO-MAGNON MAN is correctly shown in this reconstruction by Burian as having been robust and tall, but has been prematurely given a bow and arrow, invented later. He used spears.

Enter Cro-Magnon Man

The people who entered Europe from the Middle East were fully modern men, identical in appearance to today's European. Known to us as the Cro-Magnons *(above)*, they apparently arrived with a culture of their own, which flourished as their way of life gradually improved. Hunter-gatherers, they made themselves better weapons with which to bring down their prey, and better tools with which to cut and stitch skins into rudimentary clothes. Like the Neanderthalers, they still occupied caves and rock shelters, but in larger groups and on a more permanent basis. In addition, they put up tents of sorts at camp sites, and during severe winters, built for themselves partially subterranean dwellings or dome-shaped huts made snug with skins and turf.

THE LASCAUX CAVES, France's fourth most popular tourist attraction until damaging algae forced their closing in 1963, contain animal paintings dating back as much as 25,000 years.

The Magic of Art

With the Europeans of the Upper Paleolithic, art may be said to have begun—reflecting the degree to which their culture had advanced. The paintings and stone engravings they left behind are so meticulously done that only one conclusion is possible: they were the work of experienced artists, men who could take time out from the hunt. Their art seems

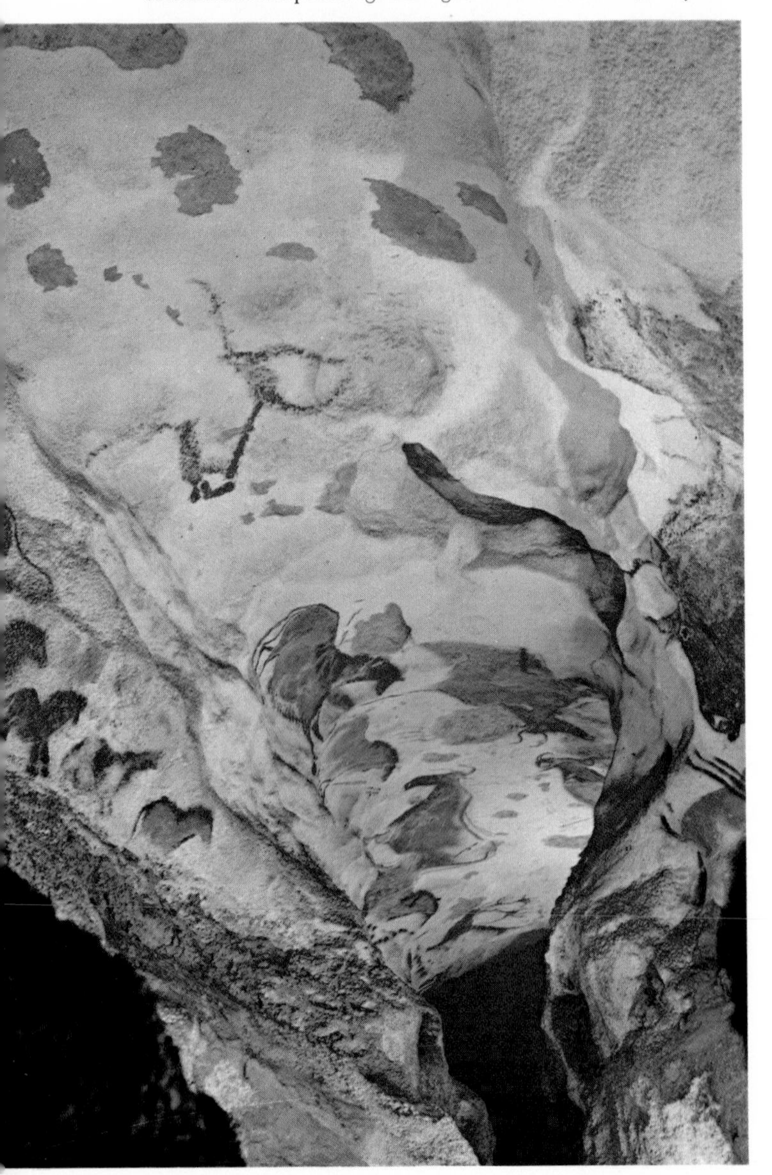

A DECORATED CHAMBER in Lascaux shows the excellent state of preservation of the paintings before algae struck them. Schoolboys discovered the caves in 1940.

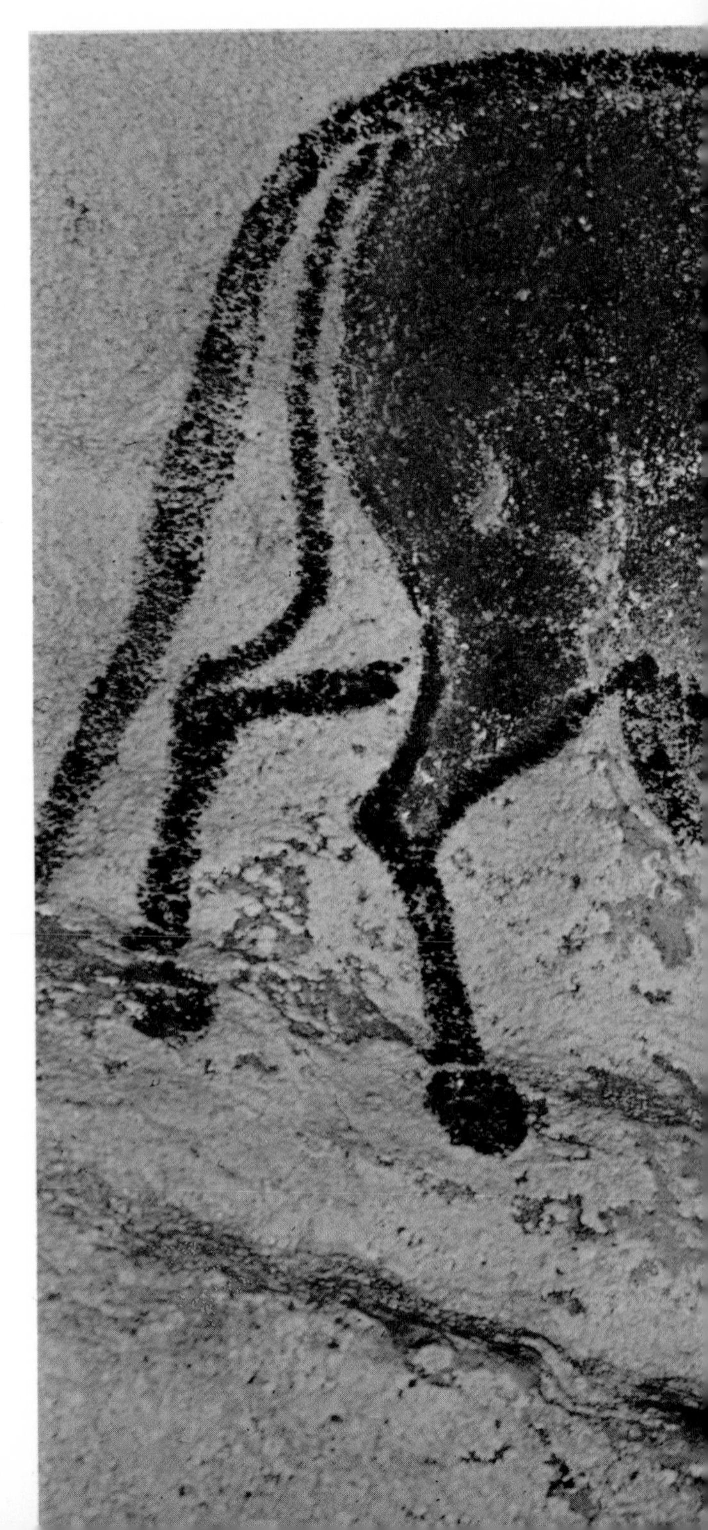

A PREGNANT HORSE gallops across the limestone ceiling of Lascaux. The slash marks above its shoulders may indicate spears drawn in for their magical effect.

to have been magical in intent. Some of the caves in which their work is found, in France and Spain, were undoubtedly sanctuaries, open only to the privileged few who worked there for the benefit of all. Most of the paintings show migratory animals like the horse and reindeer, herd animals like the aurochs and bison, or carnivores like the lion and bear, all of which affected the lives of Paleolithic man in some way, either as sources of food or objects of dread. By reproducing such beasts on the walls and ceilings of caves, these early artists were apparently attempting to gain power over them, striving to ensure the fertility of the animals and to make them vulnerable to the hunters' spears.

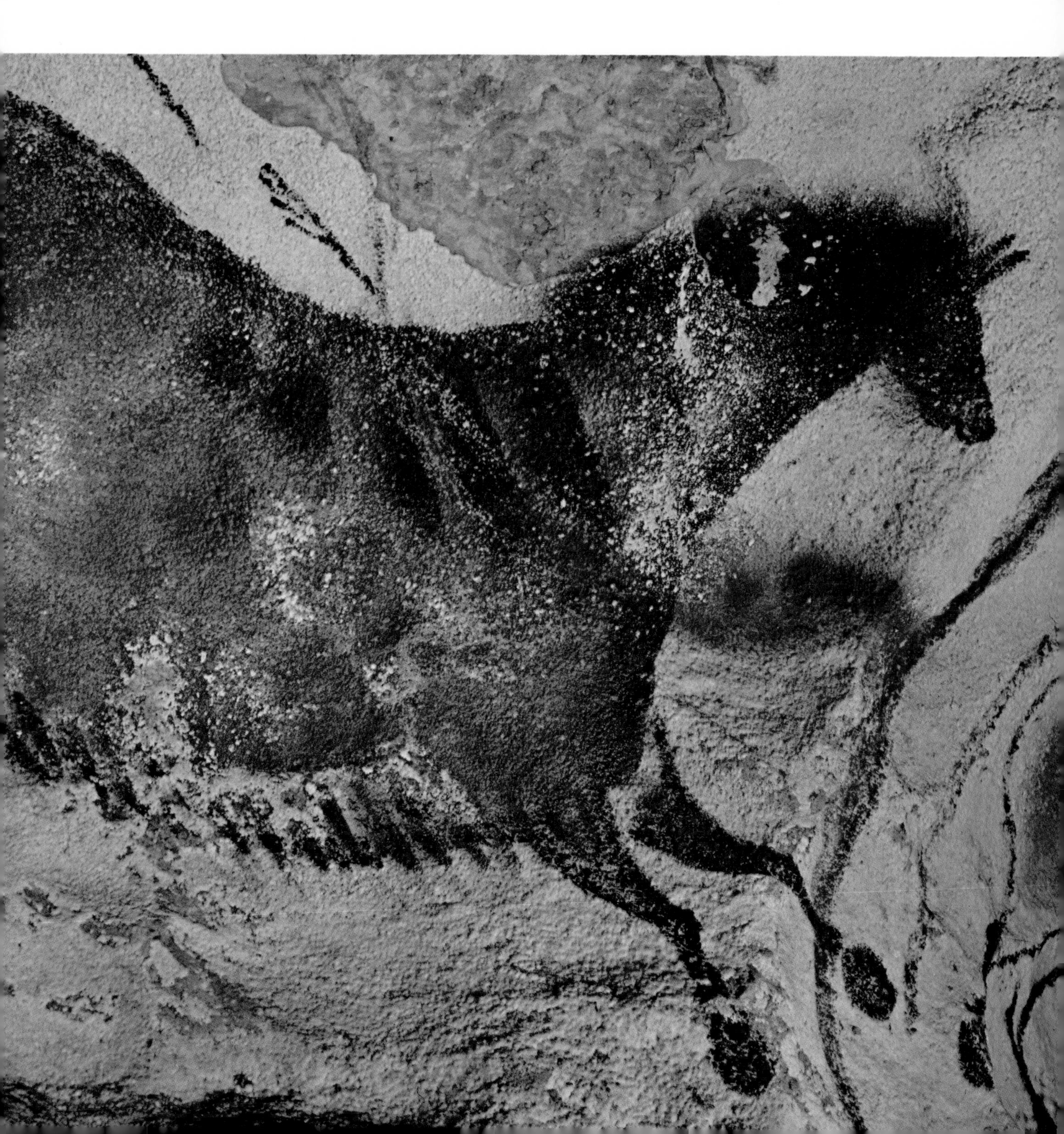

WOOLLY MAMMOTHS cut in stone are two of some 1,000 representations of this animal in the Rouffignac caves of France.

AN ENGRAVED SALMON in France's Gorge d'Enfer is surrounded by drill holes: speculators once tried to remove it.

A PAINTED HIND in Spain's Altamira cave shows how the artist strengthened the illusion of form by careful use of color.

A HUMAN HAND floats over a horse in France's Pech-Merle caves. Such hands are among the earliest forms of cave art.

OUTLINED BISON seem to crowd a section of the Niaux cave of France. Cave artists often superimposed animal paintings.

STRANGE SYMBOLS like these squares recur in caves and may represent traps or nets for prey; the dots may be a calendar.

The Wide Scope of Paleolithic Art

While the content of Upper Paleolithic art remained fairly constant, as the samples shown here demonstrate, techniques varied. Considering how limited the artists' materials were, this is amazing. For paints, they had only such natural substances as ocher; for brushes, they used chewed branches or pads of feathers and fur. Paintings were done in several ways—some simply by outlining an animal in black, others by first filling in the outlines and then scraping or washing away excess colors to obtain the proper shading and desired blend. Engravings were made with a sharp-edged stone tool, the burin. With this artists accomplished not only deep-cut, at times almost sculptural, renderings of animals but also the most delicate scratchings, such as those which decorate the small objects shown below.

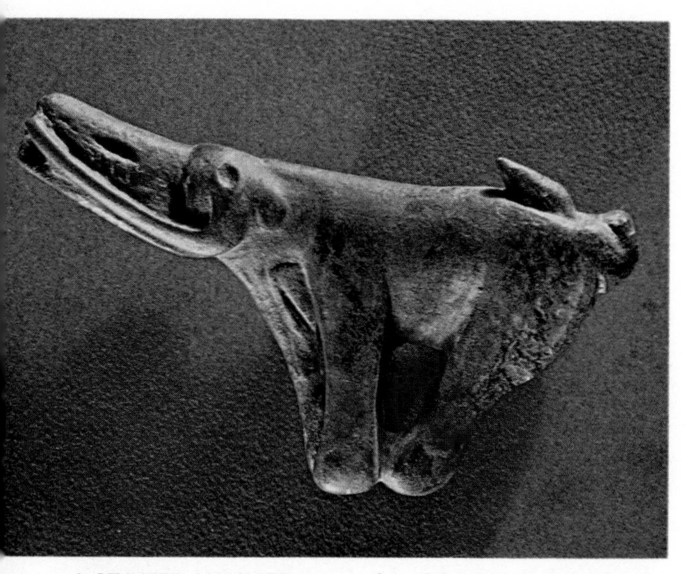

A STYLIZED MAMMOTH, carved in Magdalenian times, departs from the earlier, more realistic approach of cave painting.

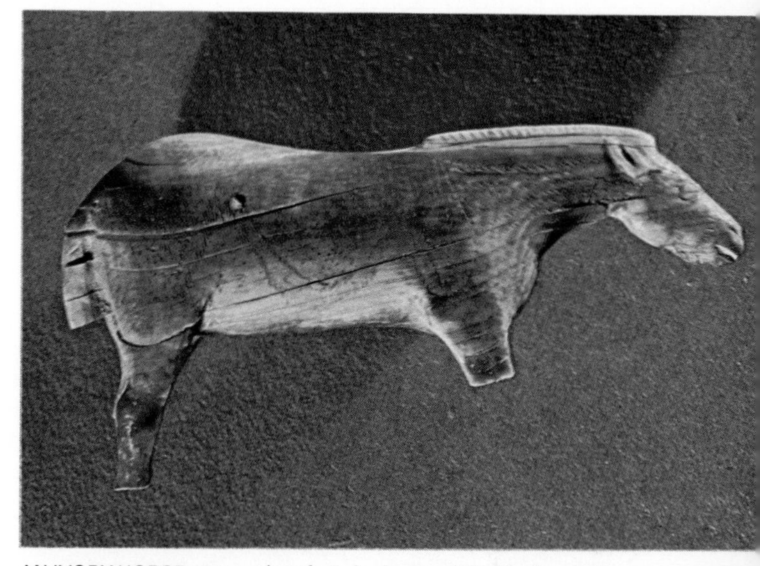

AN IVORY HORSE, measuring three inches and dating from the Magdalenian period, has little scratch marks to indicate hair.

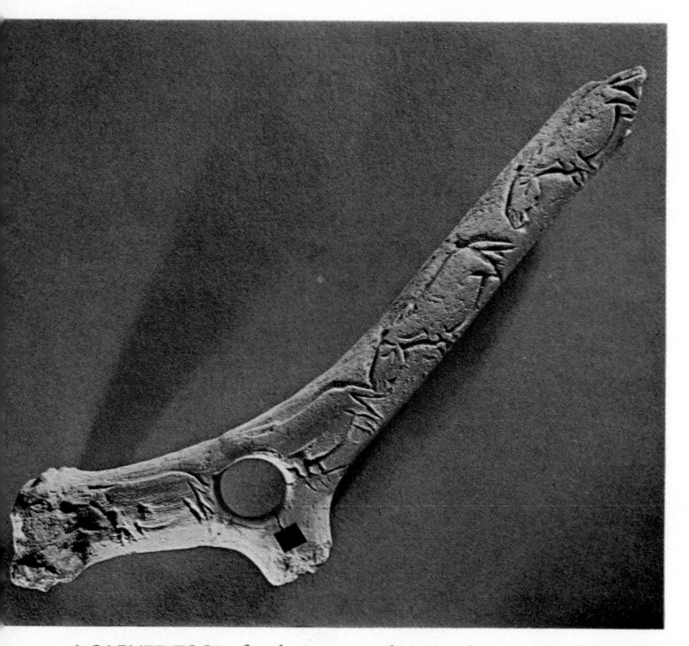

A CARVED TOOL of unknown use bears a horse motif. Similar tools are utilized by Portuguese fishermen today to make rope.

DELICATELY INCISED FIGURES of reindeer and salmon cover a broken antler that may have served as a priestly baton.

In Praise of Women

All but absent from the art he created is Paleolithic man himself. He rarely crops up in the cave paintings, and when he does, he is usually portrayed as a stick figure or disguised as an animal, perhaps because pictures were regarded as potent magic, and leaving them exposed on walls might be dangerous to the men thus represented. But of Paleolithic women there are several bold examples, like the early carvings and statues shown here. Small enough to have been carried around by different tribes, these seem to have been objects of veneration and, as their curved lines and voluptuous contours suggest, may have been used in fertility rites.

THE LADY
OF BRASSEMPOUY,
FRENCH, IVORY

HE VENUS OF LAUSSEL,
RENCH, STONE

THE VENUS
OF WILLENDORF,
AUSTRIAN, STONE

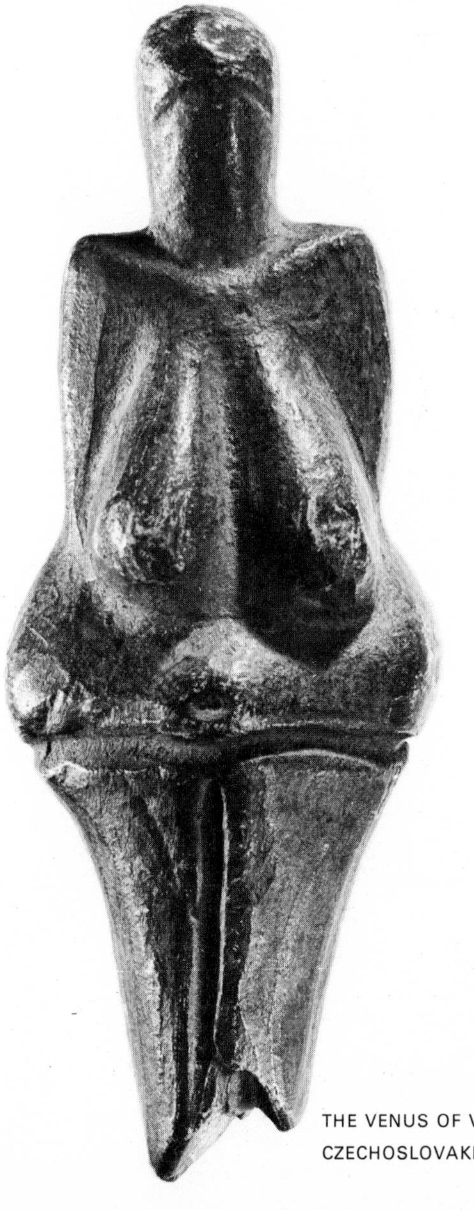

THE VENUS OF VESTONICE,
CZECHOSLOVAKIAN, CLAY

THE VENUS OF ABRI PATAUD, the armless body of a woman incised in a small piece of rock, is one of the few art objects found at the excavation. It was made some 20,000 years ago.

Uncovering a Way of Life

The Venus shown here comes from the Abri Pataud *(above, right)*. This rock shelter in the cave region of France, where excavations were completed in September 1964, promises to reveal more about the daily life of the Cro-Magnons who dwelled in its shadow than has any other Upper Paleolithic site in western Europe. Part of the reason for this is the scientific exactness with which Hallam L. Movius Jr. *(right)*, Professor of Anthropology at Harvard, conducted the excavations. No item having a human connection was too insignificant to plot in

BLACK WITH CARBON, hearths yield clues to the past. The small ones at bottom, in which bones were burned, are the earliest; those in the middle contain cooking stones, a sign of advancing technology. The late hearth at top is much bigger, suggesting larger social units.

UNDULATING LIMESTONE CLIFFS loom over the excavation at the Abri Pataud in Les Eyzies, France. In addition to the anthropologists and archeologists who worked here, there were paleontologists to identify the bones, geologists to study the rocks and paleobotanists to determine from fossil pollen what plants grew in the vicinity thousands of years ago.

position, photograph *(left)*, catalogue and preserve for future study. During six seasons of work, more than 50,000 flint tools of all sizes and use were taken from 14 levels of occupation, and more than 25 large wooden crates were filled with animal bones, bone fragments and teeth. It may be a dozen years before all this evidence is pieced together, but once it is we will have a chronicle of Cro-Magnon people, showing how they responded to the changing conditions of the Upper Paleolithic—and what kinds of cultural and technological advances they made.

HOLDING A SKULL IN HIS PALM moments after disengaging it from the soil, Movius picks at it with his penknife. In an extremely good state of preservation, the skull belonged to a teen-age girl who lived at the Abri Pataud some 18,000 years before the birth of Christ.

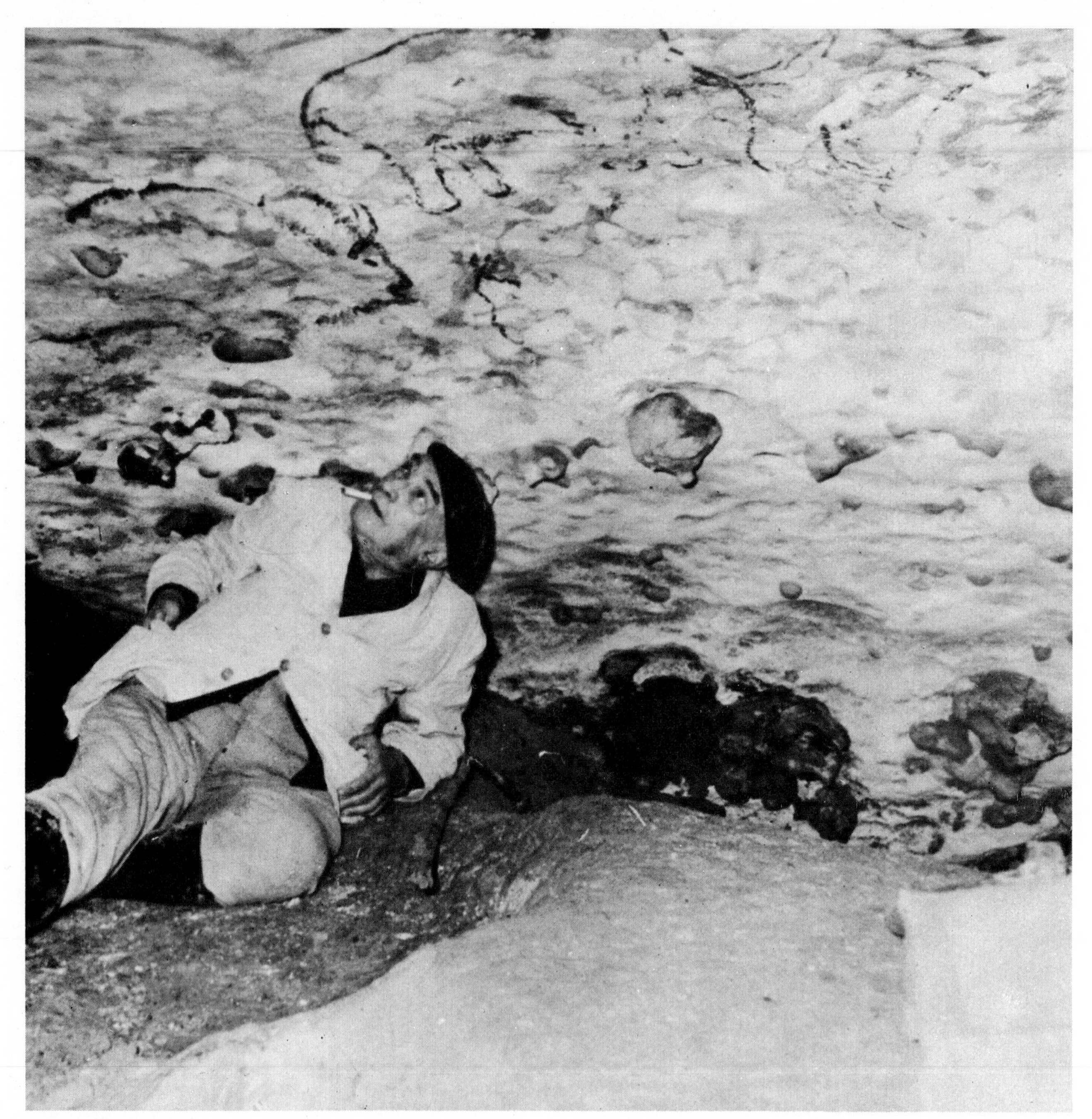

EDGING INTO A CREVICE, the Abbé Breuil examines a rhinoceros frieze discovered with other paintings in 1956 in the Rouffignac caves. Although the Abbé declared the art authentic, controversy still rages as to whether it may be fake. Some critics insist that the paintings were not there before 1948 and that they were added, a few at a time, until their "discovery."

Defender of the Faith in Early Man

Much of what is known today about cave art can be traced to the work of one man, the Abbé Henri Breuil, a French priest who devoted his life to its study until his death in 1961 at 84. He spent long hours in the cold, clammy atmosphere of underground passages, often on his back, examining and copying animals that predated Christ by thousands of years. The Abbé was among the first to maintain that the paintings were Paleolithic and spent years winning over skeptics. As late as 1956, he had to uphold fresh finds in the Rouffignac caves *(above)*, this time before the French Institute *(opposite)*.

THE ABBÉ IS CONGRATULATED AT THE FRENCH INSTITUTE AFTER AUTHENTICATING THE ROUFFIGNAC ART

HUNTER-GATHERERS STILL, Bushmen like the ones shown here with anthropologist Richard Lee are a successful people who cling to this ancient way of life for a simple reason—it suits the harsh conditions of Africa's arid Kalahari Desert.

8 The Persistent Savage

THE previous chapter brought the chronicle of early man to the point of ancestors anyone might be willing to acknowledge: Cro-Magnon peoples. Between them and contemporary peoples there still lie some 10,000 years—but we are going to jump that entire span and in this final chapter discuss what early men can teach us about our own 20th Century lives. This may seem like a startling thought—that *Australopithecus*, *Homo erectus*, *Neanderthal* and all the others have anything to say to us today—but that is precisely the point of the new paleoanthropology, which seeks not simply museum collections of old bones and imaginative reconstructions for children to gawk at, but quite specific relationships between present-day men and their ancestors.

One of the hardest things for a man to do is to think dispassionately about his own ancestry. He may want to be open-minded, but his ideas about how a human being should look and act are so strongly affected by the way he himself looks that he will automatically regard anything different from himself as less than human. That, in a nutshell, explains a good deal about our prevailing attitudes toward Neanderthalers. A receding forehead and chin, a squat shambling bent-kneed figure—dirty, hairy and possibly naked—all these things remind us of something that still embarrasses enormous numbers of people: that they are descended from apes. And apes being humiliatingly stupid, it follows that Neanderthalers must have been pretty stupid too.

Although it cannot be proved, this is almost certainly a fallacy. If Neanderthal man was stupid, so are we. Our society, from the point of view of a coldly rational intellect observing us from outer space, is unforgivably stupid in its aggressiveness, its prejudices, its superstitions and in its misuse of the powers and opportunities that our technology has given us. To repeat: Neanderthal man seems backward because he looks primitive. Let us now add that he also seems primitive because of the meagerness and simplicity of his culture compared to our own. Put the two together and we get a completely distorted idea of the capacities of a man who was probably scarcely inferior to ourselves.

There is a second fallacy that is almost the reverse of the first. Stumbling shamefacedly up from our confrontation with Neanderthal man, we are so grateful to encounter somebody like Cro-Magnon man—somebody who looks like us—that we tend to endow him with more than his share of virtues. This may explain why so many of the paintings and drawings that attempt to re-create the daily life of Cro-Magnon man manage to misrepresent him so. He is all too often depicted as a kindly philosophical fellow with pure motives and noble thoughts, who spent a good deal of his time gently instructing bright-eyed boys in the arts of toolmaking and cave painting.

This, too, is almost certainly a fallacy. We know absolutely nothing about Cro-Magnon man that would indicate that he was either pure or noble. On the contrary, he was undoubtedly as cruel, as untrustworthy, as emotionally unstable and superstition-ridden as any of the most backward peoples living today—and perhaps a good many of the so-called enlightened ones.

WHY bring this up? There is a very good reason, and it has to do with the purpose of anthropology. We study ancient man not simply out of curiosity to find out where we came from, but to learn about ourselves. There is a great deal about modern man, about the structure of his society, about his deepest beliefs, about his sudden and lamentable lapses into savagery, about his secret psychic life that is not well understood. We will learn more about these matters if we understand their origins better. To do that, it is necessary to become more familiar with our ancestors, and for that we must understand that the gap that separates us from them is small as far as innate capacity is concerned, but large as far as culture is concerned. There is little reason to suspect that peoples living ten or twenty thousand years ago would have done any worse with the tools that we have at our disposal than we are doing today. There is equally little reason to think that if we were put back there—with no metals, no agriculture, no domestic animals, no written language, and, most important, no idea that any of these things were possible—we would do any better than they did. That is what we critics of prehistoric peoples are constantly forgetting: they did not have those four principal assets on which modern society is based. To their credit, they invented them; we did not.

Thus a more charitable view of ancient man's capacities is necessary if we are to understand ourselves. Once we get the idea that when we study him we are actually studying culturally simplified versions of ourselves, then the strong current emphasis of modern paleoanthropology on total site development begins to make real sense. Scientists of many disciplines are desperate to learn more about how early man lived. We infer a great deal, but hard knowledge is terribly limited. We know, for example, that Cro-Magnon hunters made eyed needles, and we can safely infer from this that they wore stitched clothing made from animal skins and sewed together with sinew. But we have absolutely no idea whether the clothing was made by men or by women, and we don't know what it looked like. Was it trousers, saronglike wraps or heavy coatlike garments? And was it worn only by hunters or did women and children dress too? Did men and women dress differently? They do today, but when did they start and why did the differences appear?

The type of clothing worn, although interesting, would be less important to know than who made it. Do the bone needles and other delicate tools reflect a woman's tool kit, or were there male artisans who specialized in tailoring? In short, was there a division of labor? These behavioral aspects of early life could shed light on patterns which show up in human societies later on: sexual division of labor, a male work force segregated into specialties, menial versus dignified occupations and many other such matters.

It is these patterns of behavior that the paleoanthropologist is interested in reconstructing. The examples cited above are not nearly as basic as other earlier patterns which we must learn to understand. Take the idea of food-sharing. Man is the only primate who makes a practice of sharing his food with his fellows. How, where and why did he get this idea? Cro-Magnon man obviously did, so did Neanderthal man, and so, apparently, did *Homo erectus*. All of them had home bases of varying degrees of permanence to which the hunters brought back food. So, perhaps, did *Australopithecus*, for animal fossils are also found in his sites. In short, we see the practice already developed. It is obviously one of critical importance to human evolution since close family ties, child care and teaching are all fundamental requirements of human society. But when did it start? We do not know.

Nor do we know where the idea of permanent mates arose. Study of primates in the wild, another of the modern side-disciplines of anthropology which is increasingly being used to help interpret the past, reveals that none of them, not even the higher apes, have long-term male-female relationships. Mating partners are taken only for short periods of time. And yet contemporary peoples marry and form lifelong pairs, and they presumably have done so for many thousands of years. But we cannot be sure of this. We are in complete ignorance of the marital customs of Cro-Magnon man, let alone those of all his predecessors. All we know is that modern man is sexually possessive. This trait is deep-seated, and although the ethical and religious teachings of most (but not all) societies encourage it, it is still too much a part of our makeup to be explained as having been inculcated in man by historically recent concepts of morality. It obviously goes a long way back.

What the most primitive modern societies do have in common with each other and with paleolithic societies is that they are all based on hunting and gathering as a way of life, and not on agriculture. That kind of an existence imposes strict limitations on the size of social units since large numbers of men cannot practice it in a small area and survive. Bands of aborigines seldom exceed 50 individuals and are often limited to the members of a single family group. That is not to say that they do not know and mingle occasionally with other tiny groups like their own. This they do, sometimes walking for many miles to attend large song-and-dance festivals. Their society is loosely organized into larger groups according to complex blood relationships. And these larger groupings have clearly defined territories within which each small family band operates, although tending to stay within a smaller territory of its own. But the basic unit is the family and it is monogamous. In a hunter-gatherer society a man cannot support more than one wife.

It is impossible not to speculate that prehistoric hunting societies also lived in small groups and that they, too, were basically monogamous. It may be that monogamy had its start in the gradual development of a home, which, in turn, may have had its origin in hunting. As long as the emphasis was on gathering, a band of hominids probably acted much like a band of apes, moving slowly about, eating what it could find in the way of vegetables, berries, fruits and nuts, along with occasional young and injured small animals. There was probably a minimum of food-sharing, since all members of the band could be presumed to be equally adept at food-gathering from the time they were weaned. However, as a shift of emphasis from gathering to hunting took place, getting food became more and more the responsibility of the males. It became more and more unsuitable for females and young to tag along and expose themselves to the dangers of the hunt, and also probably impossible for them to keep up if the hunt was a long and arduous one. For females and infants, then, hunting undoubtedly came to mean waiting at some safe spot for the hunters to return with food. From this we may speculate that hunting, food-sharing, homemaking and monogamy all grew up more or less together.

To make any of these inferences we have had to go largely by what we know of modern man rather than by what we have been able to dig out of the past. This hammers home a belief held by David Hamburg, Professor of Psychiatry at the Stanford University Medical Center in California, who maintains that one of the best relics we have of early man is modern man. It is no accident that this statement should come from a psychiatrist. It illustrates once again the eclecticism of modern anthropology, for it pulls together the fossil expert and the psychologist, each leaning to the other to help bridge the gap that lies between them. Psychologists and physiologists are currently hard at work trying to learn more about the problems of stress and aggression in modern life and how these forces affect the physical and emotional health of people today. In their search for causes they quickly find themselves talking to paleoanthropologists, sharing ideas and data in an effort to lay bare the origins of emotional patterns that are assumed to have arisen in man thousands of years ago.

It has long been suspected that emotional states are associated with bodily changes, but the exact nature of some of these—how and why they take place and what use they are to man—has not been clearly documented until this century. In the 1920s a physiologist, Walter Cannon, made a classic study of a set of physiological changes that took place in cats and dogs during periods of excitement. He worked with the hormone adrenalin and its effects on the nervous system and discovered that it acted like a shot in the arm at times of stress, calling forth carbohydrates from storage in the liver and pouring them into the bloodstream in the form of sugar for quick conversion to energy. He also found that adrenalin increased the flow of blood to the heart, lungs, central nervous system and limbs, while decreasing the flow to the abdominal organs. These changes, as Cannon showed, help to mobilize the muscular and nervous reserves of the individual; they enable him to withstand fatigue, move more speedily and have greater endurance.

Obviously adrenalin has great survival value for the individual in a "fight-or-flight" situation. But how does it get into the system? Cannon was able to answer this question by demonstrating that it is released during periods of intense emotion, whether or not they are followed by activity. All man has to do is feel a rush of fright or anger and his system's emergency reaction will prepare him for what he has to do next. Fear does not always paralyze him; on the contrary, it keys him up and improves his chances of reacting in a crisis, such as avoiding the charge of a wounded animal.

THIS all checks out very well with observations made of hunter-gatherers today. Harvard University's Irven DeVore, co-author of the previous book in this series, and his associate, Richard Lee, have recently completed a field study of Bushmen in Bechuanaland in Africa. Their findings make it clear that Bushmen in their daily lives are steadily confronted by situations that are greatly eased by adrenalin. The anticipation of the chase, the excitement of seeing and stalking an animal, trigger off the hormonal response that will be needed to attack and kill it in a sudden burst of exertion.

The interesting thing about Bushman activities is that these bursts of exertion are only part of their hunting activity. They often follow an animal's spoor for many weary miles before coming upon it. Then, tired as they may be, they must still summon the energy to sprint forward in the hope of planting a poisoned arrow before the animal runs out of range. If it is a large one, the poison will take effect slowly and it may become necessary for the Bushmen to follow it doggedly for many miles, and sometimes for several days, before they are able to close in and kill it. During this protracted chase they may eat only a handful of food from time to time to sustain them as they run. Nevertheless, they have had the all-important stimulus, and with the flow of adrenalin that has resulted, they are able to call on their body resources to help them in this prolonged effort. Other materials such as cholesterol and fatty acids also build up in the bloodstream, to be worked off again during the long tracking that is part and parcel of a hunter-gatherer's life.

This discussion of adrenalin may appear to have taken us rather far from the behavior of ancient and modern man, but that nasty word, cholesterol, brings us right back—and back to David Hamburg, whose recent studies at Stanford have been in the new field of what might be called stress biology, the study of the effects of reactions to stress situations on the human body. The relevance of all this to the main theme of this chapter is that modern man, although he no longer lives a hunting life, is still physically a hunter-gatherer. He is still an efficient machine for facing daily perils, surviving long periods of deprivation while tracking prey, and possessing built-in energy reserves for sudden and unforeseen action. His glands react accordingly, as they have been reacting for hundreds of thousands of years. Unfortunately he does not have the chance to burn off the materials that once aided him; instead he lives in a sedentary environment in which the stresses come one after another, their side effects building up in his system and doing him all kinds of harm. Many modern physiologists have addressed themselves to this problem. They notice that we are biologically equipped for one kind of life but live another, and then go on to ask the question: "Is there any connection between the primitive hunter-gatherer's emotional reaction, like aggression, and the killing ailments of modern society, like heart disease?"

Logically, there could be a connection. For example, modern medicine is extremely suspicious of the role cholesterol may play in coronary heart disease. If strong emotions mobilize cholesterol in a man, if his way of life no longer provides him with an opportunity of disposing of it, and if its build-up is bad for him, then the point is clear: modern man is not equipped for modern life but is still back in the Stone Age emotionally—and the strain is killing him.

Consider the plight of the businessman on his way from his home to an important conference. Success or failure for him may ride on how well he aggressively takes charge of the meeting, beats down the arguments of others, rallies support to his own point of view. Although no physical energy will be expended, this promises to be a real battle nonetheless, and in preparation for it his system has been churning out hormones ever since breakfast. Thoroughly aroused by a challenging situation, and repeatedly re-aroused as further crises in the meeting itself trigger off still higher levels of cholesterol and fatty acids in his blood, he leaves the meeting at the end of the morning and sits down to a heavy lunch preceded by a couple of cocktails. Then the meetings continue in the afternoon. If they go badly for him, the tension remains and may so remain through the evening and far into the night.

His glandular system cannot be blamed. It has responded loyally and with great efficiency to the demands made on it, but if he is not able to behave appropriately himself and engage in the kind of vigorous physical activity needed to burn up the accumulations in his bloodstream, then our businessman is in serious trouble. His safety valve is gone. He cannot change the activities of his glands or his nervous system since a stressful situation will make him feel angry whether he shows it or not. The only other alternative is to change his way of life. Odd as it may seem, there may be real practical value in learning as much as we can about the ways of hunter-gatherers, if only to find out what our systems were actually designed for, so that we may perhaps behave more like these primitive forebears and lead healthier lives.

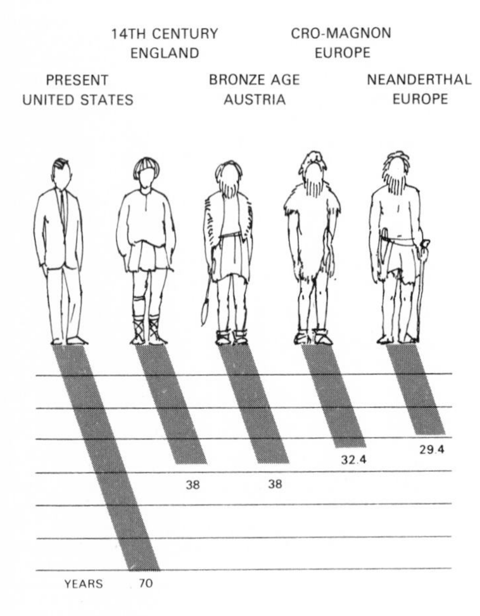

MAN'S LENGTHENING LIFE

As this chart shows, the life expectancy of human beings has more than doubled in the 100,000-odd years since Neanderthal man. Most of this increase has taken place within the last 500 years—since 1900, 10 years have been added—due to better medicine, sanitation and a less rigorous physical existence. No one knows the potential for a long life. But men continue to live longer and modern biology is faced with a whole new set of problems—the health of the aged.

THE solution cannot be as simple as taking a walk after a tension-building situation, but that might help. Many heart specialists have advocated walking and cycling as man's most beneficial exercise, arriving at that conclusion through observations of many patients. The paleoanthropologist might have come to the same conclusion, but from an entirely different direction. He would have noted that man is a creature whose evolutionary history has been one of adaptation to efficient upright striding and that his way of life as a hunter-gatherer required a great deal of steady walking. To ignore this way of life, he would conclude, may well be dangerous—just as dangerous as keeping a hunting dog cooped up in a city apartment or trying to adapt a lowland marsh plant to life on a mountaintop. Neither dog nor flower would do very well in its alien environment. The surprising thing about man is that he does as well as he does.

This is not to say that man is not changing in response to his new environment; the principles of natural selection are certainly still working for him as they always have. Therefore, if our environment were to stay as it is for a long enough time, we could assume with every confidence that the aggressive tendencies that we have inherited from our ancestors would ultimately prove so inappropriate and so damaging to us that they would eliminate themselves by killing off, through heart attacks and other ailments, those of us who still carried those primitive traits. Certainly the modern world would be a nicer and much safer place to live in if its human inhabitants were gentler and more patient than they are. We might even make a long guess that the present very high death rate among American men from coronary heart disease may be natural selection working on a segment of the population that is well adapted to short-term success but poorly adapted to survival in our society. Given time, survival should win out over success.

The problem is that there is not enough time; the modern world does not stand still. What characterizes human culture is the increasingly rapid rate of its development. It leaves biological man absolutely flat-footed, tied to the ponderous machinery of selection, which, as we have seen, requires periods of time on the order of hundreds of thousands of years before it can produce significant differences in the human species. As René Dubos of the Rockefeller Institute has said: "Even when man has become an urbane city dweller, the paleolithic bull which survives in his inner self still paws the earth whenever a threatening gesture is made on the social scene." Given emotionally archaic men like that and the fearsome power that modern technology has put in their hands, the situation may well become self-correcting, with archaic emotions winning out over culture by blowing culture up. Then, should we find ourselves scampering about after our food once again, at least we can console ourselves that we will be doing what our bodies were designed for. We are not doing it now.

All of this may convey the impression that there is something damaging about culture—if all it can do is produce more heart attacks and worse wars. Nothing could be further from the truth. Success, as has already been explained, is not measured by the fates of individual members of a species but by the species as a whole. And as a species man has been overwhelmingly successful. His sheer numbers prove it. Edward S. Deevey of Yale University has estimated that the hominid population of the earth two million years ago was not much over 100,000 individuals, presumably all of them australopithecines living in Africa. Three hundred thousand years ago, toward the end of *Homo erectus*' known tenancy, the human population had climbed probably to a million, and 25,000 years ago, during the time of the Cro-Magnon peoples, it had jumped to more than three million. Its rise has been at an increasingly steep pace since then. Something of the extraordinarily rapid mushrooming of today's peoples is brought home by Deevey when he points out that about three per cent of all the human beings who have ever lived are alive right now.

People are also living longer. Neanderthal man had a life expectancy of about 29 years; today's American has a life expectancy of about 70 years.

The increase in population, according to Deevey, has not gone in a steady curve. Rather, it has had a series of surges, reflecting the great cultural innovations associated with the evolution of man. The first, of course, was the development of stone tools. This allowed for population increase in two different ways: it enabled hominids to venture out into the world, ultimately to the point of inhabiting a number of different kinds of environments that toolless populations could not have survived in; it also made populations more efficient, enabling them to exploit various environments more intensively. In the days of the crude chopping-tool industry of the Oldowan, the population density of Africa has been estimated to have been only one per hundred square miles. By the end of the Paleolithic, men had spread throughout Europe and Asia as

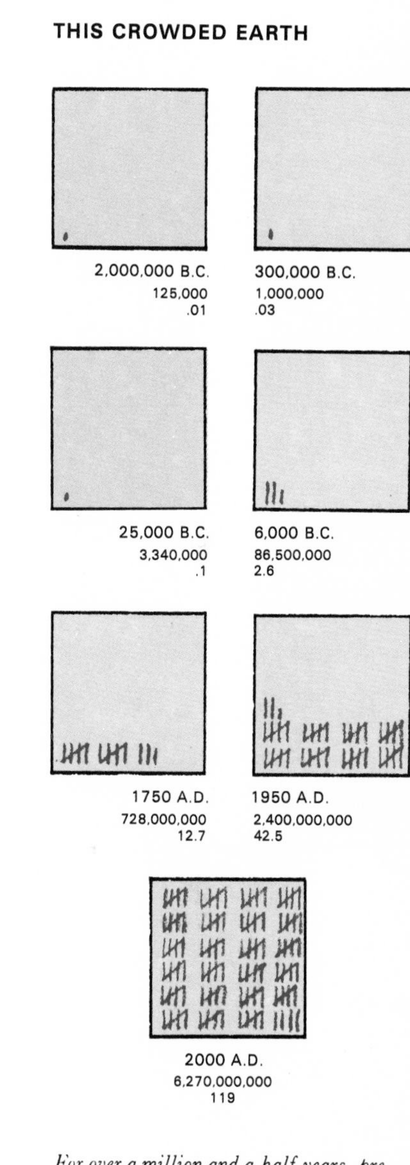

For over a million and a half years, prehumans were among the least numerous of the earth's creatures. Then, with Homo erectus (second box) human numbers began to swell. In the time of the Cro-Magnons (third box), parts of nearly all of the earth's habitable space had been occupied, and the modern problem of overcrowding began. The figures above illustrate the progression of that story; boxes represent one square mile of habitable land; a tally mark stands for one individual. Numbers below boxes give date, total population and individuals per square mile. The last square shows a projected figure of almost 120 people per square mile—more than twice today's figure—in the year 2000.

well as Africa, and their density had risen tenfold, to one per ten square miles.

The second innovation was the double discovery of how to grow crops and how to domesticate animals. This came about 10,000 years ago. It enabled people to settle down permanently for the first time, and for the first time to live together in large numbers. Even nomadic herdsmen could exist in far greater concentrations on a given area of land than hunters could. The effect on world population was staggering. In 4,000 years it jumped from an estimated five million to 86 million.

The third innovation was the industrial age. It had its beginnings about 300 years ago when the population was in the neighborhood of 550 million. It has been ballooning ever since and today is nudging three billion. It is expected to double within 50 years.

While these figures are profoundly impressive, they are not as impressive as the general speed-up that has been taking place. It took a million years to get through the first phase mentioned above. The second took only 10,000 years, and the third has been going on for only a few hundred. How long it will continue or what the human population of the earth will ultimately be is anybody's guess. But, since the surface of the earth is finite, as are its resources, present rates of increase should bring us to the bearable limit pretty quickly.

How man will handle this critical problem is also impossible to predict. The present—and projected—enormous numbers of peoples, together with the poverty and political instability that accompany them in many parts of the world, are of great concern to economists and sociologists everywhere. It is all very well to talk about the success of the species as a whole, but if this can be accomplished only at the expense of uncontrolled crowding and almost worldwide misery, then there is something wrong. Man is not just another species of animal. He is the first in the history of the world who at last understands something of his place in it and the laws that govern his own activities here. This makes him unique in having within his grasp the possibility of doing something sensible about the dreadful dilemma of his numbers. But the mere fact that he has access to this kind of knowledge is no guarantee that he will use it. The evidence is all around us; it screams from the front pages of our newspapers every day that the human condition—emotionally—is still one of discouraging savagery. It is not enough that we damage ourselves individually with unwanted and uncontrollable jolts of things like cholesterol; we are doing even worse things to each other on a world scale by our inability to control our actions.

For all the surface glitter of his culture, the one thing of value that modern man has achieved is a rather impressive amount of knowledge and understanding of himself and the world. Much of this knowledge is not yet available to large numbers of men; sadly, it is rejected by many others. Nevertheless it is there. The principles of evolution enunciated in this book are true, and their truth can be demonstrated to any open-minded person. We ignore them at our peril. They have a vital bearing on man's understanding of himself and thus they affect the future of us all, since it is surely only a matter of time before we will have it in our power to direct the course of our own evolution. Here—and not in moon shots—lies man's greatest challenge. For the first time in the two-billion-year history of life will come an opportunity to attempt to combine the good of the species with the good of the individual, a dilemma that has not been resolved very well in the past and is certainly not being resolved very well by the human species today.

DRINKING LUXURIOUSLY, a Bushman boy is watched by his sister as he lets water from a "sponge" made of dried grass and bark trickle down his chest. His source is a pool in the crotch of the tree, filled during the brief summer rain.

The Timeless People

Wherever hunter-gatherers may live in the world today, they have certain basic social and economic patterns in common. To anthropologists this is significant, for what is true of such people today was probably true of their—and our—remote ancestors. As one of the most numerous of these peoples, the Bushmen of Africa's Kalahari Desert are a particularly fascinating subject. Physically distinct from their Negro neighbors, they may even be descendants of the continent's original inhabitants.

HOLDING UP A PLANT, Irven DeVore, a lecturer on anthropology at Harvard, asks Bushmen, through an interpreter, to tell him when it grows, where it is found and what its uses are.

RECONSTRUCTING MEALS, Richard Lee, who carried out this study of Bushmen, has bones identified at an abandoned camp. In his pocket is a basic tool of the anthropologist—a notebook.

ON THE TRAIL, Lee carries his own equipment as he sets out with a family to a seasonal camp. Lee spent 15 months among these people and eventually learned their click-filled language.

PLOTTING A VILLAGE SITE, photographer Stanley Washburn uses a plane table on which all dwellings and their human appurtenances will be marked with the precision of a surveyor.

Mirror to the Past

The anthropologists shown at work here in the northern Kalahari belong to a new breed of scientist out after a new kind of information. Not content merely to interview their subjects, they followed them on trips, went over old camp sites with them, collected and preserved samples of their plant foods for study, and recorded all their various activities in photographs—the basis of this picture essay. Even more important, they plotted every square foot of several villages and camps, fixing the position of every hut, hearth and rubbish heap. They counted the number of adults and children per hut and hearth, noted the daily intake of vegetables and meat and even measured garbage piles after varying lengths of time and diets. In a sense, what these scientists were doing was living archeology—looking at a Bushman village as though it were a site that had just been excavated. Now back in the United States they are hoping that their data will add a new perspective and richer details to the story being unfolded by archeologists on the trail of early man.

Water: The Basis of Life

The Bushmen chosen by the anthropologists for their study live in one of the more hospitable sections of the Kalahari Desert. Even so, they can ill afford to roam more than some 15 miles from their single permanent source of water. For most of the year there is little or no rain, and all possible sources of moisture must be exploited, even to the water-storage organs of drought-resistant plants *(right)*. When the rain does come, it is confined almost entirely to a short season in the summer, during which storms may dump as much as 13 inches on the sands. The greater part of this fall immediately soaks into the ground and is lost, but where there are underlying strata of limestone, some may seep into pools formed by narrow clefts in the rock.

WRINGING OUT THE PULP of a desert plant that stores moisture in its root, a Bushman fills a can with drinkable liquid—a last resort when water runs short in the long dry season.

HANDING UP PAILS, women take a day's supply of water from the village's only permanent reservoir. The tiny pool lies some 15 feet below the surface, which safeguards it from animals.

STOOPING AT A PUDDLE, a far-ranging hunter luxuriates in the brief abundance of the rainy season, when water may be caught and held for a while by the subsurface limestone.

AT A TEMPORARY CAMP MANY MILES FROM THEIR WATER HOLE, WOMEN ROAST MUNGONGO NUTS FOR CONSUMPTION. THE GRASS HUTS PROTE

The Quest for Daily Bread

Although called hunter-gatherers, the Bushmen might better be called gatherer-hunters, since plant foods, rather than meat, constitute the basis of their diet. The area in which these photographs were made supports a surprisingly varied flora despite the low rainfall. The desert here is ribbed by fixed sand dunes, 50 or more feet high, on the crests of which grow the mungongo tree *(above)*, whose oil-and-protein-rich nut is a staple of the Bushman diet. When the villagers have exhausted the supply of nuts on the dunes nearest to their well, they must make longer and longer forays into the surrounding

THE TWO FAMILIES STAYING HERE FROM THE SUN AND SEASONAL RAINS.

countryside to fill their larders. With the coming of the rains they can afford to move to the outlying dunes, some 12 to 15 miles away, where they take advantage of seasonal water supplies and set up temporary camps. While the women gather nuts, the men hunt in the depressions between the dunes.

CRACKING A MUNGONGO NUT with a stone, a woman dexterously exposes the kernel inside. She has already removed the sweet outer husks which, when boiled, will serve as a gruel.

In Sign Language—
A Running Commentary on the Hunt

THE BIRDS

SECRETARY BIRD

THE SMALLER ANIMALS

SCRUB HARE

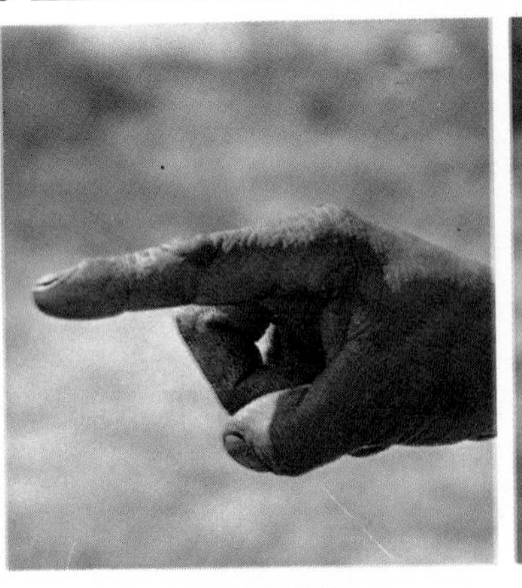

SPRINGHAAS

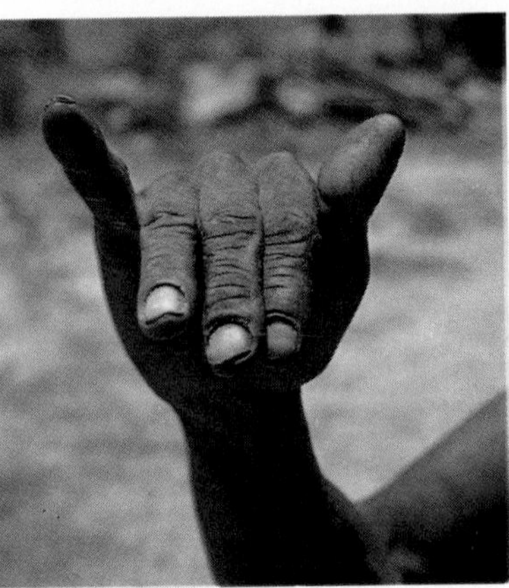

BAT-EARED FOX

PANGOLIN

THE LARGER ANIMALS

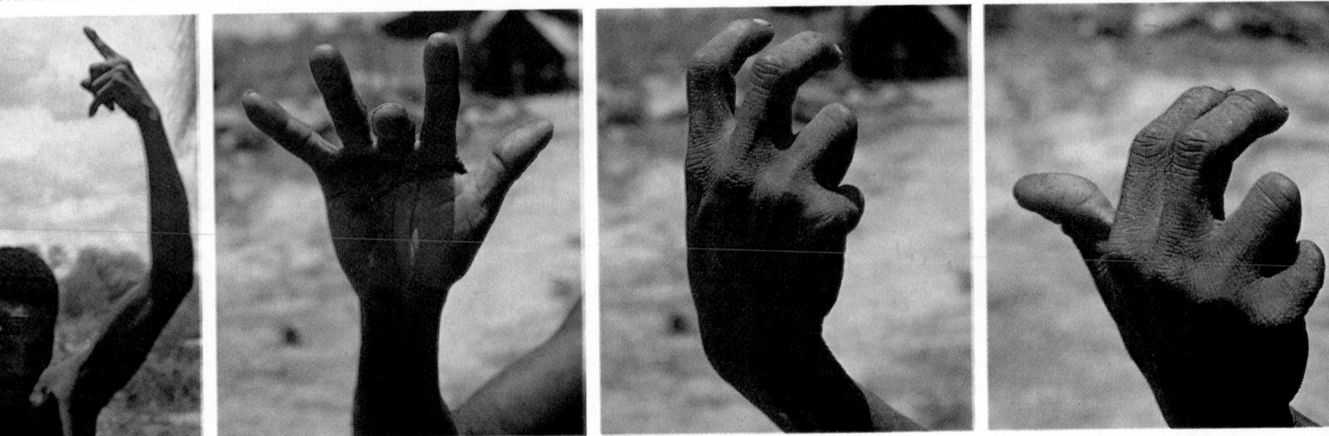

GREATER KUDU

GIRAFFE

HARTEBEEST

ROAN ANTELOPE

Hunting in pairs, Bushmen chatter with each other a great deal, but once an animal is sighted or its spoor picked up, they stalk in silence, using signals to keep each other informed. Most often these identify an animal by its most salient feature. Thus, upheld arms and outstretched index fingers suggest big horns—and indeed, as seen in the picture at bottom left *(above)*, they stand for the greater kudu. In the adjacent picture, however, it is not the giraffe's long neck that is being mimicked but its

HAWK

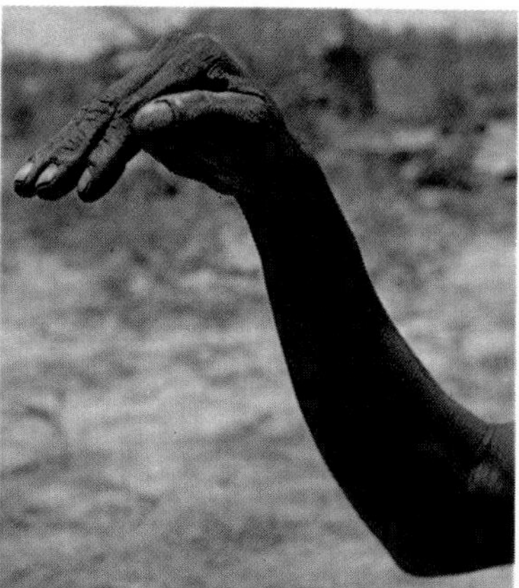

OSTRICH

CROWNED GUINEA FOWL

DUCK

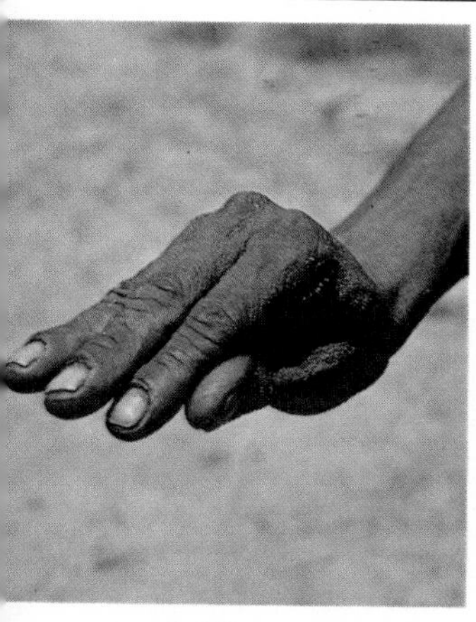

RATEL

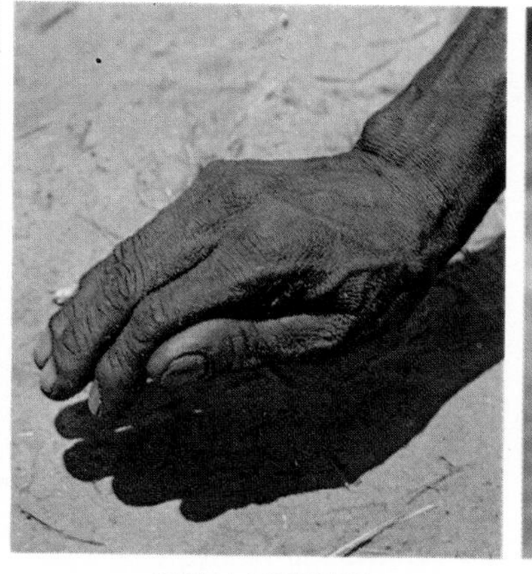

SMALL TORTOISE

PORCUPINE

VERVET MONKEY

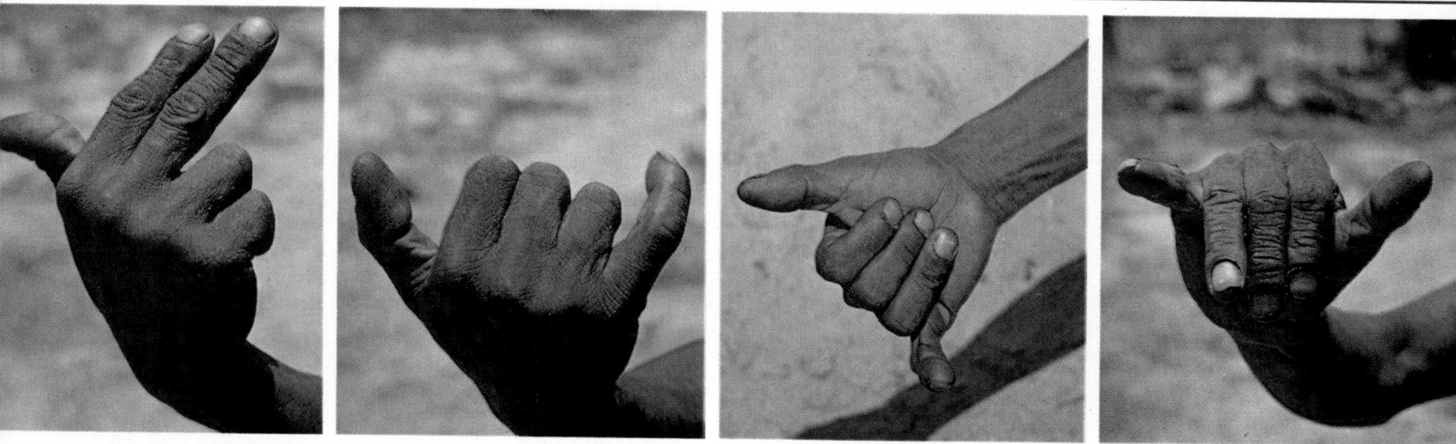

ELAND

GNU

WART HOG

LION

head, with the spread, slightly curling fingers representing the ears and stubby horns; this distinguishes it from the signal for ostrich *(top row, third photograph)*, in which an arm forms the bird's neck. When an animal defies description, the signal may be an animated one, copying the prey's movement, like the hopping of the springhaas. The signal for vervet monkey *(middle row, far right)* mimics neither movement nor appearance; it is simply an upturned palm indicating that the vervet is "like a man."

WITH A PLUCKED GUINEA HEN strung on his digging stick, a Bushman rests on the homeward trek. Small animals like this one need not be shared with anyone but the hunter's family.

High Hopes, Small Returns

Killing a big animal like an antelope is a prestigious act for the Bushman male. Not only does it prove his prowess but it demonstrates his worth to the tribe, since the meat is shared by all. Big animals, however, are relatively scarce in the Kalahari Desert, and days or even months may pass before a hunter brings one down with the bow and poisoned arrows he carries with him at all times. Far more likely is an encounter with the much more common springhaas, or jumping hare, which he snares in its burrow with a hooked pole *(below)* and finally captures with the help of a digging stick, a handy tool that also serves if the hunt is unsuccessful and he must dig up roots or plants to bring home. He may even be lucky enough to bag two springhase a day. Weighing about five and a half pounds, a springhaas has about twice the meat of a jackrabbit,

TO CATCH A SPRINGHAAS, a nocturnal animal that sleeps by day in its burrow, two men work as a team. At left, a hunter begins to dig toward the springhaas, which has been trapped

which makes catching and killing it well worth the effort.

When a Bushman hunter does kill a larger animal, it is more than likely to be immature, like the steinbok kid at right. Young animals tire faster than the adults when the hunters' dogs pursue them and, once wounded, need not be trailed for long, the poisoned arrow having its effect in a few hours instead of one or two days.

Master naturalists, Bushmen are ever ready to exploit quirks of animal behavior for their gain. The hunter at left, for example, got his guinea fowl and her clutch of nine eggs with practically no effort at all: he simply removed one egg from the nest and placed it at the edge, confident that when the frightened mother returned, she would attempt to roll it back inside—and trip the snare he set for her.

TRAILED BY THEIR DOG, two hunters trudge along with a slain steinbok kid. The one carrying the dead animal was enjoying a rare lucky streak: in only 17 days he made 29 kills.

in its burrow by his partner, who has hooked it with the metal tip of a long, flexible pole. Above, the digger, furiously casting dirt to the side, crouches shoulder-deep in the hole.

Here he triumphantly captures the springhaas by the tail. He will then club it to death with the digging stick and break its bones, turning it into a limp bundle, easy to carry home.

PLAYING A MUSICAL BOW, an instrument adapted from the hunting bow, a Bushman presses one end against the inside of his cheek and strikes the wire string. The resulting sound is like two flutes being played at once.

The Dance: Recreation, Relaxation and Cure

Bushmen were once extremely adept in the plastic arts, as thousands of centuries-old paintings in rock shelters show, but today they do little more than decorate a few scant items of apparel. They are, however, excellent musicians, their playing, singing and dancing all being beautifully developed. Dancing, their favorite recreational activity, goes on when food is abundant. While the women sit in a circle, singing and clapping their hands rhythmically, the men weave slowly around them, executing intricate steps and only occasionally bursting into song. Such dances are generally relaxed, all-night affairs that often continue well into the next day, with the participants taking time out for eating, story-telling, sleeping and joking.

While basically recreational, Bushman dances serve important medical and magical functions, and in a society without a formal priesthood, they seem to express a reaching out to the divine. Most men over 30 practice curing. As the dance progresses, some may fall into a deep trance, shaking, sinking into a catatonic state. Some, in this condition, may walk barefoot over live coals or pick them up in their hands. Bushmen believe that a man in a trance has special power which enables him to grapple with the spirits of the dead and to draw out the afflicting evil from a person who is ill *(opposite)*.

LIGHTING A CARTRIDGE SHELL PIPE filled with tobacco, the only stimulant Bushmen know, a woman listens to the plaintive twang of a thumb piano. This instrument is played by pressing down and releasing its metal prongs.

DEEP IN A TRANCE produced by all-night dancing, a curer with cocoon rattles around his ankles embraces a patient wearing coffee-can-key earrings.

(NEXT PAGE) DANCING UP THE DAWN, TWO SILHOUETTED BUSHMEN RAISE CLOUDS OF GOLDEN DUST.

Bibliography

General

Bibby, Geoffrey, *The Testimony of the Spade*. Alfred A. Knopf, 1956.

Boule, Marcellin and Henri V. Vallois, *Fossil Men*. Holt, Rinehart & Winston, 1957.

Braidwood, Robert J., *Prehistoric Men*. Oceana Publications, 1961.

Brodrick, Alan Houghton, *Early Man*. Hutchinson & Co., 1948. **Man and His Ancestry*. Hutchinson & Co., 1960.

*Clark, W. E. Le Gros, *The Antecedents of Man*. Quadrangle Books, 1960. *History of the Primates* (4th ed.). University of Chicago Press, 1963.

†Hammond, Peter B., ed., *Physical Anthropology and Archaeology: Selected Readings*. Macmillan, 1964.

Howell, F. Clark, *The Emergence of Man*. Random House (in press).

Howells, William, *Mankind in the Making*. Doubleday, 1959.

Pfeiffer, John E., *The Search for Early Man*. American Heritage Publishing Co., 1963.

Tax, Sol, ed., *Horizons of Anthropology*. Aldine, 1964.

Von Koenigswald, G.H.R., *Meeting Prehistoric Man*. Harper & Brothers, 1956. †*The Evolution of Man*. University of Michigan Press, 1962.

Weidenreich, Franz, *Apes, Giants and Man*. University of Chicago Press, 1946.

Historical

Daniel, Glyn E., *A Hundred Years of Archaeology*. Gerald Duckworth & Co., Ltd., 1952. †*The Idea of Prehistory*. Penguin Books, 1962.

*Eiseley, Loren, *Darwin's Century*. Doubleday, 1958.

*Greene, John C., *The Death of Adam*. Iowa State University Press, 1959.

Senet, André, *Man in Search of His Ancestors*. McGraw-Hill, 1955.

Weiner, J. S., *The Piltdown Forgery*. Oxford University Press, 1955.

*Wendt, Herbert, *In Search of Adam*. Houghton Mifflin, 1955.

Classification, Evolution and Behavior

†Barnett, Anthony, *The Human Species*. Penguin Books, 1961.

Clark, W. E. Le Gros, *The Fossil Evidence for Human Evolution* (2nd ed.). University of Chicago Press, 1964.

Coon, Carleton S., *The Origin of Races*. Alfred A. Knopf, 1962.

*Darwin, Charles, *The Origin of Species and the Descent of Man*. Modern Library Giants, 1936.

Dobzhansky, Theodosius, *Mankind Evolving*. Yale University Press, 1962.

Gavan, James A., ed., *The Nonhuman Primates and Human Evolution*. Wayne State University Press, 1955.

Howells, William W., ed., *Ideas on Human Evolution*. Harvard University Press, 1962.

*Huxley, Thomas Henry, *Man's Place in Nature*. University of Michigan Press, 1959.

Knapp, Peter H., ed., *Expression of the Emotions in Man*. International Universities Press, 1963.

Scott, John Paul, *Aggression*. University of Chicago Press, 1958.

Von Bonin, Gerhardt, *The Evolution of the Human Brain*. University of Chicago Press, 1963.

Washburn, Sherwood L., ed., *Classification and Human Evolution*. Aldine, 1963.

Geology and Dating

Brothwell, Don and Eric Higgs, eds., *Science in Archaeology*. Basic Books, 1963.

Butzer, Karl W., *Environment and Archeology: An Introduction to Pleistocene Geography*. Aldine, 1964.

Dunbar, Carl Owen, *Historical Geology* (2nd ed.). John Wiley & Sons, 1960.

Flint, Richard Foster, *Glacial and Pleistocene Geology*. John Wiley & Sons, 1957.

Oakley, Kenneth P., *Frameworks for Dating Fossil Man*. Aldine, 1964. †*The Problem of Man's Antiquity: An Historical Survey*. Bulletin of the British Museum (Natural History) Geology (Vol. 9, No. 5), London, 1964.

Zeuner, Frederick E., *Dating the Past*. Methuen, 1962.

Specific Early Men and Regional Books

Broom, R., *Finding the Missing Link*. Watts & Co., 1951.

†Clark, J. Desmond, *The Prehistory of Southern Africa*. Penguin Books, 1959

Cole, Sonia, *The Prehistory of East Africa*. Macmillan, 1963.

†Dart, Raymond A. with Craig, Dennis, *Adventures with the Missing Link*. Viking, 1959.

Howell, F. Clark and François Bourlière, eds., *African Ecology and Human Evolution*. Aldine, 1963.

Thomas, Elizabeth Marshall, *The Harmless People*. Alfred A. Knopf, 1959.

Toit, Alex. L. Du, ed., *Robert Broom Commemorative Volume*. Royal Society of South Africa, 1948.

Von Koenigswald, G.H.R., ed., *Neanderthal Centenary 1856-1956*. Wenner-Gren Foundation, 1958.

Culture

*James, Edwin O., *Prehistoric Religion*. Barnes & Noble, 1961.

†Leakey, L.S.B., *Adam's Ancestors* (4th ed.). Harper & Brothers, 1960.

Maringer, Johannes, *The Gods of Prehistoric Man*. Alfred A. Knopf, 1960.

Montagu, Ashley, ed., *Culture and the Evolution of Man*. Oxford University Press, 1962.

*Oakley, Kenneth P., *Man the Toolmaker*. University of Chicago Press, 1957.

Semenov, S. A., *Prehistoric Technology*. Cory, Adams & Mackay, 1964.

Spuhler, J. N., ed., *The Evolution of Man's Capacity for Culture*. Wayne State University Press, 1959.

Tax, Sol, ed., *Evolution after Darwin*, Vol. II, *The Evolution of Man*. University of Chicago Press, 1960.

Washburn, Sherwood L., ed., *Social Life of Early Man*. Aldine, 1961.

Art

Augusta, Josef and Zdeněk Burian, *Prehistoric Man*. Tudor Publishing Co., 1961.

Bandi, Hans-Georg, Henri Breuil, Lilo Berger-Kirchner, Henri Lhote, Erik Holm and Andreas Lommel, *The Art of the Stone Age*. Crown, 1961.

Bataille, Georges, *Lascaux or the Birth of Art*. Skira, 1955.

Breuil, Abbé Henri, *Four Hundred Centuries of Cave Art*. Montignac, 1952.

Celebonovic, Stevan and Geoffrey Grigson, *Old Stone Age*. Phoenix House, 1957.

Graziosi, Paolo, *Paleolithic Art*. McGraw-Hill, 1960.

Maringer, Johannes and Hans-Georg Bandi, *Art in the Ice Age*. Frederick A. Praeger, 1953.

Sieveking, Ann and Gale, *The Caves of France and Northern Spain: A Guide*. Vista Books, 1962.

Willcox, A. R., *The Rock Art of South Africa*. Thomas Nelson & Sons, 1963.

Articles

Bordes, François, "Mousterian Cultures in France." *Science* (Vol. 134, No. 3482), September 22, 1961.

Howell, F. Clark, "Isimila: A Paleolithic Site in Africa." *Scientific American* (Vol. 205, No. 4), October 1961. "The Villafranchian and Human Origins." *Science* (Vol. 130, No. 3379), October 2, 1959.

Napier, J. R., "The Evolution of the Human Hand." *Scientific American* (Vol. 207, No. 6), December 1962.

Robinson, J. T., "Australopithecines and the Origin of Man." *Annual Report of the Smithsonian Institution*, 1961.

Simons, Elwyn L., "The Early Relatives of Man." *Scientific American* (Vol. 211, No. 1), July 1964. "Some Fallacies in the Study of Hominid Phylogeny." *Science* (Vol. 141, No. 3584), September 6, 1963.

Smith, Philip E. L., "The Solutrean Culture." *Scientific American* (Vol. 211, No. 2), August 1964.

Solecki, Ralph S., "Prehistory in Shanidar Valley, Northern Iraq." *Science* (Vol. 139, No. 3551), January 18, 1963.

Sonneville-Bordes, Denise de, "Upper Paleolithic Cultures in Western Europe." *Science* (Vol. 142, No. 3590), October 18, 1963.

Washburn, Sherwood, L., "Tools and Human Evolution." *Scientific American* (Vol. 203, No. 3), September 1960.

*Also available in paperback.
†Only available in paperback.

Appendix

Major Human Fossil Sites of the Old World

Here is a selection of human fossil sites chosen not only because of their archeological and artistic interest but because each of them was a milestone in the unfolding history of early man. To locate each site in time, the Pleistocene epoch has been divided into six parts, each with an approximate span of years. The most significant facts relating to each site are summarized. A separate section lists some of the more beautiful and significant Paleolithic cave-art sites of France and northern Spain. Most of these caves are open to the public and arrangements to visit them may usually be made locally.

Pleistocene time scale

B	(Basal)—starting 2,000,000 years ago	U	(Upper)—100,000-10,000
L	(Lower)—1,000,000-275,000	EU	(Early Upper)—100,000-35,000
M	(Middle)—275,000-100,000	LU	(Late Upper)—35,000-10,000

AUSTRALOPITHECINES

Transvaal

TAUNG-(B). First recognized *Australopithecus*. STERKFONTEIN-(B). First postcranial remains of *Australopithecus;* stone artifacts found with *Australopithecus* teeth. KROMDRAAI-(L). First discovery of *Paranthropus*. SWARTKRANS-(B/L). First hip and thigh bones and abundant skeletal remains of *Paranthropus;* coexistence with advanced *Australopithecus*.

Tanzania

OLDUVAI BED I-(B). *Paranthropus* and advanced *Australopithecus* found with stone tools on occupation sites. First hand and foot; stone structures.

HOMO ERECTUS

Tanzania

OLDUVAI BED II-(L). Succession of *Homo erectus* fossils indicates evolutionary stages. Tools of Oldowan-Chelles / Acheul industry.

Algeria

TERNIFINE-(L). First clear demonstration of *Homo erectus* in Africa with hand-axe (Chelles/Acheul) associations.

China

CHOUKOUTIEN-(L). First population sample (Peking man) and only cave occupation known of *Homo erectus*. Abundant cultural evidence—hunting, tools and fire.

Java

TRINIL-(L). First discovery of *Homo erectus* (controversial Java man). SANGIRAN-(L). First find in one site of successive deposits with *Homo erectus* and perhaps an australopithecine.

Germany

MAUER-(L). Oldest human fossil remains in Europe. The lone mandible, from near Heidelberg, is similar to *Homo erectus*.

HOMO SAPIENS (EARLY)

Germany

STEINHEIM-(M). First skeletal remains from the time gap between *Homo erectus* (Mauer) and Neanderthal.

Britain

SWANSCOMBE-(M). First found and still oldest human remains in Europe directly associated with Acheulian tools. Evidence of fire.

HOMO SAPIENS (NEANDERTHAL)

Germany

EHRINGSDORF-(EU). Oldest occurrence of Neanderthals associated with Mousterian culture. First open site. NEANDERTHAL-(EU). Type site—i.e., here first fossil find was made which gave this type of man his name.

Belgium

SPY-(EU). First demonstrated occurrence of Neanderthals with Mousterian culture, extinct animals and burials. ENGIS-(EU). Neanderthal remains were first discovered here, but not recognized as such for 100 years.

France

LA FERRASSIE-(EU TO LU). First "family" Neanderthal burial situation with evidence of ritual. LA QUINA-(EU TO LU). First occurrence of Neanderthal remains in multiple levels of an occupation site. REGOURDOU-(EU). First confirmed occurrence of Neanderthal remains with bear cult. Stone constructions. ARCY-SUR-CURE-(EU to LU). Valley locality with many caves, some of which have collapsed. Mousterian occupation surfaces, some with human remains, and a succession of Upper Paleolithic occupations (including huts with the rare Chatelperronian industry), some with art. LE MOUSTIER-(EU). Type site for Mousterian culture, subsequently yielding a Neanderthal burial. COMBE GRENAL-(EU). Longest occupation of a Mousterian site, with 64 known levels and the oldest known posthole. Some skeletal remains.

Italy

MONTE CIRCEO-(EU). Early Mousterian ritual is indicated by Neanderthal skull elaborately positioned on an occupation floor in a sealed-up cave.

Yugoslavia

KRAPINA-(EU). Largest Neanderthal population sample and first demonstrated evidence of cannibalism in Mousterian times.

U.S.S.R.

TESHIK-TASH-(EU). Farthest known easterly occurrence (Siberia) of Neanderthal man. One burial site, a male child.

Iraq

SHANIDAR-(EU TO LU). Neanderthal occupation cave with several individuals crushed and preserved by rock falls.

Israel

TABŪN-(EU). First Neanderthal burial found in the Middle East. SKHŪL-(EU). Large Neanderthal population sample; organized cemetery burial. Physical characteristics transitional to Cro-Magnon people.

Morocco

DJEBEL IRHOUD-(EU). Limestone cave shows adult and juvenile Neanderthal skulls not unlike those from the Middle East. Extensive and repeated Mousterian occupation is indicated, but careful excavation must await preparation of the site.

Northern Rhodesia

BROKEN HILL-(EU TO LU). A single skull was unfortunately removed from its primary location, making associations of this African Neanderthal uncertain.

HOMO SAPIENS (MODERN)

Czechoslovakia

DOLNI VESTONICE-(LU), PAVLOV-(LU) and PREDMOST-(LU). Large and unique Upper Paleolithic mammoth-hunter encampments with huts and burials.

France

ABRI PATAUD-(LU). One of several large and long-occupied shelters in the heart of Les Eyzies. Upper Paleolithic occupation with 14 successive levels, hearth and settlement patterns. Human remains are from the proto-Magdalenian level—an occurrence found at only one other site. CAP BLANC-(LU). A shelter with a fine frieze of Solutrean horses. COMBE CAPELLE-(EU TO LU). A rare instance of the early Upper Paleolithic industry, the Chatelperronian, perhaps associated with Cro-Magnon skeleton. CRO-MAGNON-(LU). This type site gave Cro-Magnon man his name; it is also the first well-documented occurrence of Upper Paleolithic industries in a shelter with associated Cro-Magnon skeletons. LA MADELEINE-(LU). This type site for Magdalenian culture shows multiple occupations and art. LAUGERIE BASSE-(LU). Like La Madeleine, a fine succession of Magdalenian occupations. ISTURITZ-(LU). Longest single Mousterian Upper Paleolithic site in French Pyrenees with fine Magdalenian art. MAS D'AZIL-(LU). Type site for the Azilian, a terminal Paleolithic industry.

Italy

GRIMALDI-(LU). Numerous caves with long Upper Paleolithic occupations. Some Mousterian industries.

U.S.S.R.

KOSTIENKI-(LU). A site in the locality of the Don River with multiple Upper Paleolithic settlements, including various huts and other habitations. Long, repeated occupations.

Lebanon

KSÂR 'AKIL-(EU TO LU). A coastal shelter with the Middle East's longest unbroken Mousterian/Upper Paleolithic succession.

CAVE ART OF FRANCE AND NORTHERN SPAIN

The Dordogne

LASCAUX. Generally recognized as the finest painted cave in France, it was closed to the public in 1963 after an alga—perhaps caused by air conditioning—began to spread over its walls. Whether the numerous Upper Paleolithic paintings can be saved remains uncertain.
FONT-DE-GAUME. A cave with 198 painted and engraved animals, first discovered in 1901 and one of the main landmarks in Paleolithic art. Important are two friezes of polychrome bison, an engraved mammoth and a kneeling reindeer.
LES COMBARELLES. Of particular interest because of its predominance of engravings: 116 panels, each showing one or more animals. No other cave contains nearly so many.
PECH-MERLE. One of the largest and finest painted caves, with horses like those in Lascaux, elegant black line drawings of mammoths and wild cattle, and human footprints.

Pyrenees region

NIAUX. Famous for its Salon Noir, which contains what is generally considered to be the finest group of Magdalenian paintings in the Pyrenees. All are painted in black outline, some heavily shaded.
LES TROIS FRÈRES and LE TUC D'AUDOUBERT. The sanctuary of Les Trois Frères contains some of the finest of all Paleolithic engravings, apparently specifically associated with religious ceremony. Both caves are on private land; special permission is needed.
LE PORTEL. One of the principal caves for animal paintings in the Aurignacian style, with nearly 100 paintings and engravings, well preserved and easily visible.
MONTESPAN. This partially flooded cave, which may only be visited with special equipment and by arrangement with local archeologists, is interesting for its clay statues and engraved round-up hunting scene.
GARGAS. Chiefly notable for the enormous number of its Aurignacian stenciled hand paintings. Many of the hand outlines appear mutilated, as if some finger joints had been cut off, possibly in association with a form of religious ceremonial.

Northern Spain

ALTAMIRA. This most famous of all the painted caves contains a spectacular collection of polychrome paintings—the first Paleolithic cave paintings to be discovered anywhere. There are 15 bison, 3 boars, 3 female deer, 2 horses and a wolf.
PINDAL. Most notable for its elephant painted in red outline, and one of the Paleolithic's rare engravings of a fish.
PASIEGA. A fine collection of excellently preserved paintings, most of which are done in red outline. Seven successive techniques or styles of painting have been distinguished, most from the earlier Aurignacian-Périgordian cycle.

Credits

The sources for the illustrations which appear in this book are shown below.
Credits for the pictures from left to right are separated by commas, from top to bottom by dashes.

Cover—Lee Boltin and Paul Jensen courtesy William Howells, Peabody Museum, Harvard University
8—Courtesy Musée de l'Homme
10, 11—Drawings by Joe Cellini
14, 15—Drawings by John Newcomb
17—Robert Lackenbach—Black Star
18, 19—Robert Mottar—courtesy Musée Calvet in Avignon, The Bettmann Archive
20, 21—Culver Pictures colored by Matt Greene
22—Robert Morton
23—Courtesy The American Museum of Natural History
24, 25—Left; courtesy The American Museum of Natural History—The Williams Collection courtesy The American Museum of Natural History right; Neave Parker—Peter Stackpole
26, 27—Robert Morton
28, 29—Drawings by Leo and Dianne Dillon
30—Jean Hurzeler
32—Map by Lowell Hess
33—Drawings by Rudolf Freund reprinted with permission. (c) 1964 by Scientific American, Inc. All rights reserved
34—Drawings by Margaret L. Estey
35—Drawings by Margaret L. Estey adapted with permission. (c) 1964 by Scientific American, Inc. All rights reserved
36—Drawing by Margaret L. Estey
37—Drawings by Margaret L. Estey reprinted with permission. (c) 1964 by Scientific American, Inc. All rights reserved
39, 40—F. Clark Howell
41 through 45—Charts by George V. Kelvin—figures by Rudy Zallinger
46—A. R. Hughes, University of Witwatersrand, Johannesburg
48—Map by Lowell Hess
51—Drawings by Enid Kotschnig courtesy John T. Robinson
53—Drawings by Enid Kotschnig adapted from drawings by John T. Robinson courtesy Wenner-Gren Foundation for Anthropological Research
55—Drawings by Otto van Eersel
57—Drawing by Jay H. Matternes
58—Ernest Shirley
59—Kenneth MacLeish except left; Jerry Cooke
60, 61—Left; William B. Terry—John T. Robinson right; Yale Joel—John T. Robinson
62 through 69—Drawings by Jay H. Matternes
70—J. Desmond Clark—Joe McKeown, F. Clark Howell
71—J. Desmond Clark
72 through 75—Paintings by Jay H. Matternes
76—Walter Bosshard from Black Star—courtesy Musée de l'Homme, courtesy The American Museum of Natural History
78—Map by Lowell Hess
81—Drawings by Enid Kotschnig
83—Drawing by Matt Greene
85, 86, 87—F. Clark Howell
88, 89—Drawing by Matt Greene
90, 91—Painting by Stanley Meltzoff, F. Clark Howell
92, 93—Painting by Stanley Meltzoff—drawing by Matt Greene
94, 95—F. Clark Howell—Painting by Stanley Meltzoff
96, 97—Painting by Stanley Meltzoff, F. Clark Howell
98, 99—Painting by Stanley Meltzoff
100—Lee Boltin courtesy The American Museum of Natural History
103—Drawings by Lowell Hess
105—Drawings by Lowell Hess
107—Drawings by Enid Kotschnig
109—J. Desmond Clark
110 through 115—Drawings by Lowell Hess
116—Lee Boltin
117—Dmitri Kessel, courtesy Musée de l'Homme
118, 119—Marc Riboud from Magnum
120, 121—J. Desmond Clark
122—Robert Morton
124—Map by Lowell Hess
125—Drawing by Matt Greene
126, 127—Drawings by Enid Kotschnig. (c) 1960 by Alfred A. Knopf, Inc. Redrawn and adapted with the permission of the publisher from *Gods of Prehistoric Man* by Johannes Maringer
128, 129—Drawings by Otto van Eersel
131 through 135—Paintings by Z. Burian courtesy Paul Hamlyn Ltd. copied by Walter Sanders
136, 137—Robert Morton
138—Drawing by Matt Greene based on drawing by François Bordes and Pierre Laurent
139—Drawings by François Bordes and Pierre Laurent, Robert Morton
140, 141—Ralph S. Solecki
142—Top; Photos Jacques bottom right; courtesy Musée de l'Homme
143—By permission of the Trustees of the British Museum (Natural History) courtesy Kenneth Oakley except top right; Famille Lohest
144, 145—Courtesy Musée de l'Homme
146—Map by Lowell Hess
147—Drawing by Enid Kotschnig adapted with permission from Z. Burian courtesy Paul Hamlyn Ltd.
148—Reprinted with permission of Alfred A. Knopf, Inc. from *Gods of Prehistoric Man* by Johannes Maringer (c) 1960
149—Reprinted with permission of Paul Hamlyn, Ltd. from *Prehistoric Man* by Josef Augusta (c) 1960
151—Drawings by Lowell Hess
152, 153—Drawings by Otto van Eersel
155, 156, 157—Paintings by Z. Burian courtesy Paul Hamlyn Ltd., copied by Walter Sanders
158, 159—Ralph Morse except top left; René Burri from Magnum
160—Romain Robert courtesy Cultural History Research, Inc.
161—Dmitri Kessel courtesy Musée de l'Homme
162—Dmitri Kessel courtesy The Heirs of Dr. Lalanne, collection of the Musée de l'Homme
163—Courtesy Musée de l'Homme except top; Dmitri Kessel, courtesy Musée de l'Homme
164—Hallam L. Movius Jr. except top right; Gordon Tenney
165—Robert Morton—Hallam L. Movius Jr.
166—Robert Cohen from AGIP
167—Loomis Dean
168, 169—Irven DeVore
174, 175—Drawings by John Newcomb
177—Irven DeVore
178—Stanley Washburn—Irven DeVore
179—Stanley Washburn—Irven DeVore
180—Stanley Washburn
181—Irven DeVore—Stanley Washburn
182, 183—Stanley Washburn
184, 185—Irven DeVore
186, 187—Top; Irven DeVore bottom; Stanley Washburn
188—Irven DeVore
189—Irven DeVore—Stanley Washburn
190, 191—R. B. Lee

Acknowledgments

The editors want to thank the following people, who gave their time and special knowledge to various sections of this book: Guy de Beauchien, Musée de l'Homme, Paris; Shirley Beresford, Library Assistant, The New York Historical Society; François Bordes, Professor, Laboratory of Prehistory, University of Bordeaux, France; Harvey Bricker, Harvard University; Wallace S. Broecker, Professor of Geochemistry, Columbia University; Karl W. Butzer, Associate Professor of Geography, University of Wisconsin; J. Desmond Clark, Professor of Anthropology, University of California, Berkeley; H.B.S. Cooke, Professor of Geology, Dalhousie University, Halifax, Nova Scotia; Irven DeVore, Lecturer, Departments of Anthropology and Social Relations, Harvard University; Jack F. Evernden; Richard F. Flint, Chairman, Department of Geology, Yale University; C. Lewis Gazen, Head Curator, Division of Vertebrate Paleontology, Museum of Natural History, Smithsonian Institution; Frederick C. Grant, Union Theological Seminary; Richard L. Hay, Associate Professor of Geology, University of California, Berkeley; Harold F. Heady, Professor of Forestry, University of California, Berkeley; Lawrence E. Hinkle Jr., Associate Professor of Medicine, Cornell University Medical College; Ralph J. Holmes, Professor of Geology, Columbia University; William Howells, Professor of Anthropology, Harvard University; Richard G. Klein, University of Chicago; Pierre Laurent, University of Bordeaux, France; Louis S. B. Leakey, Honorary Director, Coryndon Museum Center, Nairobi; Richard Lee, Department of Anthropology, University of California, Berkeley; André Leroi-Gourhan, Professor, University of Paris; Malcolm C. McKenna, Assistant Curator, Department of Vertebrate Paleontology, The American Museum of Natural History; Hallam L. Movius Jr., Professor of Anthropology, Harvard University; Kenneth P. Oakley, Deputy Keeper in charge of Anthropology, Department of Paleontology, British Museum (Natural History), London; John T. Robinson, Professor of Anthropology, University of Wisconsin; Gale Sieveking, Department of British and Medieval Antiquities, British Museum, London; Elwyn L. Simons, Associate Professor of Geology, Curator of Vertebrate Paleontology, Peabody Museum, Yale University; Ralph Solecki, Associate Professor of Anthropology, Columbia University; T. Dale Stewart, Director, Museum of Natural History, Smithsonian Institution; S. L. Washburn, Professor of Anthropology, University of California, Berkeley; and Stanley Washburn.

Index

Numerals in italics indicate a photograph or painting of the subject mentioned.

Production Staff for Time Incorporated

John L. Hallenbeck (Vice President and Director of Production), Robert E. Foy, James P. Menton, Caroline Ferri and Robert E. Fraser

Text photocomposed under the direction of Albert J. Dunn and Arthur J. Dunn

Printed by R. R. Donnelley & Sons Company, Crawfordsville, Indiana,

and by Livermore and Knight Co., a division of Printing Corporation of America, Providence, Rhode Island

Bound by R. R. Donnelley & Sons Company, Crawfordsville, Indiana

Paper by The Mead Corporation, Dayton, Ohio

Cover stock by The Plastic Coating Corporation, Holyoke, Massachusetts